INTRODUCTION TO KINETIC THEORY STOCHASTIC PROCESSES IN GASEOUS SYSTEMS

by

TOYOKI KOGA

PERGAMON PRESS

OXFORD · LONDON · EDINBURGH · NEW YORK
TORONTO · SYDNEY · PARIS · BRAUNSCHWEIG

Pergamon Press Ltd., Headington Hill Hall, Oxford
4 & 5 Fitzroy Square, London W.1
Pergamon Press (Scotland) Ltd., 2 & 3 Teviot Place, Edinburgh 1
Pergamon Press Inc., Maxwell House, Fairview Park, Elmsford,
New York 10523
Pergamon of Canada Ltd., 207 Queen's Quay West, Toronto 1
Pergamon Press (Aust.) Pty. Ltd., 19a Boundary Street, Rushcutters Bay,
N.S.W. 2011, Australia
Pergamon Press S.A.R.L., 24 rue des Écoles, Paris 5e
Vieweg & Sohn GmbH, Burgplatz 1, Braunschweig

First edition 1970

Library of Congress Catalog Card No 76–93474

Printed in Hungary

08 006538 4

Contents

Preface

THE theme of this monograph is the stochastic nature of kinetic-theoretical processes which occur in gases exhibiting gas-dynamical phenomena. The particles constituting a gas are assumed to be classical-mechanical; in other words, a gas considered here is of low density and of high energy. A short note on the kinetic theory of quantum-mechanical systems is added in Appendix E.

Kinetic theory was initiated by Krönig, Clausius, Maxwell, and Boltzmann, based on the assumption that a gas consists of discrete particles (molecules), each of which behaves according to universal mechanical laws. Maxwell postulated the existence of a demon which can see a particle in a gas. We may also assume the existence of a mathematical demon, similar to Laplace's demon, which can solve the equations of motion of the particles constituting a gas. To these demons, the behaviors of the molecules in a gas are completely in order. Of course we are not such demons. We cannot solve precisely more than two-body problems. At the same time, we realize that we do not need to solve precisely those non-linear equations of enormous complexity, since our experimental observation to be predicted by the analyses is extremely coarse. We recall that Poincaré, last century, solved the non-linear equations governing the motion of a planet by a method of coarse-graining; that is to give perturbation factors in terms of coarse-grained trajectories. Coarse-graining creates a situation in which the hypothesis of equal *a priori* probabilities may be conditionally introduced. We also notice that Maxwell and Boltzmann made molar disorder and molecular order compatible by means of the Stosszahlansatz. There is no essential difference

between Poincaré's method of celestial mechanics and Maxwell–Boltzmann's method of kinetic theory, in view of the use of coarse-graining methods and the hypothesis of equal *a priori* probabilities. It is obvious that the hypothesis was a conditional convenience for Poincaré, Maxwell and Boltzmann to compensate their limited ability in mathematics.

Gibbs's statistical mechanics was developed from the gas theory constructed by Maxwell and Boltzmann. To Gibbs, however, the hypothesis of equal *a priori* probabilities was an unconditional principle rather than a conditional convenience. (At the same time, Gibbs did not necessarily insist that a system consists of discrete particles.) To Maxwell and Boltzmann, kinetic theory, including ergodic theory as a special case, was deducible, while to Gibbs statistical mechanics was inducible.

In statistical physics, in general, the concept of probability is indispensable. The history of the concept may be traced back to the time of Aristotle. But great progress in the mathematics of probability was made by Laplace, Legendre, Gauss, and others in the first half of the last century. The basic view of those pioneers is deterministic. In other words, they regarded nature as precisely determined; only because of the coarseness of our observation, probability has room in our scientific thought. As has been stated, the same view was inherited by Krönig, Clausius, Maxwell, and Boltzmann, who developed gas theories in the second half of the last century. We note that a rough observation corresponds to a mathematical coarse-graining. On the other hand, Mach, Ostwald, Helmholz, and Planck, as well as Gibbs, seemed to have some hesitation in supporting the deterministic view. In treating thermodynamical phenomena, they were somewhat skeptical in taking the classical-mechanical deterministic view. In this century, in the course of the development of quantum mechanics, it had become obvious that the classical concept of probability made on the basis of deterministic view was not convenient. Conforming to the demand, the probability in quantum mechanics is not the shadow cast by the real nature which can be seen precisely by a demon; instead it is nature itself, and there is no

divine demon beside us. (It is well known, however, that de Broglie, Einstein, Bohm, and others raised a question regarding the quantum-mechanical concept of probability. The question does not seem to have been closed and still appeals to us.) We should note the significant difference between the concept of probability molding quantum mechanics and the old one of gas theories. Naturally, modern statistical physics since Gibbs has been influenced very much by the modern (quantum-mechanical) concept of probability.

The question raised here is which concept, classical or modern, would be more feasible in treating problems of statistical physics. This is a serious question. If we take the old one, a statistical law may be derived from basic laws by a rational process of coarse-graining. On the other hand, according to the new one, a statistical law is to be induced from experimental evidences. I myself would like to stress the significance and necessity of coarse-graining for treating many-body systems in the kinetic-theoretical sense. In other words, as far as we are interested in transient (non-uniform) phenomena in many-body systems, the old concept of probability is essential even in the pragmatical sense. Then the hypothesis of equal *a priori* probabilities is only conditionally valid. Probabilities in statistical physics are *a posteriori* rather than *a priori*. Since a many-body system consists, ultimately, of quantal particles, the above statement might sound paradoxical. The situation is explained in Appendix E. (This situation should be differentiated from the more basic one questioned by Bohm and others; the statement in Appendix E is pertinent within the ordinary framework of quantum-mechanical interpretations.) The author believes that he can show much evidence of confusion in the modern kinetic theory which has been influenced by Gibbs's view and by the quantum-mechanical view of probability: The modern kinetic theory fails to deal with systems where microscopic behaviors of particles are governed by non-linear equations.

Then, the reader might ask: Why has Gibbs's statistical mechanics been so successful? The secrets are the following:

1. Statistical mechanics is mainly concerned with energy which is an integral of motion of an isolated system.

2. The scales of time and space of statistical-mechanical phenomena are indefinitely large. In other words, statistical mechanics views a system in a statistically stationary state.

Because of the two conditions Gibbs's statistical mechanics has been successful. But the success of Gibbs does not necessarily assure us of the feasibility of Gibbs's view in the kinetic theory which is intended to deal with stochastic phenomena in a many-body system. The reasons are:

1. Kinetic theory is concerned with non-uniform distributions of mass, momentum, and energy of a system in time and space. Densities of mass, momentum, and energy are not invariant. A system viewed by kinetic-theoretical eyes is more in order than a system viewed by statistical-mechanical eyes. In other words, we tend to be closer to Maxwell's demon by kinetic theory.

2. Scales of time and space of kinetic-theoretical phenomena are conditionally finite. Kinetic theory views a system in the process of its evolution which is, in the microscopic sense, governed by non-linear equations.

Phenomena considered by kinetic theory constitute only a minor part of the vast world of statistical-physical phenomena which are mostly statistical-mechanical, at least in view of our general concern today. As long as we are interested in kinetic-theoretical phenomena, however, the peculiar nature of those phenomena should not be ignored.

It was one hundred years ago that Maxwell published his paper *On the Dynamical Theory of Gases* in 1866. It is of particular interest to recall various events which have occurred in kinetic theory since then. The fate of kinetic theory in this century has been gloomy, being obscured behind the brilliance of quantum mechanics and statistical mechanics. My interpretation of the history is summarized in Appendix G.

The present study was begun soon after the Second World War, probably inspired by one of my teachers, the late Professor Takuzo Sakai, Tokyo University. Recalling the long course, I realize that I owe very much to the discussions and encouragement of many of

my colleagues; particularly mentioned are R. L. Chuan, H. Grad, E. P. Gross, N. Marcuvitz, H. Motz, A. Papoulis, A. E. Ruark, D. Scarl, B. Senitzky, J. Weinstock, and D. C. Youla. I wish to express my cordial gratitude to M. H. Bloom and W. B. Thompson. The gratitude to Dr. Bloom, the Director of the Preston R. Basset Research Laboratory, Polytechnic Institute of Brooklyn, is for his generosity in giving me the opportunity to complete the work, which has been regarded as speculative, at his laboratory. The gratitude to Dr. Thompson is for his reading of the original manuscript and for his comments which have helped me to elaborate upon the manuscript. I also would like to acknowledge the generosity and judgement of Dr. D. ter Haar in choosing this monograph as one in the physics monograph series of which he is the editor. Of course, Miss Jean Tucholski deserves due acknowledgement for her help in preparing the manuscript. The study in the last three years has been made under Contracts Nonr 839(34) and Nonr 839(38) for PROJECT DEFENDER of the Advanced Research Projects Agency under Order No. 529 through the Office of Naval Research.

Alhambra, California   T. KOGA

On Mathematical Symbols

BOLD-face type is used for three-dimensional vectors. For example

$$\text{momentum:} \quad \mathbf{p} = p_x, p_y, p_z$$

$$\text{position:} \quad \mathbf{r} = r_x, r_y, r_z$$

$$\mathbf{U} = \begin{pmatrix} 1 & 0 & 0 \\ 0 & 1 & 0 \\ 0 & 0 & 1 \end{pmatrix}$$

The components of vectors are given with respect to a Cartesian coordinate system. Subscripts x, y, z are often used for specifying the directions of components. A pair of $\mathbf{p}$ and $\mathbf{r}$ which denote the momentum and position of a particle is often represented by X; for example

$$X_i = \mathbf{p}_i, \mathbf{r}_i$$

denotes the momentum and position of particle i.

Scalar products:

$$\mathbf{A} \cdot \mathbf{B} = A_x B_x + A_y B_y + A_z B_z$$

$$\mathbf{A} \cdot \frac{\partial \varphi}{\partial \mathbf{r}} = \left(A_x \frac{\partial}{\partial r_x} + A_y \frac{\partial}{\partial r_y} + A_z \frac{\partial}{\partial r_z} \right) \varphi, \quad \text{etc.}$$

Vector products:

$$\mathbf{p} \times \mathbf{r} = p_y r_z - p_z r_y, \; p_z r_x - p_x r_z, \; p_x r_y - p_y r_x, \quad \text{etc.}$$

Formation of dyadics (tensors):

$$\mathbf{AB} = \begin{pmatrix} A_xB_x & A_xB_y & A_xB_z \\ A_yB_x & A_yB_y & A_yB_z \\ A_zB_x & A_zB_y & A_zB_z \end{pmatrix}$$

$$\mathbf{AB}:\mathbf{CD} = \sum_i \sum_j A_iB_jC_jD_i, \quad \text{etc.}$$

The following three symbols of integration are used with the same meaning:

$$\int d^3\mathbf{p} = \int d\mathbf{p} = \iiint dp_x\, dp_y\, dp_z.$$

Similarly

$$\int dX_i = \iiiint dp_{ix}\, dp_{iy}\, dp_{iz}\, dr_{ix}\, dr_{iy}\, dr_{iz}$$

$$\int dX_i\, dX_j = \iint dX_i\, dX_j.$$

CHAPTER 1

Introduction

1.1. Distinction of kinetic theory

Kinetic theory is interested in the time evolution of the state of a system, while statistical mechanics is interested in the average state of a system in thermal equilibrium. The relation may be explained by the following heuristic analogy: Suppose that an astronomical observatory has recorded a series of radio waves during a span of time from t to $t+\tau$. One way of analyzing the record is to find the sum of the time periods, in each of which the intensity of the wave is between E and $E+\Delta E$. The sum of the time periods divided by $\tau \Delta E$ may be called the frequency of appearance. Thus we obtain a diagram showing the relation between the frequency of appearance and E. This diagram may give us information such as the average intensity, the degree of fluctuation from the average, the probability of appearance of fluctuations of a given intensity, and so forth. By this analysis, however, the stochastic nature of the series of waves is completely ignored. The diagram made above never gives us any signal which might be implied by the mode of time evolution of the wave; the analysis of the mode is the very subject of modern communication theory. The role of statistical mechanics is similar to making a diagram to show the relation between intensity and frequency, while that of kinetic theory is to seek information on the stochastic evolution of the wave as is done by communication theory.

Kinetic theory is intended to provide laws of macroscopic phenomena of systems based on the hypothesis of molecular structure of a system and dynamical laws of discrete molecules. With respect to gaseous systems, the hypothesis that a system consists of discrete molecules is believed to be plausible. However, the validity of the hypothesis of molecular structure in its literal sense is not obvious with respect to systems not in gaseous states. Besides, it is difficult to investigate stochastic processes in such systems in a consistent manner. Considering these situations, we are obliged to eliminate investigation of systems not in gaseous states. (Of course, it is not proper to state that kinetic theory is interested in gaseous systems only.) If the dynamical equations of the molecules constituting a gas are given, it is impossible to deal with those equations simply by mathematical analyses because of the enormous number of simultaneous equations. The fatal deficiency in our mathematical ability is compensated, however, by the hypothesis of equal *a priori* probabilities. There is more than one usage of the hypothesis; a different usage results in a different conclusion. Therefore the interpretation of the hypothesis is to constitute an essential part of kinetic theory. The hypothesis bears various appearances under different circumstances. The present study of kinetic theory is the study of feasible applications of the hypothesis to systems in various gas-dynamical conditions.

Gibbs's ensembles are stationary ensembles in statistical equilibrium. By choosing an ensemble and making averages of physical quantities over the ensemble, statistical mechanics predicts thermodynamical phenomena exhibited by a real system in thermal equilibrium. An ensemble consists of many similar systems whereas our physical observation is conducted with respect to a single system.[†] Why and how is there a good agreement between the prediction of statistical mechanics and the result of our observation? Some au-

---

[†] A constituent particle (molecule, electron, etc.) may be called a system. In this book, however, we mean by a system the collection of all the particles constituting a gas which is supposed to be under our investigation. The group of particles which constitutes a part of a gas is called a subsystem; a particle is a subsystem.

thors, for example Tolman (1938), think that the statistical-mechanical method is a physical postulation; as long as the method has proved itself feasible in many cases, there is no need of explanation. But ergodic theory[†] has attempted to explain the reason for the agreement between statistical-mechanical predictions and observations. The thermodynamical observation of a single system cannot be done at an instant of time; it needs a span of time. Ergodic theory considers that a span of time necessary for a thermodynamical observation is extremely long compared with the time scales of microscopic phenomena in the system. Thereby ergodic theory shows that the averages of physical properties of the system over an infinitely long time exist uniquely and coincide with the ensemble averages. In those procedures of reasoning, we note the following: (1) Ergodic theory is not interested in the procedure of the evolution of the state of a system. (2) The system under consideration is in thermal equilibrium; the state is specified by the total energy of the system. The total energy is one of the integrals of motion of an isolated system; the others are the total momentum and the total angular momentum.[‡] Kinetic-theoretical and gas-dynamical phenomena are often regarded as fluctuations appearing in statistical-mechanical and thermodynamical systems. This interpretation is misleading. In order to explain the situation, let us consider a few examples of gas-dynamical phenomena as follows:

1. Suppose that we conduct an experiment observing the shock wave produced in a gas enclosed in a shock tube. One performance of the experiment is supposed to begin at time 0 of a stop-watch when the valve (diaphragm), dividing the gas in the tube into two

[†] For example, see the account given recently by Farquhar (1964).

[‡] These are well known; but there is no proof that these are all, as discussed by Grad (1949) and Farquhar (1964). Fowler and Guggenheim (1960) call an integral of motion of an isolated system a uniform integral. They define accessible states as specified by those uniform integrals in addition to energy. It is noted that it is not known whether the domain of the phase space specified by an arbitrary set of uniform integrals is continuously connected or separated into more than one portion. From the ergodic-theoretical viewpoint, the situation is a serious matter.

parts of different pressures, is suddenly opened and ends at time τ when the shock front arrives at an end of the tube for the first time. We may repeat the same procedure with the same gas under the same macroscopic condition, if the shock tube is equipped properly with gas pumps, cooling devices, valves, and so forth. During the period of time between 0 and τ the gas is not in thermal equilibrium due to the particular initial and boundary conditions. (As the initial difference between the pressures in the two parts decreases, the state of the gas becomes closer to thermal equilibrium. However, as long as we observe gas-dynamical phenomena in the gas, no matter how slight, the gas is not in thermal equilibrium.) As time passes, the state of the gas changes toward thermal equilibrium. If we extend the period of observation sufficiently long beyond τ, the gas is almost in thermal equilibrium on the average, because the duration τ is a minor part of the entire period of observation.

2. Let us consider a gas enclosed between two coaxial and circular walls. The internal wall is at rest while the external wall is driven from the outside to rotate around the axis with a constant speed. As the speed of rotation increases and the distance between the two walls decreases, the deviation of the state of the gas from thermal equilibrium will increase. In this example, the state is stationary; the energy supplied for keeping the outer wall rotating is converted to heat, but the walls are equipped with cooling devices in order to keep the state stationary.

3. Suppose that a rarefied and ionized gas is injected into a strong magnetic field. The motion of a charged particle perpendicular to lines of magnetic force is restrained and hence the thermalization process is retarded. The state of the ionized gas may keep deviating from thermal equilibrium for a notably long time.

In these examples, we see that the definition or distinction of a state as deviating from thermal equilibrium depends on the scales of time and space of our observation in comparision with the relevant scales of phenomena. Particular boundary and initial conditions, as well as external forces, prolong the necessary extension of time and space for the thermalization of a system so that those scales of

time and space are "macroscopic". *Thermal equilibrium is a statistical state of a system defined with an infinitely long extension of time.* Therefore it is expected that temporal and spatial non-uniformities of microscopic causes may occur in a system in thermal equilibrium.[†] A non-uniformity may occur in a system regarded as in thermal equilibrium as well as in another similar system regarded as not in thermal equilibrium. However, the statistical weight of the non-uniformity in the former system is much smaller than the statistical weight of the same non-uniformity in the latter. The difference is due to the difference between the statistical-mechanical time and kinetic-theoretical time scales. With respect to the first of the three examples mentioned previously, a shock wave may occur with certainty at each time when we open the diaphragm, and continues to exist for τ immediately after our opening the diaphragm. The same process of forming a shock wave may occur as a thermal fluctuation in the gas in thermal equilibrium in the shock tube; but it occurs only rarely, and the frequency of occurrence is negligibly small.

The recognition of the difference of statistical weight is never trivial in view of the application of the hypothesis of equal *a priori* probabilities. Kinetic theory is not a special case of statistical mechanics; rather statistical mechanics treating a gas may be said to be a special case of kinetic theory where the scales of time and space of our observation are indefinitely larger than those scales of transient phenomena in the gas.

Historically speaking, the molecular hypothesis on which kinetic theory was founded in the last century was abandoned by Gibbs (1902). By so doing Gibbs was successful in establishing principles of statistical mechanics of general systems. Encouraged by the success, many authors since Gibbs have ignored the distinction of kinetic theory and have regarded kinetic theory as an auxiliary and heuristic branch of statistical mechanics. One may see this situation in the review of statistical mechanics given by Ehrenfest (1912). In general, gas-dynamical phenomena have failed to attract due attention from

† Those non-uniformities may be specified in terms of various quantities. Those quantities are not necessarily integrals of motion of an isolated system.

5

physicists. As a result, one tends to believe that if the Boltzmann equation is assumed to be valid, thermal equilibrium is attained in a gas very "quickly" according to the H-theorem; hence, there is no artificial (harnessed) means to keep the state of the gas deviating significantly from thermal equilibrium. As stressed by ter Haar (1950), most statistical-physical phenomena are statistical-mechanical. However, those gas-dynamical phenomena mentioned previously are out of the scope of Gibbs's statistical mechanics and also out of the category of thermal fluctuation. Nevertheless, we are often inclined to regard those concepts of statistical mechanics as the sole norms for investigating those gas-dynamical phenomena. It is also noted that, together with our tendency of anticipating that a gas state will deviate only slightly[†] from thermal equilibrium, quantum-mechanical principles of uncertainty and degeneracy seem to have affected the development of kinetic theory. We often see the evidence in some authors' over-simplified justification and application of the hypothesis of equal *a priori* probabilities in kinetic theory. In view of these circumstances, kinetic theory in its literal sense is yet in the early stage of its development in spite of Boltzmann's old comment that gas theory (kinetic theory) was out of fashion in 1895.[‡]

Kinetic theory begins with the following premises: (1) A system consists of many particles. (2) The dynamical laws (the equations of motion and the interparticle force law) governing the motions of the constituent particles are known. (3) Macroscopic laws governing the behavior of the system are deducible from the dynamical laws governing the motions of constituent particles by logical reasoning.

Of course, these are matters of belief and speculation. The feasibility of kinetic theory must be put to the trial of comparison with experiments. Thus far, ergodic theory, that is kinetic theory under a special condition, has shown that rules of statistical mecha-

† The degree of deviation is not the essential matter. As long as we intend to investigate the evolution of a system exhibiting gas-dynamical phenomena, the approach must be kinetic-theoretical, instead of being ergodic-theoretical (or statistical-mechanical); the ergodic theory is not interested in the procedure of the evolution of a system.

‡ In the foreword of his *Lectures on Gas Theory* (1898).

nics are compatible with the above premises; the Boltzmann equation which is derivable based on the above premises has been supported by experimental results. But there are many results of kinetic theory which have not been compared with relevant experimental results. It might be possible to say that the status of kinetic theory is still uncertain at this moment. Until the final trial, however, kinetic theory must do its best to be faithful to its premises.

1.2. Main problems

A set of differential equations was introduced more than ten decades ago[†] and has been serving as a reliable foundation for gas dynamics. These are the equation of continuity (the mass conservation law), the Navier–Stokes equation (the momentum conservation law), and the equation of energy (the energy conservation law), and are referred to as the Navier–Stokes equations. Originally these equations were derived by considering a gas as a continuum. However, the progress of kinetic theory since then has enabled us to derive them from the complete set of Newton's equations of motion, or equivalently the Liouville equation, of the molecules constituting a gas under certain conditions. The procedure of the derivation is divided into the following two steps: The first step is the derivation of the Boltzmann equation from the Liouville equation by means of the Bogoliubov–Born–Green–Kirkwood–Yvon theory,[‡] or the BBGKY theory; the second step is the derivation of the Navier–Stokes equations from the Boltzmann equation by means of the Chapman–Enskog theory. The procedure utilizes two main assumptions: (1) Most interactions among the molecules are binary in the first step, and (2) the gas under consideration is of moderately high

[†] According to Lamb (1932), those equations were proposed independently by Navier (1822), Poisson (1829), de Saint-Venant (1845), and Stokes (1845).

[‡] As will be discussed in detail in Appendix B, the theory, as proposed by the initial authors, fails to derive properly the Boltzmann equation from the Liouville equation. The failure is due to the misuse of the hypothesis of equal *a priori* probabilities (symmetry assumption) by those authors. It is necessary to reformulate the original theory, as will be discussed later.

7

density and at the same time is almost in equilibrium in the second step. Those assumptions mentioned above restrict the feasible application of the Navier–Stokes equations to a part of the entire regime of gas dynamics. We wish gas dynamics to deal with all the macroscopic dynamical phenomena of gases. One of the main themes of the present study is to clarify the difficulties implied by the above two assumptions and to propose approaches to deal with the difficulties.

There are two cases where the first assumption is not feasible. If the density of a gas constituted of neutral molecules becomes higher, the assumption of binary interaction becomes less feasible; then the Boltzmann equation must be modified although the BBGKY theory might remain valid. If a gas is constituted of electrically charged particles, again the assumption is not feasible because of the long range of the Coulomb force governing those particle interactions. In this case there is evidence that the application of the BBGKY theory is narrowly restricted. The feasibility of the second assumption of almost thermal equilibrium is often violated in dynamical behavior of rarefied gases.

These situations are illustrated schematically in Fig. 1.2-1. The vertical double line indicates the procedure of the derivation of the Navier–Stokes equations from the Liouville equation. The ionized gas theory deviates from the main line at its beginning. The dense

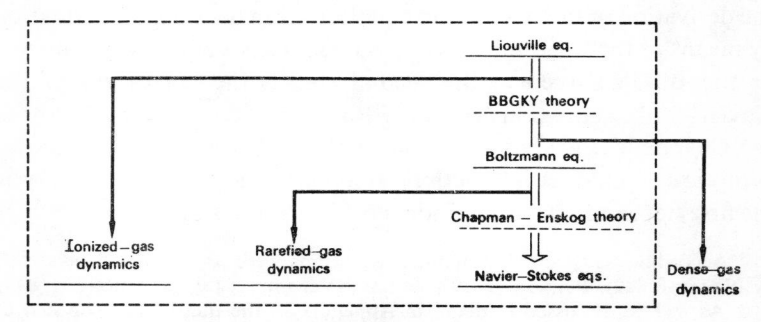

FIG. 1.2-1.
A schematic presentation of the entire system of kinetic theory. The domain enclosed by the dotted lines is the field of the present study.

gas theory departs from the main line before arriving at the Boltzmann equation, and the rarefied gas theory soon after the Boltzmann equation.

The consideration of dense gases of neutral molecules is omitted from the present study. The mode of interaction among molecules in a dense gas is more complex than the mode of the Boltzmann collision process which assumes that a binary collision begins and ends at indefinitely long distances between two molecules participating in the collision and that the two molecules are completely free at such long distances. The chance of binary collision in its literal sense decreases as the density of a gas increases. A strong and seemingly binary collision may begin and end between two molecules only at finite distances. Also the net volume of the space occupied by the molecules constituting a gas is not negligible compared with the space volume in which the gas exists;† in thermal equilibrium the situation results in a modification of the equation of state, that is, we have to consider the van der Waals equation, in general an equation of state with virial coefficients, in place of the Boyle–Charles equation. But the comparative complexity of molecular interactions in a dense gas does not seem to make the dynamical characteristics of the gas much different from the characteristics derived from the Boltzmann equation. The situation seems to be due to two reasons: (1) Strong and effective interactions at short distances are still binary, although each begins and ends at finite distances between participating molecules; (2) the state of a dense gas tends to be close to thermal equilibrium. The detail of those modifications of kinetic theories necessary for a dense gas has been studied by many authors,‡ but is out of the scope of the present study.

† If each molecule is assumed to be a material point with its force field given by eq. (1.2-1) and if the force is repulsive to other molecules, the molecule appears to occupy a volume of space from which the other molecules are excluded; the molecule causes the same effect as a solid body. Of course the volume decreases as the relative velocity with which the molecule collides with another molecule increases.

‡ There are theories which have been developed through attempts to extend the kinetic theory of gases into the liquid region by generalizing the Boltzmann equation, as reviewed by Green (1960).

The effect of the intrinsic structures of molecules, ionization, dissociation and radiation processes, are also ignored in our consideration. The consideration of these effects is indispensable to our investigation of real systems as have been discussed by Massen and Burhop (1954), Mayer (1958), Rowlinson (1958), Gross (1965) and others. It is assumed that one may take these effects into account separately after constructing the kinetic-theoretical bases by ignoring those phenomena related to intrinsic mechanisms. Radical treatments of these processes are to be quantum-mechanical, while kinetic-theoretical treatments of gas behaviors without those processes are feasible in classical mechanics. The separation provides for us the great advantage of simplicity. By unifying these processes simultaneously we have to deal with intolerable complexity. Of course, such a complexity itself cannot be the excuse of the separation. The feasibility of the separation may exist if each elementary and microscopic quantum-mechanical phenomenon takes place as a local and discrete event and is separable from ordinary collisions. We hope it is not necessary to remodel completely the main system of theory (constructed by ignoring these effects) when taking into account these effects afterwards.

According to the above considerations, the molecules treated in this study are material points in the classical-mechanical sense. They are assumed to interact mutually due to certain intermolecular forces. The force exerted on particle (molecule) i by particle j is given by

$$\mathcal{F}_{ij} = \varkappa_{ij} \frac{\mathbf{R}_{ij}}{R_{ij}^{s+1}}, \quad s = 2, 3, \ldots \tag{1.2-1}$$

Where $\mathbf{R}_{ij}$ is the position vector of particle j relative to the position of particle i, and $\varkappa_{ij}$ represents constants characterizing species of particles in interaction. (If the particles are electrons, then $\varkappa_{ij} = e^2$. Here e is the electronic charge.) Among these forces, the Coulomb force, of which $s = 2$, causes a special situation. It denies the Boltzmann collision integral any convergency; it denies the validity of the BBGKY theory in general. The forces represented by eq. (1) do

not include magnetic inter-particle forces which are essential in interactions among charged particles of extremely high energies; of course dynamics of these particles should be relativistic and are not considered in this study.

In Part I, the main course indicated with the double line in Fig. 1.2-1 is presented partly because of its merit of providing for us the opportunity to review the classical standards, and partly for the convenience of raising the questions which will be answered in the following parts. Rarefied gases are investigated in Part II and ionized gases in Part III. It is emphasized that in those treatments the proper recognition of the specific time scales and the comparative significance of each of those physical processes involved in the problems is the essential clue of solution.

In summation, the main problems raised and discussed in this study are as follows: (1) What is the physical implication of the BBGKY theory? (2) How is the Boltzmann equation properly derived from the Liouville equation without the assumption of weak collisions? (3) What is the kinetic-theoretical significance of a rarefied gas? (4) What is the kinetic-theoretical significance of an ionized gas?

In order to answer the questions raised above, we will note the following: (1) Each procedure of gas-dynamical experimentation is conducted with respect to a single system. (2) Significant phenomena (behaviors) of a gas occur and evolve with finite scales of time and space. (3) Significant quantities specifing these phenomena are not necessarily integrals of motion of an isolated system. (4) Due to initial and boundary conditions controlled in the macroscopic sense and due to external forces, these quantities which are not integrals of motion of an isolated system may exist in a gas in the secular sense.

The inter-molecular force law given by eq. (1) is after all a simplified approximation, and dynamics of constituent particles based on this force law does not dictate precisely the dynamical behavior of real gases. The question when, where and how the conclusions derived from the present force law deviate from real phenomena

11

which we intend to predict is open.[†] This is a matter of trial. We simply think that general modes of dynamics would be well presented by this model. If it fails in some cases, it will give us the direction of choosing another trial in the future.

[†] There are several other force laws considered for the basis, as reviewed, for example, by Hirschfelder *et al.* (1950), Chapman and Cowling (1950), and Waldmann (1960). Particularly, Lennard–Jones's force law has been useful for treating dense gases and liquids.

CHAPTER 2

The Liouville equation

2.1. Dynamics of N particles[†]

We investigate dynamical behavior of the particles (material points) constituting a gas which is known, throughout the entire period of time of our investigation, to be present in a part of the configuration space whose volume is V (Fig. 2.1-1). The domain may be called domain V. By this statement, we do not necessarily mean that the whole domain V is filled with the gas. There may be some parts which are completely empty of particles; the gas may be in a container which occupies only a part of domain V; the gas may be in the process of expansion toward the boundary of domain V; sometimes there may be walls and force fields which disturb its free expansion. In the above consideration we should note that the velocity and acceleration of a particle are always finite and that the time periods of our investigation are also finite.

There are two main roles of a container such as considered in the above: (1) One is simply a convenience of keeping the maximum spatial extent of a system; (2) the other is to provide the initial and boundary conditions to be imposed upon a gas contained in it. It may be misleading to assume that the container is made of walls

[†] The reader might think that the treatment in the following is primitive. The analytical treatment in accordance with Hamilton's formalism is simpler. See Whittaker (1937). But abstract formalisms often lead us to the axiomatization of treatments which tends to obscure matters critical for kinetic theories. Let us follow, for a while, primitive and primary reasoning.

13

which are solid, fixed, insulating heat and so forth. The walls are under control in the macroscopic sense as a part of the procedure of experiment; they may be flexible, deformable, sliding, may conduct

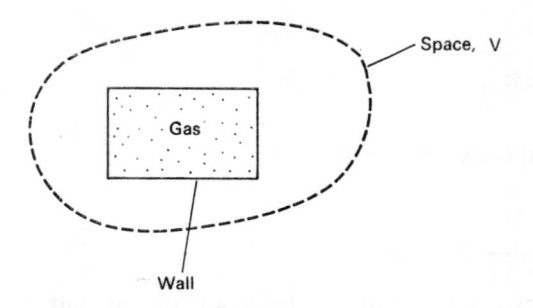

FIG. 2.1-1.

A gas (system) is known to be present within space V throughout the entire period of time of our observation. The gas may be in a container of which the volume is smaller than V; the gas may also be free and in the process of expansion.

heat, and so forth. Those walls are represented by force fields. As will be seen later in due course, our theory is made so that the conclusion is valid with respect to subsystems which are remote from any of the walls; the complex interaction between a subsystem of the gas and a real wall is substituted by a statistical boundary condition hypothetically imposed upon the statistical distribution function of molecules belonging to the subsystem. (It may be said, at this moment, that no kinetic theory has ever treated the interaction between a gas and a wall in the genuinely kinetic-theoretical sense. Unfortunately we have to follow the same tradition.)

The number of the particles in a system is denoted by N; the particles are of a single species, and each is a material point of mass m. Since we assume that each individual particle is discrete and there is no strong and permanent aggregation among them such as seen in a system in liquid and/or solid state, it is rather misguiding to introduce any generalized coordinate system such as usual in analyt-

14

ical dynamics treating general many-body systems.[†] Thus we specify the state of each individual particle, particle i for example, by position vector $\mathbf{r}_i$, and momentum $\mathbf{p}_i$; the state is often represented by X_i;

$$X_i \equiv (\mathbf{r}_i, \mathbf{p}_i), \quad i = 1, 2, \ldots, N. \tag{2.1-1}$$

If it is convenient, we use the coordinates with respect to a rectangular Cartesian coordinate system:

$$\mathbf{r}_i \equiv (r_{ix}, r_{iy}, r_{iz}), \tag{2.1-2}$$
$$\mathbf{p}_i \equiv (p_{ix}, p_{iy}, p_{iz}).$$

Time is denoted by t.

Newton's law of motion of particle i is given by

$$\dot{\mathbf{r}}_i \equiv \frac{d\mathbf{r}_i}{dt} = \frac{\mathbf{p}_i}{m} \tag{2.1-3}$$

$$\dot{\mathbf{p}}_i \equiv \frac{d\mathbf{p}_i}{dt} = \mathcal{F}_i, \tag{2.1-4}$$

where $\mathcal{F}_i$ is the force exerted on particle i:

$$\mathcal{F}_i = \mathcal{F}_{io} + \mathcal{F}_{iw} + \sum_{j=1}^{N} \mathcal{F}_{ij}, \quad \mathcal{F}_{ii} = 0, \tag{2.1-5}$$

$\mathcal{F}_{io}$ is the force exerted from the outside of the domain V and $\mathcal{F}_{iw}$ represents the effect of the walls, while $\mathcal{F}_{ij}$ is the force exerted by particle j in the same system. Let us assume that force $\mathcal{F}_{io}$ is electromagnetic and/or gravitational, and is a function of $\mathbf{r}_i$, $\mathbf{p}_i$, and t only. But force $\mathcal{F}_{iw}$ is to be more complex. A wall is also constituted of molecules which are subject to certain dynamical laws. In a strict sense, the walls and the gas in contact with them are to be considered to constitute a system. Force $\mathcal{F}_{iw}$ is a function not only of $\mathbf{r}_i$ and $\mathbf{p}_i$

[†] Gibbs (1902) abandoned the molecular hypothesis from the beginning of his statistical theory. Furthermore his interest is in integrals of motion of an isolated system. Therefore he considered generalized coordinate systems. See the quotation of his statement about this matter in Appendix G. If we take generalized coordinate systems, our standing point will be obscured.

15

but also of the states of all the molecules constituting the walls. Of course the states change as time passes. We assume, however, that the molecular structure of a wall is extremely stable compared with the state of the gas in contact with it. The wall may obtain and/or lose some energy by its collision with particles constituting the gas contained in it; its structure may change by the collisions. But the microscopic change is slight so that the microscopic state of the container is almost stationary.[†] Thereby we may assume that $\mathcal{F}_{iw}$ is defined as a function of $\mathbf{r}_i$, $\mathbf{p}_i$, and t only, if the function is complex. If $\mathbf{r}_i$ and $\mathbf{p}_i$ are given, the temporal change of $\mathcal{F}_{iw}$ is secular.

Because of those complex forces, it is not possible to solve completely those simultaneous equations given by eqs. (3) and (4). As a matter of principle, however, $\mathbf{r}_i$ and $\mathbf{p}_i$ are functions of t and of the initial values of all the quantities representing the states of the particles. Since the initial value of each component of the position vectors and momentums of the N particles may be chosen as independent of the others, the number of the degrees of freedom of the gas is $6N$. Hence, each of the variables, $\mathbf{r}_i$ and $\mathbf{p}_i$, are considered as independent of the others.[‡] It is possible to introduce some restrictive conditions such as

$$p_{ix} = \varphi(r_{ix}, p_{iz}).$$

But the introduction of such restrictive conditions is assumed to be equivalent to the consideration of some proper external forces and initial and boundary conditions represented by $\mathcal{F}_{iw}$; our present approach to treat the variables $\mathbf{r}_i$ and $\mathbf{p}_i$ as independent ones is not encumbered by those restrictive conditions.

Let us define the variation of the states of particles Δ by

$$\Delta = \prod_{i=1}^{N} \Delta^3\mathbf{r}_i \, \Delta^3\mathbf{p}_i, \quad \Delta^3\mathbf{r}_i = \Delta r_{ix} \Delta r_{iy} \Delta r_{iz}, \quad \text{etc.} \quad (2.1\text{-}6)$$

[†] But the state of the wall may change in the macroscopic sense as explained in the beginning of this section.

[‡] By varying the initial values of those variables properly, we may vary only one variable at time t, for example p_{iz}, without varying any of the other $(6N-1)$ variables at the same time. On the other hand, the variables $\dot{\mathbf{p}}_i$, defined by eq. (4) are not independent.

16

As shown in Fig. 2.1-2, we consider an elementary partial space
(1, 2, 3, 4) in the $r_{ix}r_{iy}$-space at time t. Here $\Delta r_{ix} = \overline{12}$, etc. By time
$t' = t + \Delta t$, point 1 which represents in part a state of particle i has
moved to $1'$, and 2 to $2'$, and so forth, each according to eqs. (3) and
(4). Then at time t', $\Delta r'_{ix}$ corresponding to Δr_{ix} at time t is given by

$$\Delta r'_{ix} - \Delta r_{ix} = (\dot{r}_{ix})_{\text{at 2}}\,\Delta t - (\dot{r}_{ix})_{\text{at 1}}\,\Delta t$$

$$= \left[\left(\dot{r}_{ix} + \frac{\partial \dot{r}_{ix}}{\partial r_{ix}}\,\Delta r_{ix}\right) - \dot{r}_{ix}\right]_{\text{at 1}}\Delta t$$

$$= \frac{\partial \dot{r}_{ix}}{\partial r_{ix}}\,\Delta r_{ix}\,\Delta t$$

or

$$\frac{d\,\Delta r_{ix}}{dt} = \frac{\partial \dot{r}_{ix}}{\partial r_{ix}}\,\Delta r_{ix}.$$

By considering the displacement with respect to each of the components, we obtain

$$\frac{d}{dt}\Delta = \sum_i \left(\frac{\partial}{\partial \mathbf{r}_i}\cdot\dot{\mathbf{r}}_i + \frac{\partial}{\partial \mathbf{p}_i}\cdot\dot{\mathbf{p}}_i\right). \tag{2.1-7}$$

Substitution of eqs. (3) and (4) in eq. (7) leads to

$$\frac{d}{dt}\Delta = \left(\sum_i \frac{\partial}{\partial \mathbf{p}_i}\cdot\mathcal{F}_i\right)\Delta. \tag{2.1-8}$$

As assumed by eq. (1.2-1), the inter-particle forces are functions of
the $\mathbf{r}$'s only. Hence, $\partial/\partial\mathbf{p}_i\cdot\mathcal{F}_{ij} = 0$. When $\mathcal{F}_{io}$ is a gravity and/or
electric force, it also holds that $\partial/\partial\mathbf{p}_i\cdot\mathcal{F}_{io} = 0$. If $\mathcal{F}_{io}$ is a magnetic
force, $\mathcal{F}_{io}$ is a function of $\mathbf{p}_i$. But the component of $\mathcal{F}_{io}$ in a direction
is independent of the component of $\mathbf{p}_i$ in the same direction, and
hence again $\partial/\partial\mathbf{p}_i\cdot\mathcal{F}_{io} = 0$. The effect of the container wall has
been represented by $\mathcal{F}_{iw}$. If the collision of particle i with the wall is
elastic and $\mathcal{F}_{iw}$ is a potential force, it is most likely that $\partial/\partial\mathbf{p}_i\cdot\mathcal{F}_{iw}$
vanishes. But, if particle i loses and/or gains some energy by its

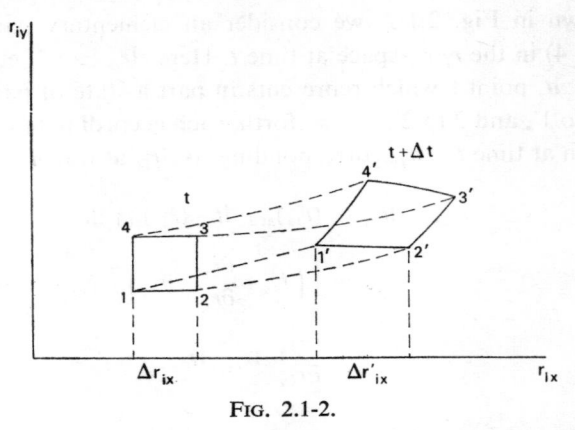

FIG. 2.1-2.

The representative points at 1, 2, 3, 4 in the $r_{ix} r_{iy}$ sub-space at time t move respectively to $1'$, $2'$, $3'$, $4'$ by time $t + \Delta t$.

collision with the wall, it does not necessarily vanish. In general, eq. (8) yields

$$\frac{d}{dt} \Delta = \left(\sum_i \frac{\partial}{\partial \mathbf{p}_i} \cdot \mathcal{F}_{iw} \right) \Delta. \tag{2.1-9}$$

If the collision with the wall is elastic regarding all the particles, we have

$$\frac{d}{dt} \Delta = 0. \tag{2.1-10}$$

Relation (10) dictates the Liouville theorem proposed by Liouville (1838).

Each of the position vectors and momentums $\mathbf{r}'_i$, $\mathbf{p}'_i$, $i = 1.2, \ldots, N$, which represent the state of a system at time t' is a function of the position vectors and momentums $\mathbf{r}_i$, $\mathbf{p}_i$ which represent the state of the same system at time t.

$$\left. \begin{aligned} \mathbf{r}'_i &\equiv \mathbf{r}'_i(\mathbf{r}_1, \mathbf{r}_2, \ldots, \mathbf{r}_N, \mathbf{p}_1, \ldots, \mathbf{p}_N; \quad t, t') \\ \mathbf{p}'_i &\equiv \mathbf{p}'_i(\mathbf{r}_1, \mathbf{r}_2, \ldots, \mathbf{r}_N, \mathbf{p}_1, \ldots, \mathbf{p}_N; \quad t, t') \end{aligned} \right\} . \tag{2.1-11}$$

From the above, it follows that

$$\prod_{i}^{N} \Delta^3 \mathbf{r}_i' \, \Delta^3 \mathbf{p}_i' = \frac{\partial(\mathbf{r}_1', \ldots, \mathbf{p}_N')}{\partial(\mathbf{r}_1, \ldots, \mathbf{p}_N)} \prod_{i}^{N} \Delta^3 \mathbf{r}_i \, \Delta^3 \mathbf{p}_i .$$

In the case where relation (10) holds,

$$\prod \Delta^3 \mathbf{r}_i' \, \Delta^3 \mathbf{p}_i' = \prod \Delta^3 \mathbf{r}_i \, \Delta^3 \mathbf{p}_i = \Delta \quad \text{(invariant)}$$

and hence

$$\frac{\partial(\mathbf{r}_1', \ldots, \mathbf{p}_N')}{\partial(\mathbf{r}_1, \ldots, \mathbf{p}_N)} = 1. \tag{2.1-12}$$

We imagine a $6N$-dimensional space of which the coordinates are given by

$$r_{ix}, r_{iy}, r_{iz}, p_{ix}, p_{iy}, p_{iz}; \quad i = 1, 2, \ldots, N.$$

The space is called the phase space. A point in the phase space may represent a complete state of a system at time t. When a point in the phase space represents the state of a system, the point is called the representative point of the system. Let us consider a closed surface[†] in the phase space at time t_1. Each point on the surface is supposed to represent a state of the same system of N particles. As time passes, according to eqs. (3) and (4), the representative surface moves and deforms. A point, representing a state, located inside the space closed by the surface at t_1 also moves as time passes. But the representative point will never cross the representative surface, if the walls of the container are elastic and $\partial/\partial \mathbf{p}_i \cdot \mathcal{F}_{iw}$ vanishes. If the representative point were on the representative surface at time $t_2 > t_1$, two different states at time t_1, one inside the closed surface and the other on the surface, should have resulted in one single state at time t_2. Since Newton's equations of motion of those particles are time-reversible when the wall is elastic, the above situation implies that an initial state results in two different states. This is not conceivable. Hence we conclude that a point representing a state of a system inside the closed

[†] To consider a closed surface in the $6N$-dimensional phase space is to consider a closed surface in each of the $2N$ three-dimensional spaces.

surface representing the states of many systems of time t_1 remains always inside the surface, no matter how the surface is deformed. If we consider v systems with their representative points inside Δ at time t, we have

$$\frac{d}{dt}\left(\frac{v}{\Delta}\right) = 0 \qquad (2.1\text{-}13)$$

in the case where eq. (10) holds.

2.2. The Liouville equation

In the last section, our approach was to follow the movement of the representative point of a system in the $6N$-dimensional phase space along the time axis. In this section, we consider an elementary domain fixed in the phase space, and observe the representative points passing through the domain.

If the states of the systems constituting an ensemble are represented by an ensemble of points distributed in the phase space at time t, we may define density $D^{(N)}$ by

$$D^{(N)} = \lim_{\Pi\,\Delta X_i \to 0} \frac{\Delta v}{\prod \Delta X_i}, \qquad (2.2\text{-}1)$$

where $\prod \Delta X_i$ is the volume of an elementary domain and Δv is the number of the representative points found inside the elementary domain. In general $D^{(N)}$ is not uniform in the phase space. Since the representative point of each system moves in the phase space as observed previously, $D^{(N)}$ is a function not only of the coordinates X_i of the point where $D^{(N)}$ is observed but also of time t. Note that a set of those coordinates represents an arbitrary point in the phase space; the set is not the representative point of a particular system moving in the phase space. If the derivatives of $D^{(N)}$ are defined with

---

† If we take $-t$ and $-\mathbf{p}_i$ respectively for t and $\mathbf{p}_i$ in eqs. (3) and (4), and assume $\mathcal{F}_i$ to be independent of the sign of time, we obtain again eqs. (3) and (4).

respect to those coordinates at time t, we may present the conservation of the number of the systems constituting the ensemble by

$$\frac{\partial}{\partial t} D^{(N)} + \sum_i \left[\frac{\partial}{\partial \mathbf{r}_i} \cdot (\dot{\mathbf{r}}_i D^{(N)}) + \frac{\partial}{\partial \mathbf{p}_i} \cdot (\dot{\mathbf{p}}_i D^{(N)}) \right] = 0, \qquad (2.2\text{-}2)$$

where the quantities $\dot{\mathbf{r}}_i$, $\dot{\mathbf{p}}_i$ are the change rates of the coordinates of a representative point passing through the fixed point under consideration. As considered previously in deriving eq. (2.1-8), we have

$$\frac{\partial}{\partial \mathbf{p}_i} \cdot \dot{\mathbf{p}}_i = \frac{\partial}{\partial \mathbf{p}_i} \cdot \mathcal{F}_{iw}. \qquad (2.2\text{-}3)$$

It may be convenient to replace the above with an operator defined by

$$\frac{\partial}{\partial \mathbf{p}_i} \cdot \mathcal{F}_{iw} = \left(\mathcal{F}'_{iw} \cdot \frac{\partial}{\partial \mathbf{p}_i} D^{(N)} \right) / D^{(N)}. \qquad (2.2\text{-}3)'$$

But $\mathcal{F}'_{iw}$, depending on $D^{(N)}$, is an unknown and possibly complicated function. According to those considerations, we obtain

$$\left. \begin{aligned} \frac{\partial}{\partial \mathbf{p}_i} \cdot (\dot{\mathbf{p}}_i D^{(N)}) &= \left(\frac{\partial}{\partial \mathbf{p}_i} \cdot \dot{\mathbf{p}}_i \right) D^{(N)} + \dot{\mathbf{p}}_i \cdot \frac{\partial}{\partial \mathbf{p}_i} D^{(N)} \\ &= (\mathcal{F}'_{iw} + \mathcal{F}_i) \cdot \frac{\partial}{\partial \mathbf{p}_i} D^{(N)}, \end{aligned} \right\} \qquad (2.2\text{-}4)$$

where

$$\mathcal{F}_i = \mathcal{F}_{io} + \mathcal{F}_{iw} + \sum_j \mathcal{F}_{ij}. \qquad (2.2\text{-}5)$$

It is a matter of course that

$$\frac{\partial}{\partial \mathbf{r}_i} \cdot \dot{\mathbf{r}}_i = \frac{\partial}{\partial \mathbf{r}_i} \cdot \frac{\mathbf{p}_i}{m} = 0. \qquad (2.2\text{-}6)$$

Substitution of eqs. (4) and (6) in eq. (2) leads to

$$\left[\frac{\partial}{\partial t} + \sum \frac{\mathbf{p}_i}{m} \cdot \frac{\partial}{\partial \mathbf{r}_i} + \sum (\mathcal{F}_i + \mathcal{F}'_{iw}) \cdot \frac{\partial}{\partial \mathbf{p}_i} \right] D^{(N)} = 0. \qquad (2.2\text{-}7)$$

21

Being a linear partial differential equation of the first order, the Liouville equation (7) has the following characteristic equations:

$$\frac{d\mathbf{r}_i}{dt} = \frac{\mathbf{p}_i}{m}, \qquad (2.2\text{-}8)$$

$$\frac{d\mathbf{p}_i}{dt} = \mathcal{F}_i + \mathcal{F}'_{iw} \qquad (2.2\text{-}9)$$

$$i = 1, 2, \ldots, N$$

$$\left(\frac{dD^{(N)}}{dt}\right)_{\text{along a trajectory}} = 0. \qquad (2.2\text{-}10)$$

Here a trajectory means a line in the phase space along which the state of a system evolves according to eqs. (8) and (9). Equation (10) presents the Liouville theorem in a broad sense.

2.3. Solutions of the Liouville equation

2.3-1. PARTICULAR SOLUTION

Let us begin our investigation of the Liouville equation with the simplest case. Suppose that we have a particle named particle 1 confined in a box; $N = 1$. Even when we do not know precisely the state, momentum, and position, it is obvious that the particle is in a single state at any moment of time. The state denoted by $X_1^*(t)$ is a function of time. In accordance with the definition given previously, the distribution function of the particle is

$$D^{(1)}(X_1; t) = \delta(\mathbf{p}_1 - \mathbf{p}_1^*(t))\delta(\mathbf{r}_1 - \mathbf{r}_1^*(t)) = \delta(X_1 - X_1^*(t)), \quad (2.3\text{-}1)$$

where X_1 and t are independent variables.[†] According to the definition of δ-function,

$$\left.\begin{array}{l} D^{(1)}(X_1; t) = 0 \quad \text{if} \quad X_1 \neq X_1^* \\ \int D^{(1)}(X_1; t)\,dX_1 = 1. \end{array}\right\} \qquad (2.3\text{-}2)$$

[†] Here

$$\delta(\mathbf{p}) \equiv \delta(p_x)\delta(p_y)\delta(p_z), \quad \text{etc.}$$

Here the domain of the integration is to be sufficiently large that the entire space inside the box and the possible maximum momentum of the particle are covered. It also holds that

$$\int \varphi(X_1) D^{(1)}(X_1; t) \, dX_1 = \varphi(X_1^*(t)).$$ (2.3-3)

There are specific functions which display the characteristics of $\delta(x)$ such as (see, e.g., Courant–Hilbert (1953))

$$\frac{a}{\pi^{1/2}} \exp(-a^2 x^2), \quad \frac{\sin(ax)}{\pi x}, \text{ etc.}$$

where a approaches ∞. It is easily shown that $D^{(1)}$ given in the above satisfies the Liouville equation

$$\left(\frac{\partial}{\partial t} + \frac{\mathbf{p}_i}{m} \cdot \frac{\partial}{\partial \mathbf{r}_i} + \mathcal{F}_i \cdot \frac{\partial}{\partial \mathbf{p}_i} \right) D^{(1)} = 0.$$ (2.3-4)

Proof: the characteristic equations of eq. (4)

$$\frac{d\mathbf{r}_i}{dt} = \frac{\mathbf{p}_i}{m}, \quad \frac{d\mathbf{p}_i}{dt} = \mathcal{F}_i$$ (2.3-5)

are the equations of motion which $X_1^*(t)$ is to satisfy; if $X_1 = X_1^*$, then the left-hand side of eq. (4) vanishes on substitution of (1); if $X_1 \neq X_1^*$, then $D^{(1)}$ vanishes itself. In any case $D^{(1)}$ satisfies (4).

If we have another similar particle, named particle 2, confined in another box, we may have similarly for the distribution function

$$D^{(1)}(X_2; t) = \delta(X_2 - X_2^*(t)).$$ (2.3-6)

The existence of particle 1 is compatible with the existence of particle 2, and they are distinguishable by being separated in two boxes. If we wish to present the distribution of the two particles by one function, we may define the joint distribution function by

$$D^{(2)}(X_1, X_2; t) = \delta(X_1 - X_1^*(t)) \delta(X_2 - X_2^*(t)).$$ (2.3-7)

Since $X_1^*(t)$ is always different from $X_2^*(t)$, it is obvious that $D^{(2)}$ is not symmetric with respect to the interchange between X_1 and X_2:

$$D^{(2)}(X_1, X_2; t) \neq D^{(2)}(X_2, X_1; t).$$ (2.3-8)

23

Let us suppose that we take off the walls of the two boxes at time t_0. From this time on, $X_1^*(t)$ and $X_2^*(t)$ satisfy the simultaneous equations of motion of the two particles in interaction, and the joint distribution function is given by eq. (8) in the same way as before. The reasons for this conclusion are that the state of particle 1 can change only continuously with finite rates of change according to $X_1^*(t)$ which presents a continuous extension from the state of particle 1 inside the first box at time t_0, and that the state of particle 2 can change similarly along $X_2^*(t)$ extending from the state of particle 2 inside the second box at time t_0. As long as $X_1^*(t)$ and $X_2^*(t)$ are mutually distinguishable, the two particles are distinguishable by their states. (Without state, no particle does exist!) If there is a time when

$$X_1^*(t) = X_2^*(t), \tag{2.3-9}$$

the above statement is not plausible after this time. As long as the two material points simulate two real particles, however, consideration of some repulsive force between the particles at short distances is necessary so that condition (9) does not occur. In general, we may extend the same argument to a system consisting of N particles:

$$D^{(N)} = \prod_{i=1}^{N} \delta(X_i - X_i^*(t)). \tag{2.3-10}$$

The distribution is not symmetric with respect to the interchange of coordinates between two similar particles in the system:

$$D^{(N}(X_1, \ldots, X_i, \ldots, X_j, \ldots, X_N)$$
$$\neq D^{(N)}(X_1, \ldots, X_j, \ldots, X_i, \ldots, X_N). \tag{2.3-10'}$$

Of course, it is a simple matter to show that $D^{(N)}$ given above satisfies eq. (2.2-7); $D^{(N)}$ given above is a particular solution of eq. (2.2-7). Investigation of the particular solution is indispensable for kinetic theory of which the main purpose is to treat stochastic processes occurring in a single system.

2.3-2. GENERAL SOLUTION

We write for $X_i^*(t)$

$$X_i^*(t) = X_i^*(t_0) + X_i'(t), \tag{2.3-11}$$

where

$$X_i'(t_0) = 0,$$

$$\frac{d\mathbf{p}_i'}{dt} = \mathcal{F}_i^* \quad \text{(a function of the } X_i^*(t)\text{'s)},$$

$$\frac{d\mathbf{r}_i'}{dt} = \frac{\mathbf{p}_i^*(t)}{m}, \tag{2.3-12}$$

and $X_1^*(t_0)$ may be chosen arbitrarily. On substitution of the $X_i^*(t)$'s defined above in eq. (10), we have

$$D^{(N)} = \prod_{i=1}^{N} \delta(X_i - X^*(t_0) - X_i'(t)) \tag{2.3-13}$$

Suppose that we have an arbitrary function of $X_1^*(t_0)$, $X_2^*(t_0)$, ...

$$\varphi = \varphi(X_1^*(t_0), X_2^*(t_0), \ldots, X_N^*(t_0)). \tag{2.3-14}$$

In terms of φ and $D^{(N)}$, we define

$$\left. \begin{aligned} \Phi(X_1, X_2, \ldots, X_N; t) &= \int \varphi D^{(N)} \prod_{i=1}^{N} dX_i^*(t_0) \\ &= \varphi(X_1 - X_1'(t), X_2 - X_2'(t), \ldots, X_N - X_N'(t)). \end{aligned} \right\} \tag{2.3-15}$$

X_i, $i = 1, 2, \ldots, N$, and t are the independent variables. When an arbitrary set of values of these independent variables is chosen, there is a set of $X_i^*(t_0)$ such that

$$\begin{aligned} X_i &= X_i^*(t) \\ i &= 1, 2, \ldots, N \end{aligned} \tag{2.3-16}$$

are satisfied according to eq. (11), if φ is defined with respect to a sufficiently large domain of the phase space. Under condition (16),

25

$D^{(N)}$ given by eq. (13) and also $\varphi D^{(N)} \prod dX_i^*(t_0)$ satisfy the Liouville equation. Therefore, Φ given by (15) is the general solution of the Liouville equation. It is noted that, according to eqs. (12) and (16), $\mathbf{p}_i'$ and $\mathbf{r}_i'$ are solutions of

$$\left.\begin{array}{l} \dfrac{d\mathbf{p}_i'}{dt} = \mathcal{F}_i \\[2mm] \dfrac{d\mathbf{r}_i'}{dt} = \dfrac{\mathbf{p}_i}{m}, \end{array}\right\} \qquad (2.3\text{-}17)$$

where the right-hand side terms are independent of t. According to eq. (17), then we have

$$\mathbf{p}_i' = \mathcal{F}_i(t-t_0)$$

$$\mathbf{r}_i' = \frac{\mathbf{p}_i}{m}(t-t_0).$$

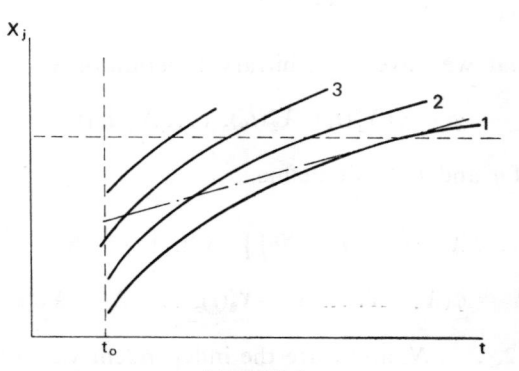

FIG. 2.3-1.

X_i and t are independent variables. Each of the solid lines is a possible trajectory of particle i on which $D^{(N)}$ given by eq. (13) may exist. Each trajectory has its own $X_i^*(t_0)$ and $X_i'(t)$. If the trajectories are numbered consecutively, we may have $X_i^*(t_0)_1$, $X_i'(t)_1$, $X_i^*(t_0)_2$, $X_i'(t)_2$, ... On the other hand, $X_i'(t)$ in φ given by eq. (15) does not belong to a particular trajectory, but consists of those which belong to many different trajectories which line $X_t = \text{const}$ cuts transversally along the time axis. The chain line is a solution of eq. (17).

Obviously these do not present a real trajectory of particle i. The situation might appear rather paradoxical. But it is not so. When X_i is given, $X_i^*(t_0)$, from which $X_i^*(t)$ in (16) is calculated according to eq. (11), changes as t changes. In other words, $X_i^*(t)$ and, also, $X_i'(t)$ are accounted for at each different time with respect to a different trajectory of particle i. See the illustration in Fig. 2.3-1.

2.3-3. ADDITIONAL REMARKS

In view of the above solutions, we note the following: the Liouville equation itself is not concerned with the nature of the initial condition of $D^{(N)}$, but simply gives the law of the time evolution of $D^{(N)}$ from one moment of time to another. The Liouville equation implies no statistical sense. Gibbs (1902) called

$$\int \prod_i dX_i$$

the extension-in-phase, and interpreted the Liouville theorem as a theorem of conservation of the extension-in-phase for an element of phase space moving with the dust of representative points. The extension-in-phase is often interpreted as the representation of the microscopic ambiguity in the state of a real system; thereby the Liouville equation is quoted as a theorem of probability conservation. This interpretation is pragmatically feasible in statistical mechanics dealing with thermal equilibrium; but the interpretation is misleading in kinetic theory dealing with the time evolution of the state of a system, as will be made clear in the following. Let us recall the first of the three gas-dynamical experiments stated in Section 1.1. That is the experiment of producing shock waves in a shock tube. Since we repeat the same procedure of the experiment with the same gas constituted of N similar particles, it is convenient to let a point in the $6N$-dimensional phase space represent the state of the gas at a moment of time (Fig. 2.3-2). Of course, we do not know precisely where the point is located. But it is obvious that

the location is a single point because the system is one. The state of the gas during one procedure of the experiment which begins at time 0 when the diaphragm is open and ends at time τ, is represented by a trajectory line in the phase space. Note that the trajectory is a single trajectory even if we do not know the location precisely. By

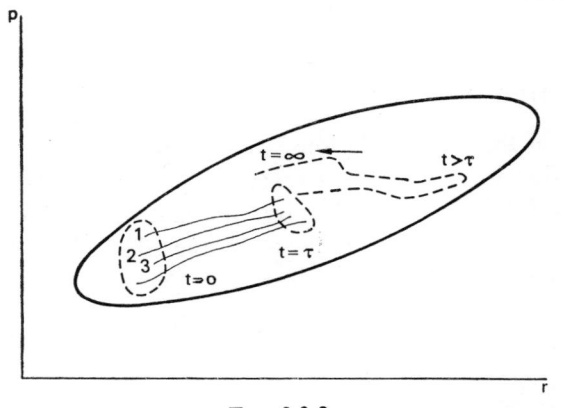

FIG. 2.3-2.

The bold solid line encircles the domain of a canonical ensemble in the phase space. A solid line beginning at $t = 0$ and ending at $t = \tau$ represents the microscopic state of a gas during a procedure of the experiment producing a shock wave in a shock tube. Microscopic states of the same gas in repeated procedures of the same experiment are represented by solid lines 1, 2, 3, ... The dotted line, extending from line 1, represents the microscopic state of the gas in thermalization after procedure 1.

repeating many procedures of the same experiment with the same gas under macroscopically the same conditions, we obtain the group of trajectories in the phase space. Since those procedures are controlled with macroscopic means, each trajectory may be different from the others in the microscopic sense. The domain of the phase space occupied by those trajectories is specified with macroscopic states of the gas.

28

2.4. Distribution functions of subsystems and their evolution

For the convenience of treatment, we always take for $D^{(N)}$ a function normalized as follows:

$$\int D^{(N)} \prod_{i=1}^{N} dX_i = 1. \tag{2.4-1}$$

The total number of the systems may be either one or more than one.[†] But the total number is invariant. Hence $D^{(N)}$, once normalized, remains so, if time passes. The normalization is always possible: Suppose $D^{(N)'}$ is not yet normalized. Then we may define $D^{(N)}$ by

$$D^{(N)} = D^{(N)'} / \int D^{(N)'} \prod dX_i,$$

which is normalized. It is known that a system is within a finite domain V of the configuration space. Therefore,

$$D^{(N)} = 0, \quad \text{if} \quad |\mathbf{r}_i| = \infty. \tag{2.4-2}$$

Also the total energy of a system is finite and hence

$$D^{(N)} = 0, \quad \text{if} \quad |\mathbf{p}_i| = \infty. \tag{2.4-3}$$

We define the F's as follows:

$$\left.\begin{aligned}
F_i^{(1)}(X_i; t) &= \int D^{(N)} \prod_j dX_j, j \neq i, \\
F_{ij}^{(2)}(X_i, X_j; t) &= \int D^{(N)} \prod_k dX_k, i \leqq j, k \neq i, j, \\
&\cdots\cdots\cdots\cdots \\
F_{1,\ldots,N}^{(N-1)}(X_1, \ldots, X_k, X_m, \ldots, X_N; t) &= \int D^{(N)} dX_l.
\end{aligned}\right\} \tag{2.4-4}$$

Here the integrations range over all the phase space. It is noted that the order of subscripts attached to, for example, $F^{(2)}$ is the

---

[†] This statement is proper, so far as the treatment in this section is concerned. In kinetic theory, however, it is necessary to begin with treating a single system.

same as the order of the same set of subscripts attached to the X's in $F^{(2)}$. This accordance of the orders means that there has been no interchange of coordinates among particles. According to the definition, it holds that

$$F_{ji}^{(2)}(X_j, X_i; t) = F_{ij}^{(2)}(X_i, X_j; t)$$

and

$$\neq F_{ij}^{(2)}(X_j, X_i; t). \tag{2.4-5}$$

Since $D^{(N)}$ is normalized, it holds that

$$\int F_i^{(1)}(X_i; t)\, dX_i = 1. \tag{2.4-6}$$

Defined by

$$f(X; t)\, \Delta X/m^3 = \sum_{i=1}^{N} \int_X^{X+\Delta X} F_i^{(1)}(X_i; t)\, dX_i \tag{2.4-7}$$

$f\, \Delta X/m^3$ gives the number of particles in states between X and $X+\Delta X$ in one system; f is the distribution function appearing familiarly in the Boltzmann equation.[†]

We integrate each member of eq. (2.2-7) as given by

$$\left[\frac{\partial}{\partial t} + \sum_i \frac{\mathbf{p}_i}{m} \cdot \frac{\partial}{\partial \mathbf{r}_i} + \sum_i \sum_j \mathscr{F}_{ij} \cdot \frac{\partial}{\partial \mathbf{p}_i} + \sum_i \mathscr{F}_{i0} \cdot \frac{\partial}{\partial \mathbf{p}_i} + \sum \frac{\partial}{\partial \mathbf{p}_i} \cdot \mathscr{F}_{iw}\right] D^{(N)} = 0, \tag{2.4-8}$$

where operator $\partial/\partial \mathbf{p}_i$ on the left-hand side of $\mathscr{F}_{iw}$ operates not only on $\mathscr{F}_{iw}$ but also on $D^{(N)}$, repeatedly with respect to the coordinates of all the particles, firstly except for particle i, secondly except for particle i and particle j, and successively increasing the number of

---

[†] f is defined as a function of velocity and space coordinates.

$$\Delta X/m^3 = \Delta \mathbf{p}\, \Delta \mathbf{r}/m^3 = \Delta \mathbf{c}\, \Delta \mathbf{r}.$$

excepted particles. Examples of integration of constituent members are shown in the following:

$$\int \cdots \int \frac{\partial}{\partial t} D^{(N)} \prod_{j \neq i} dX_j = \frac{\partial}{\partial t} F_i^{(1)},$$

$$\int \cdots \int \frac{\mathbf{p}_i}{m} \cdot \frac{\partial}{\partial \mathbf{r}_i} D^{(N)} \prod_{j \neq i} dX_j = \frac{\mathbf{p}_i}{m} \cdot \frac{\partial}{\partial \mathbf{r}_i} \int \cdots \int D^{(N)} \prod dX_j$$

$$= \frac{\mathbf{p}_i}{m} \cdot \frac{\partial}{\partial \mathbf{r}_i} F_i^{(1)},$$

$$\sum_{j \neq i} \int \cdots \int \mathcal{F}_{ij} \cdot \frac{\partial}{\partial \mathbf{p}_i} D^{(N)} \prod_{k \neq i} dX_k = \sum_j \int \mathcal{F}_{ij} \cdot \frac{\partial}{\partial \mathbf{p}_i} F_{ij}^{(2)} \, dX_j,$$

$$\int \cdots \int \mathcal{F}_{io} \cdot \frac{\partial}{\partial \mathbf{p}_i} D^{(N)} \prod_{j \neq i} dX_j = \mathcal{F}_{io} \cdot \frac{\partial}{\partial \mathbf{p}_i} F_i^{(1)}, \qquad (2.4\text{-}9)$$

$$\int \cdots \int \frac{\partial}{\partial \mathbf{p}_i} \cdot \mathcal{F}_{iw} D^{(N)} \prod_{j \neq i} dX_j = \frac{\partial}{\partial \mathbf{p}_i} \cdot \mathcal{F}_{iw} F_i^{(1)},$$

$$\int \frac{p_{jx}}{m} \frac{\partial}{\partial r_{jx}} D^{(N)} \, dr_{jx} = \frac{p_{jx}}{m} D^{(N)} \Big|_{r_{jx} = -\infty}^{+\infty} = 0,$$

$$\int (\mathcal{F}_{jix} + \mathcal{F}_{jox}) \frac{\partial}{\partial p_{jx}} D^{(N)} \, dp_{jx} = 0,$$

$$\sum_j \int \frac{\partial}{\partial \mathbf{p}_j} \cdot \mathcal{F}_{jw} D^{(N)} \prod_{k \neq i} dX_k = 0.$$

Considering the above, we obtain in the first case of integration with the exception of particle i

$$\left(\frac{\partial}{\partial t} + \frac{\mathbf{p}_i}{m} \cdot \frac{\partial}{\partial \mathbf{r}_i} + \mathcal{F}_{io} \cdot \frac{\partial}{\partial \mathbf{p}_i} + \frac{\partial}{\partial \mathbf{p}_i} \cdot \mathcal{F}_{iw} \right) F_i^{(1)}$$

$$+ \sum_{j=1}^{N} \int \mathcal{F}_{ij} \cdot \frac{\partial}{\partial \mathbf{p}_i} F_{ij}^{(2)} \, dX_j = 0 \qquad (2.4\text{-}10)$$

(*N* similar equations; $i = 1, 2, \ldots N$),

31

and in the second case

$$\left[\frac{\partial}{\partial t}+\frac{\mathbf{p}_i}{m}\cdot\frac{\partial}{\partial \mathbf{r}_i}+\frac{\mathbf{p}_j}{m}\cdot\frac{\partial}{\partial \mathbf{r}_j}+((\mathscr{F}_{io}+\mathscr{F}_{ij})\cdot\frac{\partial}{\partial \mathbf{p}_i}+((\mathscr{F}_{jo}+\mathscr{F}_{ji})\cdot\frac{\partial}{\partial \mathbf{p}_j}\right.$$
$$\left.+\frac{\partial}{\partial \mathbf{p}_i}\cdot\mathscr{F}_{iw}+\frac{\partial}{\partial \mathbf{p}_j}\cdot\mathscr{F}_{jw}\right]F_{ij}^{(2)}+\sum_{k=1}^{N}\int\left(\mathscr{F}_{ik}\cdot\frac{\partial}{\partial \mathbf{p}_i}+\mathscr{F}_{jk}\cdot\frac{\partial}{\partial \mathbf{p}_j}\right)F_{ijk}^{(3)}\,dX_k=0$$

$$(2.4\text{-}11)$$

$$(N(N-1)/2!\text{ similar equations}),$$

and in the last case

$$\left(\frac{\partial}{\partial t}+\sum_i\frac{\mathbf{p}_i}{m}\cdot\frac{\partial}{\partial \mathbf{r}_i}+\sum_i\mathscr{F}_{io}\cdot\frac{\partial}{\partial \mathbf{p}_i}+\sum_i\sum_j\mathscr{F}_{ij}\cdot\frac{\partial}{\partial \mathbf{p}_i}+\sum_i\frac{\partial}{\partial \mathbf{p}_i}\cdot\mathscr{F}_{iw}\right)F_{12\ldots km\ldots N}^{(N-1)}$$
$$+\sum_i\mathscr{F}_{il}\cdot\frac{\partial}{\partial \mathbf{p}_i}\,D^{(N)}\,dX_l=0$$

$$(2.4\text{-}12)$$

$$N(N-1)\ldots 2/(N-1)! = N \text{ similar equations.}$$

The total number of those equations is 2^N-2:

$$\left.\begin{array}{r}N+\dfrac{N(N-1)}{2!}+\ \cdots\ +\dfrac{N(N-1)\ldots2}{(N-1)!} = (1+1)^N-2 \\[2mm] = 2^N-2. \end{array}\right\} \quad (2.4\text{-}13)$$

Governing the evolutions of those (2^N-2) different distribution functions $F_i^{(1)}$, $F_{ij}^{(2)}$, ..., the above equations are in general different one after another. (If the wall is elastic, time is obviously reversible in those equations. See Section 2.1.)

Being partial differential equations, those equations are interpreted as analogous to the Liouville equation. Let us take eq. (10), for example. Since the equation is a non-homogeneous linear differential equation of the first order regarding $F_i^{(1)}$, we have for the

characteristic equations

$$\frac{d\mathbf{r}_i}{dt} = \frac{\mathbf{p}_i}{m},$$ (2.4-14)

$$\frac{d\mathbf{p}_i}{dt} = \mathcal{F}_{io} + \mathcal{F}_{iw} + \mathcal{F}'_{iw},$$ (2.4-15)

$$\frac{d\mathbf{F}_i^{(1)}}{dt} = \Phi_i,$$ (2.4-16)

where

$$\mathcal{F}'_{iw} \cdot \frac{\partial}{\partial \mathbf{p}_i} F_i^{(1)} = F_i^{(1)} \frac{\partial}{\partial \mathbf{p}_i} \cdot \mathcal{F}_{iw},$$ (2.4-17)

$$\Phi_i = -\sum_{j \neq 1}^{N} \int \mathcal{F}_{ij} \cdot \frac{\partial}{\partial \mathbf{p}_i} F_{ij}^{(2)} \, dX_j.$$ (2.4-18)

Unlike the Liouville theorem that $D^{(N)}$ is invariant along the trajectory of a system in the $6N$-dimensional phase space, $F_i^{(1)}$ is not invariant along the trajectory of the subsystem that is particle i, in the 6-dimensional phase space determined by eqs. (14) and (15) (Fig. 2.4-1):

$$F_i^{(1)}(t) = F_i^{(1)}(t_0) + \int_{t_0}^{t} \Phi_i \, dt.$$ (2.4-16)'

In fact the trajectory determined by eqs. (14) and (15) is not the real trajectory of particle i. The real trajectory is to be determined by taking into account all the forces exerted on particle i, $\mathcal{F}_{io} + \mathcal{F}_{iw} + \mathcal{F}'_{iw} + \sum_j \mathcal{F}_{ij}$. Therefore the real trajectory of particle i deviates from the fictitious trajectory determined by $\mathcal{F}_{io} + \mathcal{F}_{iw} + \mathcal{F}'_{iw}$ only. We cannot solve eq. (10) alone. $F_{ij}^{(2)}$ in the integrand is to be determined by eq. (11). But eq. (11) also cannot be solved by itself, because $F_{ijk}^{(3)}$ is to be obtained from an equation of the next rank, and so forth. Finally eq. (12) is solved only when $D^{(N)}$ is given as a solution of the Liouville equation itself. In other words, the set of equations given by (10), (11), ..., (12) are not closed. If we were given $D^{(N)}$ as an explicit function of $X_1, X_2, \ldots, X_N$, the easiest

way of obtaining the F's would be to consider (4), instead of solving those equations (10), (11), etc.

If particle i under our investigation is sufficiently remote from any wall of the vessel (container), we may ignore $\mathcal{F}_{iw}$ from the equations obtained in the above.

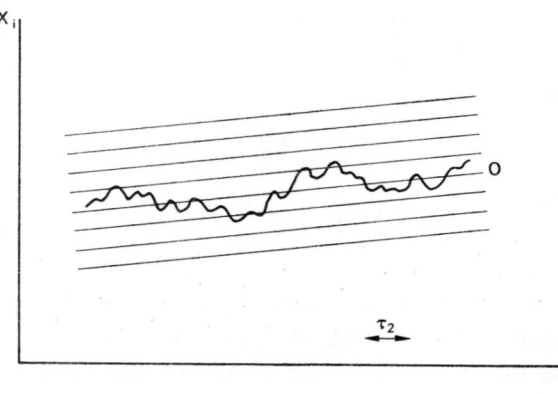

FIG. 2.4-1.

The straight lines are the trajectories determined by eqs. (14) and (15). Among them, trajectory 0 is the particular one on which $F_i^{(1)}$ represented by δ-function is carried along, when $\Phi_i = 0$. If $\Phi_i \neq 0$, $F_i^{(1)}$ is carried along the wavy line, the fluctuations of which are of time scale τ_2.

We may also derive from the Liouville equation, instead of eq. (10),

$$\left.\begin{array}{l}\left(\dfrac{\partial}{\partial t}+\dfrac{\mathbf{p}_i}{m}\,\dfrac{\partial}{\partial \mathbf{r}_i}+\mathcal{F}_{io}\cdot\dfrac{\partial}{\partial \mathbf{p}_i}+\dfrac{\partial}{\partial \mathbf{p}_i}\cdot\mathcal{F}_{iw}\right) F_i^{(1)}(X_i;\,t) \\[3mm] +\displaystyle\sum_{j,\,k}\int(\mathcal{F}_{ij}+\mathcal{F}_{ik})\cdot\dfrac{\partial}{\partial \mathbf{p}_i}\,F_{ijk}^{(3)}(X_i,\,X_j,\,X_k;\,t)\,dX_j\,dX_k = 0.\end{array}\right\} \quad (2.4\text{-}19)$$

Here each of the $N-1$ particles, except for i, is counted only once either by j or by k, and $\sum_{jk}$ means the summation with respect to $(N-1)/2$ pairs of particles. (If $N-1$ is an odd number, we may ignore one of the $N-1$ particles; ignoring the particle is not significant for

the behavior of particle i.) It is also possible to write for the integral term

$$\sum_{j,\,k,\,l} \int \left. \begin{array}{l} (\mathcal{F}_{ij}+\mathcal{F}_{ik}+\mathcal{F}_{il})\cdot\dfrac{\partial}{\partial \mathbf{p}_i}\, F^{(4)}_{i,\,j,\,k,\,l}(X_i,\,X_j,\,X_k\,X_l;\,t) \\[2mm] \times dX_j\,dX_k\,dX_l, \quad \text{etc.} \end{array} \right\} \quad (2.4\text{-}20)$$

In general, in place of each of eqs. (10), (11), $\ldots$, we may derive equations where the integral terms contain integrands constituted of F's of higher multiplicities.

$$\underbrace{\sum_{j,\,k,\,\ldots,\,m}}_{\nu} \int (\mathcal{F}_{ij}+\mathcal{F}_{ik}+\ldots+\mathcal{F}_{im})\cdot\frac{\partial}{\partial \mathbf{p}_i}\, F^{(\nu)}_{i,\,j,\,k,\,\ldots,\,m}\,dX_j\,dX_k\ldots dX_m.$$

$$(2.4\text{-}21)$$

The number of the groups, each of which consists of ν particles, is $(N-1)/\nu$. In other words, if the field particles are represented by ν particles, $(N-1)/\nu$ is the number of such subsystems. There is more than one way of grouping $N-1$ particles into such subsystems; the number of the ways is

$$\frac{(N-1)!}{(\nu!)^{(N-1)/\nu}[(N-1)/\nu]!}. \qquad (2.4\text{-}22)$$

Equation (10) and eq. (19), for example, are mutually equivalent as long as they are considered in the microscopically precise sense.

2.5. Distribution functions in generic phase spaces

Instead of representing the state of each of the individual particles in a different 6-dimensional phase space, it is possible to superpose the states of all the similar particles of a system in a common 6-dimensional phase space which may be called the generic space:

$$\frac{1}{m^3}f(X_a;\,t) = N\overline{F^{(1)}(X_a;\,t)}$$

$$= \frac{1}{\varDelta X_a}\sum_{i=1}^{N}\int_{X_a}^{X_a+\varDelta X_a} F^{(1)}_i(X_i;\,t)\,dX_i, \qquad (2.5\text{-}1)$$

4*

where

$$\Delta X_a = \Delta p_{ax} \, \Delta p_{ay} \, \Delta p_{az} \, \Delta r_{ax} \, \Delta r_{ay} \, \Delta r_{az} \qquad (2.5\text{-}2)$$

is an elementary domain of the generic space. Similarly we may define

$$(N-1)\overline{F_{i0}^{(2)}(X_i, X_b; t)} \, \Delta X_b = \sum_j \int_{X_b}^{X_b + \Delta X_b} F_{ij}^{(2)}(X_i, X_j; t) \, dX_j. \qquad (2.5\text{-}3)$$

In a 12-dimensional generic space, we define

$$\left. \begin{aligned} N(N-1)\overline{F^{(2)}(X_a, X_b; t)} \, \Delta X_a \, \Delta X_b \\ = \sum_i \sum_j \int_{X_a}^{X_a + \Delta X_a} \int_{X_b}^{X_b + \Delta X_b} F_{ij}^{(2)}(X_i, X_j; t) \, dX_i \, dX_j \end{aligned} \right\} \qquad (2.5\text{-}4)$$

In an 18-dimensional generic space, we define

$$N(N-1)(N-2)\overline{F^{(3)}(X_a, X_b, X_c; t)} \, \Delta X_a \, \Delta X_b \, \Delta X_c = \ldots, \qquad (2.5\text{-}5)$$

and so forth.

$f(X_a; t)$ defined by eq. (1) is the number density of similar particles in the 6-dimensional velocity-configuration space and is almost equivalent to the distribution function governed by the Boltzmann equation. According to our previous definitions, functions $F_i^{(1)}$, $F_{ij}^{(2)}$, etc., are discontinuously localized in the phase space. On the other hand, those functions of X_a, X_b, etc., defined above may be continuous in generic spaces, as the number density of the particles in a system increases.

Exercises

1. By assuming that

$$\mathcal{F}_{i0} = \mathcal{F}_{iw} = 0, \quad \mathcal{F}_{ij} = -\frac{d\varphi_{ij}}{d\mathbf{r}_i}$$

and defining E_i by

$$E_i = \frac{1}{2} \frac{p_i^2}{m} + \sum_j \varphi_{ij}$$

show that

$$D^{(N)} = \text{const exp } \left(-\alpha \sum_i E_i\right)$$

is a solution of the Liouville equation, if

$$\frac{\partial D^{(N)}}{\partial t} = 0.$$

A group of similar systems represented by the above solution is called the canonical ensemble by Gibbs (1902). Obviously the distribution is stationary.

2. Two material points are in interaction by a force which is independent of their momenta. Show that their motions are reversible with respect to time. (If the directions of momenta are reversed at time t_1, their positions at time $t_1 + \tau$ will be the same as those at time $t_1 - \tau$.)

3. We define

$$\Delta X_i = \Delta r_{ix} \Delta r_{iy} \Delta r_{iz} \Delta p_{ix} \Delta p_{iy} \Delta p_{iz} = \sum_{\xi=1}^{6} \Delta X_{i\xi}$$

$$D_{i\xi}^{(N)} = \frac{1}{\pi} \int_{-\infty}^{+\infty} \frac{\sin\left(\frac{1}{2} \Delta X_{i\xi}^* \varrho_{i\xi}\right) \cos\left[\varrho_{i\xi}(X_{i\xi} - \frac{1}{2}\Delta X_{i\xi}^* - X_{i\xi}^*)\right]}{\varrho_{i\xi}} d\varrho_{i\xi}$$

[Dirichlet's discontinuous factor; see Courant and Hilbert (1953).]

Then

$$D_{i\xi}^{(N)} = 1 \quad \text{if} \quad X_{i\xi}^* < X_{i\xi} < X_{i\xi}^* + \Delta X_{i\xi}^*$$

$$= \tfrac{1}{2} \quad \text{if} \quad X_{i\xi} = X_{i\xi}^* \quad \text{or} \quad X_{i\xi} = X_{i\xi}^* + \Delta X_{i\xi}^*$$

$$= 0 \quad \text{otherwise.}$$

If X^*'s are governed by the equations of motion of the particles and ΔX_i^* is the displacement (variation) of X_i^* due to a displacement of X_i^* at the initial time, then it is shown that

$$D^{(N)} = \prod_{i=1}^{N} \prod_{\xi=1}^{6} D_{i\xi}^{(N)}$$

is a solution of the Liouville equation.

Gases in Moderate States

CHAPTER 3

The BBGKY Hierarchy

3.1. Introductory remarks

In this part, we trace the way, starting from the Liouville equation and ending at the Navier–Stokes equations, which is depicted with a vertical double line in Fig. 1.2-1. The procedure of the historical development is inverse: the Navier–Stokes equations were first given for continuous media by Navier (1822), Poisson (1829), de Saint-Vernant (1845), and Stokes (1845); later Maxwell (1866) proposed, rather intuitively, equations of transfer by which the Navier–Stokes equations were shown to be derived as based on the hypothesis that a gas consists of small particles. Maxwell's equations of transfer stimulated Boltzmann (1872) to propose the Boltzmann equation of which the implication is much broader than that of Maxwell's. Finally the derivation of the Boltzmann equation from the Liouville equation has been attempted by various authors.

In the following, we first apply a certain statistical operation to eqs. (2.4-10), (2.4-11), ..., which have been derived from the Liouville equation. Secondly, by assuming that most interactions among particles are binary, we may derive the Boltzmann equation from these equations considered above. The third step is to derive the Navier–Stokes equations by means of the Chapman–Enskog method.

The first procedure was proposed independently by Yvon (1935), Born and Green (1946), Bogoliubov (1946), and Kirkwood (1946).

The chain of equations (2.4-10), (2.4-11), ..., interpreted and presented in a statistical sense is called the BBGKY hierarchy of equations after those authors. It must be noted, however, that the interpretation and presentation of the BBGKY hierarchy as proposed by these authors are not plausible and, as a result, the derivation of the Boltzmann equation is not consistent. The difficulty arises from their improper interpretations of the assumption that the distribution function of similar systems in phase space is symmetric with respect to the interchange of the phase space coordinates between any pair of similar particles. Boboliubov seems to believe that the symmetry is a basic property of the distribution function; Kirkwood appears to assert that the symmetry is achieved by coarse-graining the distribution function along the trajectory of a system in phase space; and the other authors attribute the symmetry to the effect of coarse-graining the distribution function with respect to one of Gibbs's ensembles.

It is speculated that Bogoliubov's belief has stemmed either from the hypothesis of degeneracy well established with respect to quantum-mechanical systems or from his implicit consideration of one of Gibbs's ensembles. The quantum-mechanical degeneracy is not the result of thermalization in the classical sense, but is the basic mode of the existence of a system. The degeneracy is proved to exist with respect to electrons bound in atoms and/or in metals. But the feasibility is quite doubtful when one considers an ordinary gas as a quantum-mechanical system. The microscopic symmetry of the distribution function and the Boltzmann collision model are not compatible in their radical meanings. See Appendixes E and F.

Kirkwood's assertion is primarily plausible, since each of our experimental observations is conducted with respect to a single system along the time axis. Later, however, he states that the choice of a system, to be observed along the time axis is made at random among the systems constituting one of Gibbs's ensembles. Gibbs's ensembles are defined as representing systems in statistical equilibrium in view of the partition of energy; such a system chosen at random from an ensemble of Gibbs is not expected to exhibit prop-

erly macroscopic dynamical characteristics which are specific with respect to a system under observation. In spite of his proper approach of time average, Kirkwood experiences a failure, similar to that of Bogoliubov, in the derivation of the Boltzmann equation; he has not pursued persistently his initial approach of time average, seemingly because of his strong adhesion to Gibbs's ensembles.

Since each of our gas-dynamical observations is made with a finite time scale with respect to a single system which is not in thermal equilibrium, kinetic theory dealing with phenomena which are subject to such gas-dynamical observations must be detached from Gibbs's concepts of ensembles which are defined with respect to energy (an integral of motion of an isolated system) and indefinitely long time scales of observation. Gibbs interpreted the Liouville equation as governing the probability density cloud of similar systems at the beginning of his statistical mechanics. Gibbs's interpretation of the Liouville equation means one method of coarse-graining. There are many other methods; the feasibility of a choice is not a matter of axiomatic proposition but a matter of rational investigation. (Gibbs's choice has been proved to be a feasible one, with respect to systems in thermal equilibrium.)

Some authors think that transient or gas-dynamical phenomena in a system are interpreted as thermal fluctuations in a system in thermal equilibrium. Since gas-dynamical phenomena are harnessed by initial and boundary conditions and external forces, the above interpretation is not plausible, as is discussed in Section 1.1.

As discussed in Chapter 2, the Liouville equation itself has no statistical meaning. Proper coarse-graining operations applied to the Liouville equation in Chapter 3 lead to the proper presentation of the BBGKY hierarchy. It is easy now in Chapter 4 to derive the Boltzmann equation from the hierarchy without the assumption of weak collision. Then, in Chapter 5, the Chapman–Enskog theory leads us from the Boltzmann equation to the Navier–Stokes equations; the last step is the part best paved of all the course. Section 5.3 is devoted to the presentation of an anomalous but strict iteration

method for deriving the Navier–Stokes equations from the Boltzmann equation. The merit will become obvious in Part II.

The forces $\mathscr{F}_{iw}$ are neglected in the Liouville equation and in those derived from the Liouville equation; justification will be given in Section 5.3.

3.2. The symmetry assumption of distribution functions in the microscopic sense

As was explained in Section 2.4, eqs. (2.4-10), (2.4-11), ... do not provide us any particular convenience, in spite of their somewhat simple appearances compared with the Liouville equation. If it is feasible to assume that $D^{(N)}$ is symmetric regarding the interchange of the coordinates between two arbitrary particles, however, an enormous simplicity is introduced to those equations. Here the symmetry means that

$$\left.\begin{aligned} D^{(N)}(X_1, &X_2, \ldots, X_i, \ldots, X_j, \ldots, X_N; t) \\ &= D^{(N)}(X_1, X_2, \ldots, X_j, \ldots, X_i, \ldots, X_N; t). \end{aligned}\right\} \quad (3.2\text{-}1)$$

Simpler examples are

$$\varphi_1(x^2+y^2+z^2) = \varphi_1(y^2+x^2+z^2),$$

$$\varphi_2(xy, x+y) = \varphi_2(yx, y+x), \quad \varphi_3(x/y) \neq \varphi_3(y/x).$$

The assumption implies a serious condition imposed on dynamical processes occurring in a system as will be investigated in detail later on in this chapter. Meanwhile, however, we take the assumption for granted. Then it follows that

$$\left.\begin{aligned} F_i^{(1)} &= F_1^{(1)} \quad \text{if} \quad X_i = X_1, \\ F_{ij}^{(2)} &= F_{12}^{(2)} \quad \text{if} \quad X_i = X_1, X_j = X_2, \\ F_{ijk}^{(3)} &= F_{123}^{(3)} \quad \text{if} \quad \ldots, \text{ etc.} \end{aligned}\right\} \quad (3.2\text{-}2)$$

On consideration of eq. (2), we have for eq. (2.4-10)

$$\left(\frac{\partial}{\partial t}+\frac{\mathbf{p}_1}{m}\cdot\frac{\partial}{\partial \mathbf{r}_1}+\mathcal{F}_{10}\cdot\frac{\partial}{\partial \mathbf{p}_1}\right)F^{(1)}(X_1;\,t) \left.\begin{array}{c}\\[2ex]\\[2ex]\end{array}\right\}\quad(3.2\text{-}3)$$
$$+(N-1)\int \mathcal{F}_{12}\cdot\frac{\partial}{\partial \mathbf{p}_1}\,F^{(2)}(X_1,\,X_2;\,t)\,dX_2 = 0.$$

In view of the consideration given in Section 5.4 which is relevant with respect to gases of moderate densities, we consider only those particles which are remote from the wall of the container and have eliminated $\mathcal{F}_{iw}$ from the above equation. Similarly we obtain from eq. (2.4-11)

$$\left[\frac{\partial}{\partial t}+\frac{\mathbf{p}_1}{m}\cdot\frac{\partial}{\partial \mathbf{r}_1}+\frac{\mathbf{p}_2}{m}\cdot\frac{\partial}{\partial \mathbf{r}_2}+(\mathcal{F}_{10}+\mathcal{F}_{12})\cdot\frac{\partial}{\partial \mathbf{p}_1}\right.$$
$$\left.+(\mathcal{F}_{20}+\mathcal{F}_{21})\cdot\frac{\partial}{\partial \mathbf{p}_2}\right]F^{(2)}(X_1,\,X_2;\,t)$$
$$+(N-2)\int\left(\mathcal{F}_{13}\cdot\frac{\partial}{\partial \mathbf{p}_1}+\mathcal{F}_{23}\cdot\frac{\partial}{\partial \mathbf{p}_2}\right)F^{(3)}(X_1,\,X_2,\,X_3;\,t)\,dX_3 = 0$$

$$(3.2\text{-}4)$$

Similarly, the equations for $F^{(3)}$, ... follow. The striking simplicity which distinguishes these new equations from the original ones is that we have only one equation given by eq. (3) instead of N equations given by eq. (2.4-10), one equation given by eq. (4) instead of $N(N-1)/2!$ equations given by eq. (2.4-11), and so forth. The total number of these derived equations is $N-1$, instead of 2^N-2. Furthermore, the summations $\sum_j$, $\sum_k$, ... have been substituted by the multiplications of $(N-1)$, $(N-2)$, ... The chain of those equations is named the BBGKY hierarchy after the authors who introduced the chain independently. They are J. Yvon (1935), M. Born and H. S. Green (1946), J. M. Kirkwood (1946), and N. N. Bogoliubov (1946).

45

Although the final presentation of the BBGKY hierarchy is the same, the reason for introducing the symmetry assumption varies among those authors:

1. Bogoliubov takes the assumption for granted without giving any reason.
2. Kirkwood insists that the investigation of a system must be done along the time axis with an operation of time average.
3. Yvon and Born and Green consider ensemble averages.

Leaving those interpretations of Kirkwood, Yvon, Born and Green for investigation in other sections, we first consider Bogoliubov's interpretation. Although Bogoliubov did not give any reason explicitly, later authors tend to interpret his silence as follows: a state of a system and the state obtained by interchanging the phase space coordinates between two similar particles have the same observable properties; hence the density distribution function is symmetric. So far as classical-dynamical particles are concerned, however, the above statement involves a logical difficulty. Since a procedure of experiment (observation) is conducted with respect to a single system, the distribution function is a particular solution of the Liouville equation as given by eq. (2.3-9). Of course, $X_i^*(t)$, $i = 1$, $2, \ldots, N$, are completely unknown. But it is obvious that $D^{(N)}$ is not symmetric with respect to the interchange of phase-space coordinates between two similar particles. If we dare to assume the symmetry in the microscopic sense, we obtain from eq. (2.3-9)

$$F_i^{(1)}(X_i;\ t) = \delta(X_i - X_j^*(t)),$$

where j, independent of i, may be any one of $1, 2, \ldots, N$. In other words, particle i exists at all the possible states at the same time. The situation is similar to that of a quantum-mechanical system, in which degeneracy is complete. It is known, however, that quantum-mechanical degeneracy is not significant regarding those molecules constituting ordinary gases (except for electrons bound in molecules and/or metals). See Appendix E. It is noted that eqs. (3), (4), $\ldots$ derived from eqs. (2.4-10), (2.4-11), $\ldots$, according to the present

symmetry assumption are not reduced to the Boltzmann equation without the assumption of weak collision. The situation will be discussed in Appendix B. Since the assumption allows more than one particle to occupy a single point in the space at the same time, it is necessary to assume that the interactions among those particles are extremely weak. Since a single particle is located at all the possible states at the same time, the implication of the present symmetry is also similar to what is implied by Gibb's statistical-mechanical ensembles. See footnote, p. 175; also see p. 177.

Finally it is noted that our interpretation of Bogoliubov's silence is a speculation. But the speculation has a reason. Bogoliubov is well known as a collaborator of two books treating non-linear oscillations. See Krylov and Bogoliubov (1943) and Bogoliubov and Mitropolsky (1961) in references. The main theme of the books is to develop an asymptotic method of solving non-linear differential equations which has its origin in Poincaré's treatment of planetary dynamics (perturbation method). The method consists of coarse-graining and introduction of the hypothesis of equal *a priori* probabilities. It is rather curious that Bogoliubov did not state explicitly the necessity of coarse-graining for deriving eqs. (3), (4), ... from eqs. (2.4-10), (2.4-11), ... Note that substitution of $(N-1)$, $(N-2)$, ... for $\sum_j$, $\sum_k$, ... is an application of the hypothesis of equal *a priori* probabilities. After deriving the BBGKY hierarchy and for applying the hierarchy to a gaseous system, he assumes the existence of time scales in dynamical processes in the system. But his assumption is not for the derivation of the hierarchy but for the reduction of the hierarchy to gas-dynamical equations. To Bogoliubov, the validity of the hierarchy is independent of the assumption of time scales. The only possible interpretation of Bogoliubov's unrevealed reasoning for this matter is degeneracy. (It might also be possible that he was considering an ensemble in the same way as other authors.)

3.3. The symmetry of distribution functions in time average and the derivation of the BBGKY hierarchy

As is well known, the method of coarse-graining with respect to time was initiated by Poincaré (1881–92) when he investigated the motion of a planet. The planet is moving around the sun because of the large gravitational force of the sun. But fluctuations are superposed on the motion due to various causes, for example, its satellites. If the time scale τ_1 of the main motion is much larger than the time scale τ_2 of fluctuations, it is possible to calculate the motion in the long time scale by coarse-graining the detailed motion with respect to time.[†] The length of time τ_{12} over which the coarse-graining is made must be shorter than τ_1 and longer than τ_2 so that the result of the coarse-graining is sufficiently independent of τ_{12}. In the second approximation, one may obtain more detailed motion of time scale τ_2 in terms of the first approximation. This procedure is an application of the hypothesis of equal *a priori* probabilities. The method has been developed and modified to be applied to various branches of science, for example, the theory of Brownian motion, turbulence theory, communication theory, the theory of non-linear oscillations, and so forth. See Taylor (1912, 1935), Krylov and Bogoliubov (1943), Bogoliubov and Mitropolsky (1961), and Wiener (1950). Note that, under condition $\tau_1 \gg \tau_2$, processes of time scale τ_2 may constitute a *stationary* time series as called by Wiener. In kinetic theory, Maxwell and Boltzmann used the method (or principle) when they considered the Stosszahlansatz. Their usage was rather implicit. Later the method was explicitly used by Kirkwood (1946). In his theory, however, a system to be coarse-grained with respect to time is chosen at random among those constituting a canonical ensemble, and $D^{(N)}$ is given in the probabilistic sense at the beginning of his investigation; it seems that Kirkwood applied the method of coarse-graining only for the purpose of smoothing out the result. Therefore the meaning or the role of the coarse-

---

[†] In the case of Poincaré treating a planet, the coarse-grained motion is a periodic cycling.

graining with respect to time is not significant in his theory. As a result, inconsistencies appearing in his derivation of the Boltzmann equation from the Liouville equation are similar to those in Bogoliubov's derivation in which no coarse-graining with respect to time is considered.

Since our experimental observation is made at each time with respect to a single system, the relevant theory is to begin with the investigation of a single system. The symmetry of $D^{(N)}$ is introduced after coarse-graining operations. Let us take first eq. (2.4-10). By regarding the integral term as the cause of fluctuations, we assume that the secular characteristic of $F_i^{(1)}$ is mainly determined by

$$\left(\frac{\partial}{\partial t}+\frac{\mathbf{p}_i}{m}\frac{\partial}{\partial \mathbf{r}_1}+\mathcal{F}_{io}\cdot\frac{\partial}{\partial \mathbf{p}_i}\right)F_i^{(1)}(X_i;\,t) = 0. \qquad (3.3\text{-}1)$$

The time scale of $F_i^{(1)}$ governed by eq. (1) is the time scale of the external force $\mathcal{F}_{io}$. The scale is denoted by τ_1. Let us suppose that the integral term in eq. (2.4-10) causes fluctuations of time scale τ_2. If τ_1 is much longer than τ_2, we may coarse-grain eq. (2.4-10) with respect to time over the time period τ_{12} which satisfies

$$\tau_1 \gg \tau_{12} \gg \tau_2. \qquad (3.3\text{-}2)$$

Only under this condition can the result of coarse-graining be independent of τ_{12} and be uniquely determined. We consider trajectories of particle i during the time between t and $t+\tau_{12}$ governed by

$$\left.\begin{array}{l}\mathbf{p}_i(s) = \mathbf{p}_i+\varDelta\mathbf{p}_i(s), \quad \mathbf{r}_i(s) = \mathbf{r}_i+\varDelta\mathbf{r}_i(s) \\[2mm] \dfrac{d\varDelta\mathbf{p}_i(s)}{ds} = \mathcal{F}_{io}(s), \quad \dfrac{d\varDelta\mathbf{r}_i(s)}{ds} = \dfrac{\mathbf{p}_i(s)}{m} \\[2mm] 0 \leqslant s < \tau_{12}, \quad i = 1, 2, 3 \ldots \end{array}\right\} \qquad (3.3\text{-}3)$$

with initial conditions

$$\varDelta\mathbf{p}_i(0) = 0, \quad \varDelta\mathbf{r}_i(0) = 0, \qquad (3.3\text{-}4)$$

where $\mathbf{p}_i$, $\mathbf{r}_i$, and t are independent variables. It is noted that the trajectories considered above are analogous to those presented by X_i' in eq. (2.3-11). So far as the observation of time scale τ_1 is con-

cerned, we may assume that

$$\mathbf{p}_i(\tau_{12}) = \mathbf{p}_i, \quad \mathcal{F}_{io}(\tau_{12}) = \mathcal{F}_{io}.$$

Then, we have

$$\frac{1}{\tau_{12}} \int_0^{\tau_{12}} \left[\left(\frac{\partial}{\partial t} + \frac{\mathbf{p}_i}{m} \cdot \frac{\partial}{\partial \mathbf{r}_i} + \mathcal{F}_{io} \cdot \frac{\partial}{\partial \mathbf{p}_i} \right) F_i^{(1)}(X_i; \ t) \right] ds$$

$$t \to t+s$$

$$= \left(\frac{\partial}{\partial t} + \frac{\mathbf{p}_i}{m} \cdot \frac{\partial}{\partial \mathbf{r}_j} + \mathcal{F}_{io} \cdot \frac{\partial}{\partial \mathbf{p}_i} \right) \langle F_i^{(1)}(X_i; \ t) \rangle_{\tau_{12}},$$

where

$$\langle F_i^{(1)}(X_i; \ t) \rangle_{\tau_{12}} = \frac{1}{\tau_{12}} \int_0^{\tau_{12}} F_i^{(1)}(X_i(s); \ t+s) \, ds. \tag{3.3-5}$$

On defining J_i and $\langle J_i \rangle_{\tau_{12}}$ respectively by

$$J_i = \sum_j \int \mathcal{F}_{ij} \cdot \frac{\partial}{\partial \mathbf{p}_i} F_{ij}^{(2)}(X_i, X_j; \ t) \, dX_j \tag{3.3-6}$$

and

$$\left. \langle J_i \rangle_{\tau_{12}} = \frac{1}{\tau_{12}} \int_0^{\tau_{12}} \sum_j \left[\int_{X_j} \mathcal{F}_{ij} \cdot \frac{\partial}{\partial \mathbf{p}_i} F_{ij}^{(2)}(X_i, X_j; \ t) \, dX_j \right] ds \right\} \tag{3.3-7}$$

$$t \to t+s,$$

we may obtain, by coarse-graining eq. (2.4-10),

$$\left(\frac{\partial}{\partial t} + \frac{\mathbf{p}_i}{m} \cdot \frac{\partial}{\partial \mathbf{r}_i} + \mathcal{F}_{io} \cdot \frac{\partial}{\partial \mathbf{p}_i} \right) \langle F_i^{(1)}(X_i; \ t) \rangle_{\tau_{12}} + \langle J_i \rangle_{\tau_{12}} = 0. \tag{3.3-8}$$

The statistical implications of the coarse-graining are as follows:

1. The integration with respect to s in eq. (7) is to be done after the summation with respect to j. In order to change the order of the two operations, it is necessary to assume the following: (1) The interactions are weak; (2) if the interactions are strong, τ_{12} is to be sufficiently short so that particle i interacts with only one of the other particles, at most, during the time period; (3) the interference between two particles which collide with particle i in the time period τ_{12} in

case (1) is negligibly weak, unless the interference is of a time scale much shorter than τ_2. Under the above conditions, we may write

$$\left.\begin{array}{l}\langle J_i \rangle_{\tau_{12}} = \dfrac{1}{\tau_{12}} \sum_j \int_0^{\tau_{12}} \left[\int_{X_j} \mathcal{F}_{ij} \cdot \dfrac{\partial}{\partial \mathbf{p}_i} F_{ij}^{(2)}(X_i, X_j; t) \, dX_j \right] ds \\ \\ \qquad\qquad\qquad\qquad t \to t+s. \end{array}\right\} \quad (3.3\text{-}7)'$$

2. Since we are observing $\langle F_i^{(1)}(X_i; t)\rangle_{\tau_{12}}$, $i = 1, 2, \ldots$, it is impossible and also unnecessary for us to know the precise time when, and the precise state with which a particular particle j begins to interact significantly with particle i during the time between t and $t+\tau_{12}$: In a local domain of the configuration space, particles j are mutually indistinguishable. In view of the finiteness of the velocity of each particle, the volume of such a domain is limited by $\Delta \mathbf{r}_b$. In each of the domains, the distribution of particles j is assumed to be the same in the sense of probability. According to this assumption which is equivalent to the Stosszahlansatz of Boltzmann, and according to definition (2.5-3) we replace eq. (7)′ with

$$\left.\begin{array}{l}\overline{\langle J_i \rangle_{\tau_{12}}} = \dfrac{(N-1)}{\tau_{12}} \sum_{\Delta r_b} \int_0^{\tau_{12}} \int_{\Delta r_b} \left[\mathcal{F}_{ib} \cdot \dfrac{\partial}{\partial \mathbf{p}_i} \overline{F_{io}^{(2)}(X_i, X_b; t)} \, dX_b \right] ds \\ \\ \qquad\qquad\qquad\qquad t \to t+s. \end{array}\right\} \quad (3.3\text{-}7)''$$

Here each domain of the integration with respect to dr_b is limited by $\Delta \mathbf{r}_b$ although the domain of $\mathbf{p}_b$ is unlimited, and $\sum_{\Delta r_b}$ means the summation with respect to all the local domains, in each of which the distribution of particles b is symmetric. Since $\mathcal{F}_{ib}$ decreases as the distance between particle i and particle b increases, significant interactions occur only between particle i and particles b located in $\Delta \mathbf{r}_b$ near particle i. However, the situation depends on the force law; it is possible that forces induced by many particles b, each of which is weak, may culminate in a significant force field as is seen in the case of an ionized gas. Therefore, it is not plausible to ignore the effect of interactions at large distances all at once. It is also noted that definition (2.5-3) implies a statistical sense. A statistical sense

has been introduced to eq. (7)″ by our writing

$$\mathcal{F}_{ib} \cdot \frac{\partial}{\partial \mathbf{p}_i} \overline{F_{io}^{(2)}(X_i, X_b; t)}$$

instead of

$$\overline{\mathcal{F}_{ib} \cdot \frac{\partial}{\partial \mathbf{p}_i} F_{io}^{(2)}(X_i, X_b; t)}.$$

The feasibility will be discussed in detail again as related to relation (12). Unlike $F_{ij}^{(2)}$, $\overline{F_{io}^{(2)}}$ is a continuous function of X_b; in order to retain the condition that each group of particles which are indistinguishable mutually is localized in $\Delta \mathbf{r}_b$, the domain of the integration with respect to dX_b is divided by $\Delta \mathbf{r}_b$.

3. Equations (7)″ and (8) are given particularly for particle i. According to eq. (2.5-1), these equations yield

$$\left.\langle J \rangle_{\tau_{12}} = \frac{(N-1)}{\tau_{12}} \sum_{\Delta \mathbf{r}_b} \int_0^{\tau_{12}} \left[\int_{\Delta \mathbf{r}_b} \mathcal{F}_{ab} \cdot \frac{\partial}{\partial \mathbf{p}_a} F^{(2)}(X_a, X_b; t)\, dX_b \right] ds \right\}$$
$$t \to t+s \quad$$
$$(3.3\text{-}7)'''$$

$$\left.\left(\frac{\partial}{\partial t} + \frac{\mathbf{p}_a}{m} \frac{\partial}{\partial \mathbf{r}_a} + \mathcal{F}_{ao} \cdot \frac{\partial}{\partial \mathbf{p}_a} \right) \langle \overline{F^{(1)}(X_a; t)} \rangle_{\tau_{12}} \right\}$$
$$+ \langle J \rangle_{\tau_{12}} = 0. \quad (3.3\text{-}8)'$$

4. The result of the coarse-graining must be independent of τ_{12} as long as τ_{12} satisfies (2). Otherwise, the result has no definite physical meaning. The situation depends on the distribution of particles in $\Delta \mathbf{r}_b$ and τ_{12}. If the distribution is uniform, the result is perfect. If the density of a gas is much rarefied and the distribution in the local domain is significantly non-uniform, the result may depend on the value of τ_{12}. Then the possibility of kinetic theory does not exist. This condition is equivalent to the condition that τ_1 is not sufficiently larger than τ_2.

In order to evaluate $\langle J_i \rangle_{\tau_{12}}$, it is necessary to know $F_{ij}^{(2)}$ in the integrand. $F_{ij}^{(2)}$ is governed by eq. (2.4-11). If we ignore the integral

term in the equation, we obtain

$$\left[\frac{\partial}{\partial t}+\frac{\mathbf{p}_i}{m}\cdot\frac{\partial}{\partial \mathbf{r}_i}+\frac{\mathbf{p}_j}{m}\frac{\partial}{\partial \mathbf{r}_j}+(\mathcal{F}_{io}+\mathcal{F}_{ij})\cdot\frac{\partial}{\partial \mathbf{p}_i}\right.$$
$$\left.+(\mathcal{F}_{jo}+\mathcal{F}_{ji})\cdot\frac{\partial}{\partial \mathbf{p}_j}\right]F_{ij}^{(2)}(X_i, X_j; t) = 0. \quad (3.3\text{-}9)$$

The time scale of $F_{ij}^{(2)}$ governed by the above equation is τ_2. Due to the integral term in eq. (2.4-11), fluctuations of the time scale τ_3 are superposed on the behavior of $F_{ij}^{(2)}$, when it is governed by eq. (2.4-11). For substitution in the integrand of eq. (7), $F_{ij}^{(2)}$ is necessary to be precise in the time scale τ_2. If $\tau_2 \gg \tau_3$, we may choose τ_{23} which satisfies

$$\tau_2 \gg \tau_{23} \gg \tau_3$$

for the time period over which eq. (2.4-11) is coarse-grained. Then, as is discussed with respect to J_i, particles represented by k appear to interact with particle i and particle j as if the distribution of particles k is uniform in the local sense; under conditions similar to those given with respect to the coarse-graining of J_i, we may replace operator $\sum_k$ with multiplier $(N-2)$. Thus eq. (2.4-11) yields

$$\left.\begin{array}{l}\left[\dfrac{\partial}{\partial t}+\dfrac{\mathbf{p}_i}{m}\cdot\dfrac{\partial}{\partial \mathbf{r}_i}+\dfrac{\mathbf{p}_j}{m}\cdot\dfrac{\partial}{\partial \mathbf{r}_j}+(\mathcal{F}_{io}+\mathcal{F}_{ij})\cdot\dfrac{\partial}{\partial \mathbf{p}_i}\right. \\[2mm] \left.+(\mathcal{F}_{jo}+\mathcal{F}_{ji})\cdot\dfrac{\partial}{\partial \mathbf{p}_j}\right]\langle F_{ij}^{(2)}(X_i, X_j; t)\rangle_{\tau_{23}} \\[2mm] +\dfrac{N-2}{\tau_{23}}\sum_{\Delta r_c}\displaystyle\int_0^{\tau_{23}}\left[\int_{\Delta r_c}\left(\mathcal{F}_{ic}\cdot\dfrac{\partial}{\partial \mathbf{p}_i}+\mathcal{F}_{jc}\cdot\dfrac{\partial}{\partial \mathbf{p}_j}\right)\right. \\[2mm] \left. F_{ijo}^{(3)}(X_i, X_j, X_c; t)\, dX_c\right]\, ds = 0 \\[2mm] \hspace{4cm} t \to t+s. \end{array}\right\} \quad (3.3\text{-}10)$$

In view of the difference of time scales, $\tau_{12} \gg \tau_{23}$, $\Delta \mathbf{r}_c$ in the above is to be much narrower than $\Delta \mathbf{r}_b$ in (7)''.

$$\Delta \mathbf{r}_b \gg \Delta \mathbf{r}_c \quad (3.3\text{-}11)$$

The integration with respect to s is done along the trajectories of particle i and particle j in interaction; the trajectories are determined by the characteristic equations of eq. (9). The characteristic equations are the equations of motion of the two particles. As far as eq. (7) and eq. (10) are concerned, particle i may interact with two particles at the same time. If particle i interacts with one of the two in time scale τ_2, then particle i must interact with the other in time scale τ_3. Only under this condition, are eq. (7) and eq. (10) mutually compatible. On the other hand, if $\tau_2 \simeq \tau_3$, there is no way of choosing τ_{23} which enables us to obtain eq. (10) from eq. (2.4-11). By solving eq. (10), $\overline{F^{(2)}(X_a, X_b; t)}$ in the integrand of eq. (7)''' may be provided. It is necessary to note that

$$\overline{\mathcal{F}_{ab} \cdot \frac{\partial}{\partial \mathbf{p}_a} F^{(2)}(X_a, X_b; \ t)} \neq \mathcal{F}_{ab} \cdot \frac{\partial}{\partial \mathbf{p}_a} \overline{F^{(2)}(X_a, X_b; t)}. \quad (3.3\text{-}12)$$

This is due to the following: The scale of $\varDelta \mathbf{r}_a$ and/or $\varDelta \mathbf{r}_b$ is the scale of $\tau_{12}\,\mathbf{p}/m$. This scale is obviously much larger than the scale in which $\mathcal{F}_{ab}(X_a, X_b)$ is equivalent to $\mathcal{F}_{ab}(X_a + \varDelta X_a, X_b + \varDelta X_b)$. Hence, relation (12) cannot be an equation. But, in our observation made with time scale $\tau_1 \gg \tau_{12}$, the difference vanishes, because many particles j passing successively through $\varDelta \mathbf{r}_b$ are, as a whole, distributed in $\varDelta \mathbf{r}_b$ eventually uniformly although each is present at a different time.

A significant consequence of the above consideration is noted as follows: by assuming that eq. (9) holds $F_{ij}^{(2)}$ is invariant along trajectories determined by solving the characteristic equation of eq. (9). On the other hand, $\overline{F^{(2)}(X_a, X_b; \ t)}$ is not invariant along the same trajectories.

By extending similar discussion to the third and the higher rank equations given in Section 2.4, we obtain a hierarchy of equations under the condition that there is a hierarchy of time scales.

$$\tau_1 \gg \tau_2 \gg \tau_3 \gg \ldots, \quad (3.3\text{-}13)$$

in which τ_1 is the time scale of the external and macroscopic force field, τ_2 is the time scale of two-particle interaction, τ_3 is the time

scale of the disturbance imposed on the two-particle interaction due to the third particle, and so forth. This statement does not necessarily mean that there exists such a hierarchy of time scales in dynamical processes occurring in a real system. The situation will be discussed in detail in the next section.

The derivation of the hierarchy is made possible only by those considerations stated above. Therefore the implications and the capacities of the hierarchy are quite different from those which the original authors seemed to conceive. In the following sections, the BBGKY hierarchy means the hierarchy in our sense. Finally, it is worth while to note that the set of particular trajectories along which the equation of each subsystem is coarse-grained is not one. For example, we may take another set of trajectories different from the set determined by eq. (3) as long as the two are equivalent in the time scale τ_1. This note is particularly important in view of the applications.

3.4. Physical implications of the BBGKY hierarchy

3.4-1. IRREVERSIBILITY

In the process of deriving the BBGKY hierarchy from the Liouville equation, a coarse-graining is indispensable, as is investigated in the last section. Equations (2.4-10), (2.4-11), (2.4-12) are reversible with respect to time, if the initial conditions of all the F's are set at the same time. The irreversibility is introduced into the hierarchy by our particular method of coarse-graining each equation with respect to particles. With respect to eq. (3.3-8)' the first of the BBGKY hierarchy, τ_{12} is extremely short compared with τ_1, and is extremely long compared with τ_2. The initial condition of the evolution of $F_{ij}^{(2)}$ during the period from t to $t+\tau_{12}$ is determined by assuming that $D^{(N)}$ is symmetric with respect to particles j in each local domain $\Delta\mathbf{r}_b$. In other words, uncertainty is introduced through the initial conditions. The uncertainty is of the same nature as that of the uncertainty introduced by the Stosszahlansatz of Boltzmann: By

the Stosszahlansatz, the initial condition of a particle which collides with a specified particle is chosen at random among the possible conditions of particles in molar disorder. Once the initial condition is chosen, however, the two particles collide precisely according to the equations of motion given by Newton. We introduced the same assumption of molar disorder with respect to particles j, when we wrote eq. (3.3-7)″ for eq. (3.3-7)′. Although the trajectories of two particles i and b may be precise according to the equations of motion, the condition of particle b which interacts with particle i during the time period between t and $t+\tau_{12}$ is chosen in the statistical sense among the possible conditions. Since τ_{12} is much shorter than τ_1, setting the condition of particle b appears to be made incessantly from the viewpoint of an observer of time scale τ_1. Thus the evolution of $\langle \overline{F^{(1)}} \rangle$ governed by eq. (3.3-8)′ is affected by uncertainty supplied incessantly through $\langle \overline{J} \rangle_{\tau_{12}}$. As a result, the evolution of eq. (3.3-8)′ is statistical and irreversible. The same situation is observed in the evolution of $\langle F_{ij}^{(2)} \rangle_{\tau_{23}}$ governed by eq. (3.3-10). There, the condition of particle c in the integrand is chosen at random among those which are accessible during the time period between t and $t+\tau_{23}$. We may extend the same investigation to the other equations.

3.4-2. LOCALIZATION OF SYMMETRY

In replacing $\sum_j$ with $N-1$ in eq. (3.3-7)″ it is assumed that $D^{(N)}$ is symmetric with respect to particles located near particle i. The velocity and the acceleration of each particle are finite. Also we know that the particles are spread in the domain of the configuration space of volume V. It is known that there are particles which are remote from particle i; such a particle is distinguishable from a particle near particle i during the time interval τ_{12}. Therefore, we may say at least that $D^{(N)}$ is symmetric only with respect to particles in each local space Δr_b. This consideration is indispensable as is shown in the derivation of the Boltzmann equation from the BBGKY

hierarchy. Note that in the Boltzmann collision integral the integration with respect to the space in the direction of the relative velocity of two colliding particles is limited by the distance which is equal to the magnitude of the relative velocity multiplied by unit time. If we assume the symmetry of $D^{(N)}$ literally with respect to all the particles, the integration must be extended over the entire configuration space of volume V. The failure is inevitable if a derivation is attempted based on the assumption of symmetry of $D^{(N)}$ in the microscopic sense. (See Appendix B.) A similar caution is necessary for each equation of the hierarchy. As is shown by eq. (3.3-11), the volume of a local domain of the configuration space where the symmetry is considered decreases as the multiplicity of interactions increases. In view of this situation together with eq. (3.3-13), it is likely that the BBGKY hierarchy, beyond the first and second equations, has no definite physical meaning.

3.4-3. APPLICATIONS

The feasible application of the BBGKY hierarchy is limited by the conditions necessary for the derivation of the hierarchy. The main conditions are:

1. The time scales considered for the hierarchy must coincide with the time scales of dynamical processes in a real system. In view of this condition, it is most likely that only the first two equations, at most, among those belonging to the hierarchy are physically significant.

2. A gas should be sufficiently rarefied that two particles which interact with particle i successively with time scale τ_2 are not in mutual interaction with the same time scale.

3. A gas should be sufficiently dense that the distribution of particles near particle i is uniform so that an assumption similar to the Stosszahlansatz is applicable.

4. The time scale of external force $\mathcal{F}_{io}$ is to be much longer that τ_2.

The feasibility of kinetic theory based on the hierarchy depends on the nature of the real system to which the theory is to be applied and on the accurarcy expected of the result. If the theory is to deal with a rarefied gas of neutral molecules, the extremely rare probability of more than binary interaction among particles permits us to eliminate the three-particle interaction integral from the second equation of the hierarchy. Thus, the hierarchy terminates at the second equation. The governing time scales are τ_1 and τ_2, and the theory can be applied to the real system. Under the above assumption of binary collision, the Boltzmann equation is derived from the first two equations of the BBGKY hierarchy. It is noted that the derivation cannot be consistent if the symmetry of $D^{(N)}$ is assumed in the microscopic sense, as noted in Appendix B. In a liquid at low temperatures, the interaction between a pair of nearest neighboring particles may be strong and durable with time scale τ_2. The interaction might be perturbed by third particles weakly and briefly with time scale τ_3; a third particle might have its own nearest neighbor in a close interaction with time scale τ_2, and τ_3 may be shorter than τ_2. If this is the case, the hierarchy is useful for the liquid; the integral term in the second equation may be treated in an approximation so that the hierarchy can be terminated at the second equation.

One may recall that Bogoliubov (1946), after having derived the BBGKY hierarchy, assumed the existence of three time scales in a rarefied gas in order to reduce the hierarchy to the Boltzmann equation. In this particular case, Bogoliubov's assumption is physically plausible and at the same time is consistent with assumption (3.3-13). As a matter of general principle, however, there is a significant difference between the two assumptions. Bogoliubov made his assumption as independent of the validity of the BBGKY hierarchy. According to him, it is to be feasible to use the hierarchy even in a case where it seems plausible to set a time-scale assumption contradictory to eq. (3.3-13). According to our assertion, however, the BBGKY hierarchy itself cannot be assumed to exist without assumption (3.3-13). The physical significance of the assertion may be shown in the case of an electron gas: because of the long range of

interaction due to the Coulomb force, it is difficult to conceive that the second condition mentioned in the beginning of this subsection is not satisfied in an electron gas as defined as usual. It is more likely that interactions of higher multiplicities are as significant as binary interactions, and τ_3, τ_4, ... are comparable to τ_2. The BBGKY hierarchy may be applicable to an electron gas only with a precision of the same degree as of the Vlasov equation. Thus, the shielding effect in the sense of Debye is not conceivable in an electron gas. But an ion with a large mass and a large electric charge can be shielded by electron clouds in the sense of Debye, as will be shown in Section 9.6.

3.5. The symmetry assumption of distribution functions in ensemble average

We have seen in the last two sections that proper time-average operations regarding a single system are necessary for coarse-graining eqs. (2.4-10), (2.4-11), ... properly so that we may use them for the basis of gas dynamics. As is shown below, proper ensemble average operations permit us to reach the same conclusion as obtained in the above. This fact does not deny the assertion of coarse-graining with respect to time. Instead, the fact means that the behavior of a model (imaginary) system obtained by proper ensemble average operations is equivalent to the behavior of a real system averaged over proper time spans if condition (3.3-13) exists. (Without this proof, an ensemble average has no physical significance.) We consider an ensemble of similar systems. If the system which the ensemble average is supposed to simulate is not in thermal equilibrium, the domain of the relevant phase space where the representative points of the ensemble exist is narrower than the domain of Gibbs's ensembles. The domain is to be restricted as remarked previously in advance of the investigation of time averages in Section 3.2.

Suppose that we have a proper ensemble, we then count the number of the constituent systems where X_i is between X and $X+\Delta X$.

The number of these selected systems is denoted by $v_i^{(1)}$. Among these $v_i^{(1)}$ systems, there may be a number of systems where there is no other particle significantly interacting with particle i. The number is denoted by $v_{i0}^{(1)}$. Secondly, there is a number of systems where particle j is significantly interacting with particle i. The number is denoted by $v_{ij}^{(1)}$. Here j may be 1, 2, ..., N, but not i. Then we obtain

$$v_i^{(1)} = v_{i0}^{(1)} + \sum_j v_{ij}^{(1)}. \tag{3.5-1}$$

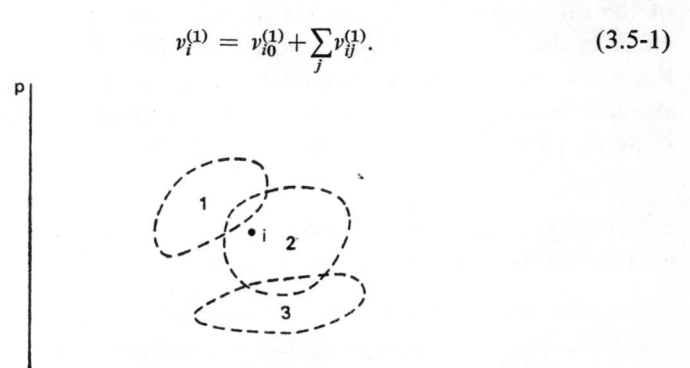

FIG. 3.5-1.

The states of particle i, 1, 2, 3, ... in similar systems, in which the state of particle i is precisely specified as common, are represented in a 6-dimensional **pr**-space. The state of particle i in those systems is represented by point i while the states of particle 1 are spread in domain 1, the states of particle 2 in domain 2, and so forth.

Here is an obvious difficulty involved in this consideration. If, for example, particle j_1 and particle j_2 are interacting with particle i at the same time in a system, the system is counted twice. As will be shown later, this difficulty is avoided if condition (3.3-13) is satisfied (assumed). Meanwhile, the difficulty is ignored in our investigation. By superposing those systems in a 6-dimensional **pr**-space and interpreting the degree of superposition of a specified particle as the degree of probability of its occurrence, one may obtain an imaginary system where particle i exists in the specified condition with a large probability while other particles interacting with particle i are spread with thin densities of probability around particle i. See the schematic illustration in Fig. (3.5-1).

60

This is the model of two-particle interaction obtained by coarse-graining an ensemble. The main characteristics of this model are:

1. The probability of particle i is concentrated at the specified conditions.

2. The probability of each second particle is spread as a cloud surrounding particle i.

3. There is no mutual interaction among these second particles surrounding particle i.

4. For particle i, we may take any of the N particles.

The model is an imaginary system. However, those conditions characterizing the imaginary system are realized in effect by particles in a real system, if the time scale τ_1 of single-particle behaviors in a real system, according to a precise observation in the secular sense, is much longer than the time scale τ_2 of two-particle interactions. (Here a precise observation in the secular sense means an observation of the gross mass density, gross momentum density, and higher order moments of single-particle distribution in terms of which the law of the secular evolution of the real system is sufficiently precisely given.) In other words, the single-particle distribution of the real system is to be almost stationary in view of the two-particle interactions so that the secular evolution of the single-particle distribution at a moment of time is affected by many independent two-particle interactions superposed seemingly at the same moment of time.

In order to investigate the situation of two-particle interactions we count in the ensemble the number of the systems in which specified particle i and specified particle j are respectively in specified conditions. The number is denoted by $\nu_{ij}^{(2)}$;

$$\nu_{ij}^{(2)} \ll \nu_i^{(1)}. \tag{3.5-2}$$

Among those systems counted above, the number of systems where third particles k are in significant interactions with particle i and particle j is counted to be $\nu_{ijk}^{(2)}$:

$$\nu_{ij}^{(2)} = \nu_{ij0}^{(2)} + \sum_k \nu_{ijk}^{(2)}. \tag{3.5-3}$$

Here $\nu_{ij0}^{(2)}$ is the number of the systems where there is no such third particle. As before, we may conclude that $\tau_2 \gg \tau_3$ is the condition necessary for the ensemble average model to be an effective imitation of a real system in view of these interactions. Here τ_3 is the time scale of the interference of a third particle.

After repeating successively similar considerations regarding more multiple interactions, we may conclude that condition (3.3-13) is the condition necessary for the ensemble average model to be an effective imitation of the real system. Then, applying the present scheme of ensemble average, it is a matter of course to obtain the BBGKY hierarchy from eqs. (2.4-10), (2.4-11), ...

Finally we recall the question raised previously regarding the difficulty that a system is counted twice in $\sum_j \nu_{ij}^{(2)}$ if particle i is interacting with particle j_1 and particle j_2 at the same time in the system. The question is now answered as follows: in fact $\sum_j \nu_{ij}^{(2)}$ is the number of systems where particle i in a specified condition interacts with second particles, at most one second particle in one system, with time scale τ_2; the interaction of particle i with the third particle in a system, if it ever exists, is to be with time scale τ_3. If there are many systems, in each of which three particles i, j_1, and j_2 interact mutually with the same time scale τ_2 at the same time, the BBGKY hierarchy, is not applicable for such systems because of the difficulty raised above. Naturally one might tend to hope that the kinetic theory would be constructed based on those ensembles in a manner similar to Gibbs's statistical mechanics. But consideration of suitable ensembles, which is conceptually possible as stated above, does not seem to provide us any particular technical convenience; such an ensemble must be specified not only by integrals of motion of an isolated system (uniform integrals by Fowler) but also by other quantities which are not integrals of motion, and inevitably the time evolutions of those quantities which are not integrals of motion must be taken into account. Thus an ensemble has to be redefined from one moment of time to another. Furthermore, we have to choose a different ensemble for a different sort of microscopic process, and the lifetime of one ensemble is different from

the lifetime of another in general. In order to justify ensemble-average operations by ergodic-theoretical consideration at each moment of time, after all, we have to perform time-average operations with time-scale consideration. To find such ensembles is not a method of kinetic theory. Instead, it seems to be the very purpose of kinetic theory.

Exercises

1. The oscillation of a simple pendulum is governed by

$$\frac{d^2\theta}{dt^2} = -\frac{g}{l}\,\theta,$$

where θ is the angle of deflection from the vertical line, g the gravitational acceleration, l the length of the pendulum and t time. If $g = g_0$ (invariant), then the period of oscillation is

$$\tau_1 = 2\pi(l/g_0)^{1/2}.$$

Supposing that

$$g = g_0 + g_1(t)$$

$$g_1(t) = g'\sin\left(\frac{2\pi}{\tau_2}t + \varphi\right)$$

$$g'/g_0 < 1, \quad \tau_1 \gg \tau_2,$$

investigate the motion of the pendulum. Also consider the case $\tau_1 \fallingdotseq \tau_2$.

2. Show that

$$\frac{1}{\tau_{12}}\int_t^{t+\tau_{12}} \psi\,dt = a\sin\left(\frac{2\pi}{\tau_1}t\right) + 0\left[\frac{b\tau_2}{2\pi\tau_{12}}\right],$$

when

$$\psi = a\sin\left(\frac{2\pi}{\tau_1}t\right) + b\sin\left(\frac{2\pi}{\tau_2}t + \varphi\right)$$

and

$$\tau_1 \gg \tau_{12} > \tau_2.$$

3. ψ is defined by

$$\psi(x; a, b) = \int_a^b \delta(x-y)\,dy$$

$$a < b.$$

Show that

$$\psi = 1 \quad \text{if} \quad a < x < b$$
$$= 0 \quad \text{if} \quad x < a \quad \text{and/or} \quad x > b.$$

4. ψ is defined by

$$\psi(x,\, t) = \frac{1}{\tau_1} \int_0^{\tau_1} \delta\left[x - a \sin\left(\frac{2\pi}{\tau_2}\,(t+s)\right)\right] ds,$$

where

$$\tau_1 \gg \tau_2, \quad a > 0.$$

Is it correct to conclude that $\psi(x,\, t)$ is independent of τ_1 and

$$\psi(x,\, t) = \text{finite} \quad \text{if} \quad a > x > -a$$
$$= 0 \qquad \text{if} \quad x < -a \quad \text{and/or} \quad x > a?$$

CHAPTER 4

The Boltzmann Equation

4.1. Introduction

The Boltzmann equation was proposed by Boltzmann (1872). It might be possible to remark that the equations of transfer of Maxwell (1866) had stimulated Boltzmann to conceive the equation. The equation governs the evolution of the density of similar particles, that is similar to f defined by eq. (2.5-1). The equation is given by

$$\left.\begin{aligned}
&\left(\frac{\partial}{\partial t}+\mathbf{c}\cdot\frac{\partial}{\partial \mathbf{r}}+\mathcal{F}_0\cdot\frac{1}{m}\frac{\partial}{\partial \mathbf{c}}\right)f'(\mathbf{c},\mathbf{r};\,t) \\
&=\int [f'(\mathbf{c}_1',\mathbf{r};\,t)f'(\mathbf{c}',\mathbf{r};\,t)-f'(\mathbf{c}_1,\mathbf{r};\,t)f'(\mathbf{c},\mathbf{r};\,t)]|\mathbf{c}_1-\mathbf{c}|\,d\varphi\,dh\,d\mathbf{c}_1.
\end{aligned}\right\}$$

$$(4.1\text{-}1)$$

According to the definition by Boltzmann, $\mathbf{c}$, $\mathbf{c}_1$, $\mathbf{c}'$, and $\mathbf{c}_1'$ must be velocities of particles only in states of free flight; therefore f' should be defined so that f' gives the number density of such particles only. Angle φ and length h are variables specifying the geometrical relation between two particles participating in a collision: The collision begins with initial (asymptotic) velocities $\mathbf{c}$ and $\mathbf{c}_1$ of the two particles at a long distance as is illustrated in Fig. 4.1-1. $\mathbf{c}'$ and $\mathbf{c}_1'$ are the final (asymptotic) velocities of the two particles at a long distance after the collision. In the Boltzmann equation $\mathbf{c}$, $\mathbf{c}_1$, and h are independent variables. In accordance with the equations of motion of two particles, however, a collision may begin either with $\mathbf{c}$ and $\mathbf{c}_1$ or with $\mathbf{c}'$ and $\mathbf{c}_1'$ and ends respectively either with $\mathbf{c}'$ and

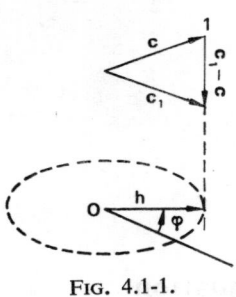

FIG. 4.1-1.

Immediately before a collision between two particles, the particle with velocity c is at 0 and the particle with velocity c_1 is at 1. $c_1 - c$ is the relative velocity. Projected on the plane which passes 0 and is perpendicular to $c_1 - c$, the vector $0 - 1$ is of length h and of direction φ. h is often called *impact parameter*.

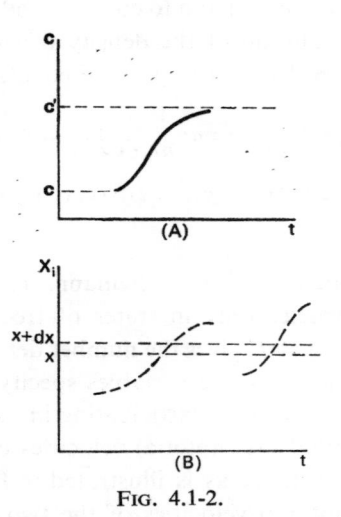

FIG. 4.1-2.

In the Boltzmann equation, the effect of a collision is an integral over the entire phase of the collision as is shown in A. On the other hand, the effect of a collision in eq. (3.3-6) is accounted for only at X_i between X and $X+dX$ as is shown in B. Reduction of eq. (3.3-6) to the Boltzmann equation is made possible by coarse-graining eq. (3.3-6) with respect to time and particles.

c_1' or with c and c_1. By the Boltzmann equation, the evolution of f' is due to the effects of many collisions accounted for in such a manner that the effect of each collision is the integral of the relevant differential effect over the entire phase of the collision. On the other hand, the evolution of $F_i^{(1)}$ according to eq. (2.4-10) is due to the effects accounted for at given X_i which may be a state of particle i during collision as well as during free flight. See the schematic comparison given in Fig. 4.1-2. Therefore f, defined by eq. (2.5-1) which counts in not only the number density of particles in free flight, but also the density of particles during collision, is not the distribution function f' governed by the Boltzmann equation. However, if the portion of a unit time during which a particle is in interaction with others is much smaller than the other portion during which the particle is in free flight, we may eliminate small and sudden fluctuations of f due to particles in states of collision, by making an average of f over a time period from t to $t+\tau$.

$$\langle f \rangle_0 = \frac{1}{\tau} \int_0^\tau f(c, r(s); t+s) \, ds, \qquad (4.1\text{-}2)$$

where

$$\frac{dr(s)}{ds} = c, \quad r(o) = r \qquad (4.1\text{-}3)$$

and it is assumed that

$$\frac{\tau}{c} \frac{dc}{ds} \div \frac{\tau}{c} \frac{\mathcal{F}_o}{m} \ll 1. \qquad (4.1\text{-}4)$$

If τ and $r(\tau)-r$ are negligibly small in the macroscopic sense and yet large in the microscopic sense, $\langle f \rangle_0$ defined above is equivalent to f in the macroscopic sense, while in the microscopic sense, $\langle f \rangle_0$, unlike f itself, is a smooth function of t presenting only the density of particles in free flight. Therefore it is more plausible to take $\langle f \rangle_0$, instead of f, for the distribution function to be governed by the Boltzmann equation

$$f' = \langle f \rangle_0. \qquad (4.1\text{-}5)$$

The Boltzmann equation is a product of intuitive but ingenious thoughts of Maxwell and Boltzmann. In spite of the intuition involved

in the original derivation, the feasibility of the equation has been tested and confirmed in many ways, as will be shown in due course. Therefore, the equation is to be appreciated as a basic, if empirical, law by itself. Hence, it is of no significance to show a radical derivation of the equation from the Liouville equation, as a means of proving the feasibility of the Boltzmann equation. On the contrary, it is more likely to be a proof of the feasibility of a kinetic-theoretical scheme that the scheme is able to derive consistently the Boltzmann equation from the Liouville equation. In other words, the derivation of the Boltzmann equation under certain conditions can be a test of the feasibility of a kinetic-theoretical scheme.

4.2. Necessary assumptions

4.2-1. THE ASSUMPTION OF BINARY COLLISION

It is necessary to assume that a gas under consideration is sufficiently rarefied. As a result, a constituent particle moves, for most of the time, as free from any disturbance from the other constituent particles. But occasionally it happens that the particle comes so close to another particle that they interact significantly with each other due to the interaction force given by eq. (1.2-1). The chance of occurrence of its interaction with more than one particle at the same time is negligibly small. The situation is similar regarding any of the constituent particles. Because of the situation, if $\mathscr{F}_{ij}$ and $\mathscr{F}_{ji}$ are significant in eq. (3.3-10), $\mathscr{F}_{ic}$ and $\mathscr{F}_{jc}$ are negligibly small in the same equation. Therefore eqs. (3.3-8)′; and (3.3-10) are closed by themselves.

$$\left.\begin{aligned}\left(\frac{\partial}{\partial t}+\frac{\mathbf{p}_a}{m}\cdot\frac{\partial}{\partial \mathbf{r}_a}+\mathscr{F}_{a0}\cdot\frac{\partial}{\partial \mathbf{p}_a}\right)\langle\overline{F^{(1)}(X_a;\,t)}\rangle_0 \\ +\,\langle J\rangle_0 = 0\end{aligned}\right\} \quad (4.2\text{-}1)$$

$$\left.\begin{aligned}\langle\overline{J}\rangle_0 = \frac{(N-1)}{\tau}\sum_{\Delta\mathbf{r}_b}\int_0^\tau\left[\int_{\Delta\mathbf{r}_b}\mathscr{F}_{ab}\cdot\frac{\partial}{\partial \mathbf{p}_a}\overline{F^{(2)}(X_a,\,X_b;\,t)}\,dX_b\right]ds \\ t\to t+s\end{aligned}\right\}$$

$$(4.2\text{-}2)$$

$$\left[\frac{\partial}{\partial t}+\frac{\mathbf{p}_i}{m}\frac{\partial}{\partial \mathbf{r}_i}+\frac{\mathbf{p}_j}{m}\cdot\frac{\partial}{\partial \mathbf{r}_j}+((\mathcal{F}_{i0}+\mathcal{F}_{ij})\cdot\frac{\partial}{\partial \mathbf{p}_i}\right.$$
$$\left.+(\mathcal{F}_{j0}+\mathcal{F}_{ji})\cdot\frac{\partial}{\partial \mathbf{p}_j}\right] F_{ij}^{(2)}(X_i, X_j; t) = 0. \qquad (4.2\text{-}3)$$

Here τ is for τ_{12} in eq. (3.3-8)′ and τ_{23} in eq. (3.3-10) is assumed to be extremely short, that $\langle F_{ij}^{(2)}\rangle_{\tau_{23}}$ is equivalent to $F_{ij}^{(2)}$; subscript 0, instead of τ, means that those averages are made along trajectories governed by eq. (3.3-3), under the condition given by eq. (4.1-4).

4.2-2. THE OCCURRENCE OF A COLLISION

The occurrence of a collision on a particle is rare: (a) the possibility of a particle to be in collision with any other particle at an arbitrary moment of time is negligibly small. We may choose a time length τ such that (b) the possibility of a particle colliding between t and $t+\tau$ is not negligible, but (c) the possibility of its collision with two or more than two particles in τ is negligible.

4.2-3. AN ASSUMPTION REGARDING $\langle F^{(1)}\rangle_\tau$

We assume that $\langle F^{(1)}\rangle_\tau$, eq. (4.2-1), accounts only for the states of particles free from the other particles. This assumption is consistent with assumption (a). In its precise meaning, a specified state presented by X_a, t occurs on a particle not only during its free flight but also during its collisions with other particles.

4.2-4. AN ASSUMPTION REGARDING $F^{(2)}$

It is assumed[†] that the following relation always holds:

$$\langle \overline{F^{(2)}(X_a, X_b; t)}\rangle_\tau = \langle \overline{F^{(1)}(X_a; t)}\rangle_\tau \langle \overline{F^{(1)}(X_b; t)}\rangle_\tau. \qquad (4.2\text{-}4)$$

[†] Since Boltzmann (1896), the implication of the assumption has been discussed by many authors, for example, H. S. Green (1952), M. S. Green (1958), and others. This is a result of application of the hypothesis of equal *a priori* probabilities in a local sense, after a coarse-graining operation.

As is assumed by eq. (2), a particle collides with others only rarely. The chance of strong correlation between two specific particles is rare during the time between t and $t+\tau$.

4.2-5. THE SPATIAL AND TEMPORAL SCALES OF COLLISION

In the macroscopic sense, $c\tau$ and $\mathcal{F}_0\tau$ are negligibly small.

$$\Delta\mathbf{p} = \int_t^{t+\tau} \mathcal{F}_{ij}\, dt$$

is not negligible even in the macroscopic sense.

4.3. Derivation

For deriving the Boltzmann collision integral from eq. (4.2-2) we remember the following three points which are commonly essential in statistical investigation:

1. In eq. (3.3-7) the summation with respect to j is made first, and then the result is averaged with respect to s. In order to make the the time average separately with respect to each of the particles j, it is necessary either to choose τ sufficiently short that particle i interacts with particles j once, at most, during the time between t and $t+\tau$, or to assume that the interactions are very weak. (Suppose that there are two strong collisions of particle i during the period between t and $t+\tau$. The effect of one collision when it occurs first is different from the effect of the same collision when it is assumed to occur second. Note that X_i is an independent variable and is the same in the two cases, but $F_i^{(1)}$ in the first case is different from $F_i^{(1)}$ in the second.) The necessity of the above condition will be discussed again with respect to eq. (4.3-15).

2. Since we are observing $\langle F_i^{(1)}(X_i;\ t)\rangle_0$, $i = 1, 2, 3, \ldots$, it is impossible and also unnecessary for us to know the precise time when the precise state with which a particular particle j begins to interact significantly with particle i. Thus we may set the same assumption as the Stosszahlansatz by Boltzmann with respect to the state with which particle j begins to interact significantly with particle i during

the time between t and $t+\tau$: particle j is one of the particles which are located near particle i at time t and among which $D^{(N)}$ may be assumed to be symmetric. We take $\Delta\mathbf{r}_b$ for the domain of the configuration space in which such particles j exist. Since we know that inter-particle forces considered by Boltzmann are of short range, $\Delta\mathbf{r}_b$ is limited to the neighbor of particle a, and eq. (4.2-2) yields

$$\langle \overline{J} \rangle_0 = \frac{(N-1)}{\tau} \int^{\tau} \int_{\Delta\mathbf{r}_b} \left[\mathcal{F}_{ab} \cdot \frac{\partial}{\partial \mathbf{p}_a} \overline{F^{(2)}(X_a, X_b; t)} \right] dX_b \, ds \quad t \to t+s$$

(4.3-1)

as analogous to eq. (3.3-7).

3. The result of the coarse-graining must be independent of τ. Otherwise, the result has no definite physical meaning. The situation depends on the distribution of particles in $\Delta\mathbf{r}_b$ and τ. If the distribution is uniform, the result is perfect. As the density of gas becomes more rarefied and the distribution of particles in $\Delta\mathbf{r}_b$ and τ becomes more non-uniform, the result tends to depend on τ. Then the possibility of kinetic theory diminishes.

Instead of $\langle J_i \rangle_0$ given by eq. (3.3-7), we may make $\langle J_i \rangle_I$ by coarse-graining J_i over time from t to $t+\tau$ along trajectories I which satisfy

$$\left. \begin{array}{ll} \dfrac{d\mathbf{r}_i(s)}{ds} = \dfrac{\mathbf{p}_i(s)}{m}, & \dfrac{d\mathbf{p}_i(s)}{ds} = \mathcal{F}_{ij}(s) \\[2mm] \dfrac{d\mathbf{r}_j(s)}{ds} = \dfrac{\mathbf{p}_j(s)}{m}, & \dfrac{d\mathbf{p}_j(s)}{ds} = \mathcal{F}_{ji}(s) \end{array} \right\}$$

(4.3-2)

(trajectories I)

with initial conditions

$$\left. \begin{array}{l} \mathbf{r}_i(0) = \mathbf{r}_i, \ \mathbf{p}_i(0) = \mathbf{p}_i \\ \mathbf{r}_j(0) = \mathbf{r}_j, \ \mathbf{p}_j(0) = \mathbf{p}_j. \end{array} \right\}$$

(4.3-3)

Thus we obtain[†]

$$\left. \begin{array}{l} \langle J_i \rangle_I = \dfrac{1}{\tau} \displaystyle\int_0^{\tau} \sum_j \int_{X_j} \left(\dfrac{d\mathbf{p}_i(s)}{ds} \cdot \dfrac{\partial}{\partial \mathbf{p}_i(s)} + \dfrac{d\mathbf{p}_j(s)}{ds} \cdot \dfrac{\partial}{\partial \mathbf{p}_j(s)} \right. \\[4mm] \left. \qquad\qquad \times F_{ij}^{(2)}(X_i(s), X_j(s); t+s) \right) dX_j \, ds. \end{array} \right\}$$

(4.3-4)

[†] The second term of the integrand is shown to vanish on integration, but is added for convenience in the future.

Equations (2) constitute the characteristic equations of eq. (4.2-3), if $\partial/\partial t$ is replaced with $\partial/\partial s$ and t with $t+s$. Therefore, by integrating eq. (3) along trajectories I given by eq. (2) we obtain

$$\left.\begin{array}{r} \int \dfrac{d}{ds} F_{ij}^{(2)}(X_i(s),\ X_j(s);\ t+s)\ ds \\[2mm] = |F_{ij}^{(2)}(X_i(s),\ X_j(s);\ t+s)|_0^{\tau} = 0, \end{array}\right\} \quad (4.3\text{-}5)$$

where

$$\left.\begin{array}{l} \dfrac{d}{ds} = \dfrac{\partial}{\partial s} + \dfrac{d\mathbf{r}_i(s)}{ds}\cdot\dfrac{\partial}{\partial \mathbf{r}_i(s)} + \dfrac{d\mathbf{r}_j(s)}{ds}\cdot\dfrac{\partial}{\partial \mathbf{r}_j(s)} \\[3mm] \qquad + \dfrac{d\mathbf{p}_i(s)}{ds}\cdot\dfrac{\partial}{\partial \mathbf{p}_i(s)} + \dfrac{d\mathbf{p}_j(s)}{ds}\cdot\dfrac{\partial}{\partial \mathbf{p}_j(s)}. \end{array}\right\} \quad (4.3\text{-}6)$$

By making the average of $\langle J_i\rangle_{\mathrm{I}}$ with respect to particles in the same way as in eq. (3.3-7)''', we obtain

$$\left.\begin{array}{r} \langle\overline{J}\rangle_{\mathrm{I}} = \dfrac{N}{\tau}\displaystyle\int_0^{\tau}\!\!\int_{\Delta \mathbf{r}_b}\left(\dfrac{d\mathbf{p}_a(s)}{ds}\cdot\dfrac{\partial}{\partial \mathbf{p}_a(s)} + \dfrac{d\mathbf{p}_b(s)}{ds}\cdot\dfrac{\partial}{\partial \mathbf{p}_b(s)}\right) \\[3mm] \times \overline{F^{(2)}(X_a(s),\ X_b(s);\ t+s)}\ dX_b\ ds, \end{array}\right\} \quad (4.3\text{-}7)$$

where $\Delta \mathbf{r}_b$ has the same implication as for eq. (1). Defining $\left[\dfrac{d}{ds}\right]_{ab}$ by

$$\left.\begin{array}{l} \left[\dfrac{d}{ds}\right]_{ab} = \dfrac{\partial}{\partial s} + \dfrac{\mathbf{p}_a(s)}{m}\cdot\dfrac{\partial}{\partial \mathbf{r}_a(s)} + \dfrac{\mathbf{p}_b(s)}{m}\cdot\dfrac{\partial}{\partial \mathbf{r}_b(s)} \\[3mm] \qquad + \mathscr{F}_{ab}(s)\cdot\dfrac{\partial}{\partial \mathbf{p}_a(s)} + \mathscr{F}_{ba}(s)\cdot\dfrac{\partial}{\partial \mathbf{p}_b(s)}, \end{array}\right\} \quad (4.3\text{-}8)$$

relation (6) yields

$$\left.\begin{array}{r} \langle\overline{J}\rangle_{\mathrm{I}} = \dfrac{N}{\tau}\displaystyle\int_0^{\tau}\!\!\int_{\Delta \mathbf{r}_b}\left(\left[\dfrac{d}{ds}\right]_{ab} - \dfrac{\partial}{\partial s} - \dfrac{\mathbf{p}_a(s)}{m}\cdot\dfrac{\partial}{\partial \mathbf{r}_a(s)} - \dfrac{\mathbf{p}_b(s)}{m}\cdot\dfrac{\partial}{\partial \mathbf{r}_b(s)}\right) \\[3mm] \overline{F^{(2)}(X_a(s),\ X_b(s);\ t+s)}\ dX_b\ ds. \end{array}\right\} (4.3\text{-}9)$$

Unlike eq. (5), $\left[\dfrac{d}{ds}\right]_{ab}\overline{F^{(2)}}$ in the above integrand does not vanish. The reason is that, as in p. 54,

$$\overline{\mathscr{F}_{ab}\cdot\dfrac{\partial}{\partial \mathbf{p}_a}F^{(2)}(X_a,\ X_b;\ t)} \neq \mathscr{F}_{ab}\cdot\dfrac{\partial}{\partial \mathbf{p}_a}\overline{F^{(2)}(X_a,\ X_b;\ t)}, \quad \text{etc.}$$

$\Delta \mathbf{r}_b$ considered in eq. (7) covers domains of the configuration space which are larger than the domain of the force field induced by a single particle; hence not all the particles among two groups of particles, one group in states between X_a and $X_a + \Delta X_a$ and the other in states between X_b and $X_b + \Delta X_b$, are really participating in binary collisions of the mode specified by eq. (6); many of them are in collisions of different mode and/or in free flight. Hence we may write for eq. (9).

$$
\left. \begin{aligned}
\langle \overline{J} \rangle_{\mathrm{I}} = {} & \frac{N}{\tau} \int_{\Delta \mathbf{r}_b} [\overline{F^{(2)}(X_a(\tau), X_b(\tau); t+\tau)} \\
& - \overline{F^{(2)}(X_a, X_b; t)}] \, dX_b \\
& - \frac{N}{\tau} \int_0^\tau \int_{\Delta \mathbf{r}_b} \left(\frac{\partial}{\partial s} + \frac{d\mathbf{r}_a(s)}{ds} \cdot \frac{\partial}{\partial \mathbf{r}_a(s)} + \frac{d\mathbf{r}_b(s)}{ds} \cdot \frac{\partial}{\partial \mathbf{r}_b(s)} \right) \\
& \times \overline{F^{(2)}(X_a(s), X_b(s); t+s)} \, dX_b \, ds.
\end{aligned} \right\} \quad (4.3\text{-}10)
$$

It will be shown that the first integral in the above yields the Boltzmann collision integral while the second integral is insignificant if the number density of particles is as low as usual.

Particles in state X_b may interact with particles in state X_a during the period of time between t and $t+\tau$ only if $\mathbf{r}_b$ at time t is chosen in the domain of the configuration space between $\mathbf{r}_b'$ and $\mathbf{r}_b''$ respectively defined by

$$
\left. \begin{aligned}
(\mathbf{r}_b' - \mathbf{r}_a) \cdot (\mathbf{p}_b - \mathbf{p}_a) &= 0 \\
\frac{(\mathbf{r}_b'' - \mathbf{r}_a) \cdot (\mathbf{p}_b - \mathbf{p}_a)}{|\mathbf{p}_b - \mathbf{p}_a|^2/m} &= -\tau
\end{aligned} \right\} \quad (4.3\text{-}11)
$$

as is illustrated in Fig. 4.3-1. Hence, by presenting $\mathbf{r}_b$ with a cylindrical coordinate system with the origin at $\mathbf{r}_a$ and the altitude in the direction of $\mathbf{p}_b - \mathbf{p}_a$, we have

$$
\Delta \mathbf{r}_b = \int d\mathbf{r}_b = -\tau \frac{|\mathbf{p}_b - \mathbf{p}_a|}{m} \int d\varphi h \, dh. \quad (4.3\text{-}12)
$$

Here φ stands for the direction angle and h the radius in the plane of zero altitude. We also assume that, before and after a collision

73

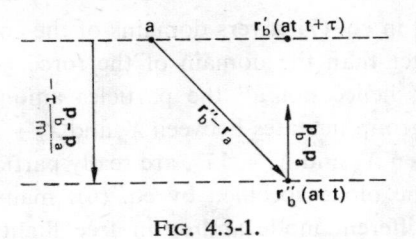

FIG. 4.3-1.

Particle a in state $(\mathbf{r}_a, \mathbf{p}_a)$ and particle b in state $(\mathbf{r}'', \mathbf{p}_b)$ at time t will be at the shortest distance at $t+\tau$, if

$$-\tau \frac{|\mathbf{p}_b - \mathbf{p}_a|}{m} = \frac{(\mathbf{r}_b'' - \mathbf{r}_a) \cdot (\mathbf{p}_b - \mathbf{p}_a)}{|\mathbf{p}_b - \mathbf{p}_a|}.$$

between two particles the correlation between the two particles is weak so that

$$\left.\begin{aligned}
\overline{F^{(2)}(X_a, X_b; t)} &= \overline{F^{(1)}(X_a; t)} \; \overline{F^{(1)}(X_b; t)} \\
\overline{F^{(2)}(X_a(\tau), X_b(\tau); t+\tau)} &= \overline{F^{(1)}(X_a(\tau); t+\tau)} \; \overline{F^{(1)}(X_b(\tau); t+\tau)}.
\end{aligned}\right\} \quad (4.3\text{-}13)$$

On consideration of eq. (12), the second term on the right-hand side of eq. (10) is of the order of

$$\left.\begin{aligned}
\frac{N}{\tau} \int \left(\tau \frac{\partial}{\partial t} + \frac{\tau \mathbf{p}_a}{m} \cdot \frac{\partial}{\partial \mathbf{r}_a} + \frac{\tau \mathbf{p}_b}{m} \cdot \frac{\partial}{\partial \mathbf{r}_b} \right) \overline{F^{(2)}(X_a, X_b; t)} \\
d\mathbf{p}_b \tau \frac{|\mathbf{p}_b - \mathbf{p}_a|}{m} \, d\varphi h \, dh \\
= \frac{N \Delta \mathbf{r}_b}{V} \left(\frac{\partial}{\partial t} + \frac{\mathbf{p}_a}{m} \cdot \frac{\partial}{\partial \mathbf{r}_a} \right) \overline{F^{(1)}(X_a; t)},
\end{aligned}\right\} \quad (4.3\text{-}14)$$

where $\Delta \mathbf{r}_b$ is given by eq. (12) and is the volume of the configuration space domain in which we find at t such particles as interact with particles of state X_a in the future between t and $t+\tau$. It is reasonable,[†] therefore, to assume that

$$0[\int d\varphi h \, dh] = \sigma^2 = 5 \times 10^{-16} \text{ cm}^2,$$

where σ^2 is of the order of cross section or σ is the maximum distance between two particles within which their interaction is significant

† These values are conveniently found in Jeans's book (1925).

and that

$$(N/V)^{-1/3} \ll 0[\tau(\mathbf{p}_b - \mathbf{p}_a)/m] \ll \text{mean free path length} = \frac{1}{2^{1/2}\pi\sigma^2 N/V}.$$

By choosing τ as in the above, we have in accordance with eq. (12)

$$\sigma^2 \left(\frac{N}{V}\right)^{2/3} \ll \frac{N\Delta\mathbf{r}_b}{V} \ll \frac{1}{2^{1/2}\pi} \doteq 0.2. \qquad (4.3\text{-}15)$$

If $N/V = 10^{21}$, then $\sigma^2 (N/V)^{2/3} = 5 \times 10^{-2}$. Under this condition it appears barely possible to choose τ so that eq. (15) is satisfied. If $N/V = 10^{24}$, then $\sigma^2 (N/V)^{2/3} = 5$, and eq. (15) does not hold.

It is noted that condition $N\Delta\mathbf{r}_b/V \ll 1$ is the very condition that τ is short so that particle i interacts with other particles once at most during the time period between t and $t+\tau$. Note the statements given at the beginning of this section. Under condition (15), the term given by eq. (14) is negligibly small compared with the first three terms of eq. (4.2-1). Thus with the help of eqs. (12) and (13), eq. (10) yields

$$\left.\begin{aligned}
\langle J \rangle_I = -N \int &\overline{[F^{(1)}(\mathbf{p}_a(\tau), \mathbf{r}_a(\tau); t+\tau) \quad F^{(1)}(\mathbf{p}_b(\tau), \mathbf{r}_b(\tau); t+\tau)} \\
&- \overline{F^{(1)}(\mathbf{p}_a, \mathbf{r}_a; t) \quad F^{(1)}(\mathbf{p}_b, \mathbf{r}_b; t)]} \\
&\frac{|\mathbf{p}_b - \mathbf{p}_a|}{m} \, d\varphi h \, dh \, d\mathbf{p}_b.
\end{aligned}\right\}$$

$$(4.3\text{-}16)$$

If we consider that τ, $\mathbf{r}_a(\tau) - \mathbf{r}_a$ and $\mathbf{r}_b(\tau) - \mathbf{r}_b$ are of microscopic scales and hence

$$\overline{F^{(1)}(\mathbf{p}_a, \mathbf{r}_a(\tau); t+\tau)} = \langle F^{(1)}(\mathbf{p}_a, \mathbf{r}_a; t) \rangle_0, \quad \text{etc.,} \qquad (4.3\text{-}17)$$

in the time scale of τ_1, we finally have

$$\left.\begin{aligned}
\langle \overline{J} \rangle_I = -N \int &[\langle F^{(1)}(\mathbf{p}_a(\tau), \mathbf{r}; t) \rangle_0 \quad \langle F^{(1)}(\mathbf{p}_b(\tau), \mathbf{r}_a; t) \rangle_0 \\
&- \langle F^{(1)}(\mathbf{p}_a, \mathbf{r}_a; t) \rangle_0 \quad \langle F^{(1)}(\mathbf{p}_b, \mathbf{r}_a; t) \rangle_0] \\
&\times \frac{|\mathbf{p}_b - \mathbf{p}_a|}{m} \, d\varphi h \, dh \, d\mathbf{p}_b.
\end{aligned}\right\}$$

$$(4.3\text{-}18)$$

Since $\langle J_i \rangle_0$ and $\langle J_i \rangle_I$ are made by averaging respectively along trajectories 0 and trajectories I, these two averages are not mutually equivalent. In the following, however, it will be shown that

$$\langle J(X_a; t) \rangle_0 = \langle J(X_a; t) \rangle_I \qquad (4.3\text{-}19)$$

after their being coarse-grained with respect to particles in the same way as is shown by eq. (2.5-1): J_i is a function of X_i and t, and exists along a solid line named J_i in the $X_i t$-space as is shown schematically in A of Fig. 4.3-2. By the assumption of binary collision, line

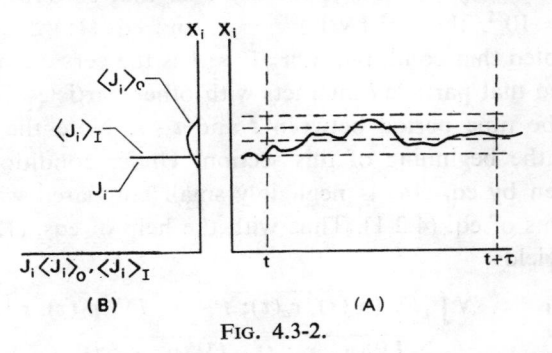

FIG. 4.3-2.

J_i and $\langle J_i \rangle_I$ appear as if they are δ-functions. But $\langle J_i \rangle_0$ is similar to an error function.

J_i coincides with one of the trajectories I. Since we are dealing with a single system, J_i vanishes unless particle i is in interaction with particle j so that $\mathcal{F}_{ij}$ is significant. Almost straight lines in the same illustration are trajectories 0. In B of Fig. 4.3-2, J_i, $\langle J_i \rangle_0$ and $\langle J_i \rangle_I$ are shown at time t. J_i appears as if a δ-function, since J_i exists only on one of the trajectories I. On the other hand, $\langle J_i \rangle_0$ made by averaging J_i along trajectories 0 is shown as if it were an error function. Obviously

$$\langle J_i \rangle_0 \neq \langle J_i \rangle_I. \qquad (4.3\text{-}20)$$

It is obvious, however, that

$$\int \langle J_i(X_i; t) \rangle_0 \, dX_i = \int \langle J_i(X_i; t) \rangle_I \, dX_i. \qquad (4.3\text{-}21)$$

This is because both are the same total intensity of J_i from t to $t+\tau$ divided by τ. If the number of particles which exist in states between X_a and $X_a+\Delta X_a$ is sufficiently large, we may assume

$$\langle \overline{J(X_a; t)}\rangle_0 = \langle \overline{J(X_a; t)}\rangle_{\mathrm{I}}, \tag{4.3-19}$$

where, of course,

$$\langle \overline{J(X_a; t)}\rangle_0 = \frac{1}{N\Delta X_a} \sum_i \int_{X_a}^{X_a+\Delta X_a} \langle J_i(X_i; t)\rangle_0 \, dX_i, \tag{4.3-22}$$

$$\langle \overline{J(X_a; t)}\rangle_{\mathrm{I}} = \frac{1}{N\Delta X_a} \sum_i \int_{X_a}^{X_a+\Delta X_a} \langle J_i(X_i; t)\rangle_{\mathrm{I}} \, dX_i. \tag{4.3-23}$$

Needless to say, condition (21) is compatible with eq. (19). According to the above, eq. (4.2-1) yields

$$\left(\frac{\partial}{\partial t} + \frac{\mathbf{p}_a}{m}\cdot\frac{\partial}{\partial \mathbf{r}_a}\right)\langle \overline{F^{(1)}(X_a; t)}\rangle_0 + \langle \overline{J}\rangle_{\mathrm{I}} = 0. \tag{4.3-24}$$

In order to reduce eq. (24) to eq. (4.1-1), it is necessary to replace $\overline{\langle F^{(1)}\rangle_0}$ with f' in accordance with

$$f'(\mathbf{c}, \mathbf{r}; t) = Nm^3 \overline{\langle F^{(1)}(\mathbf{p}, \mathbf{r}; t)\rangle_0} \tag{4.3-25}$$

$$\mathbf{c} = \mathbf{p}/m. \tag{4.3-26}$$

It is a trivial matter that we take off subscript a, replace subscript b with 1, and write mc' and mc_1' respectively for $\mathbf{p}_a(\tau)$ and $\mathbf{p}_b(\tau)$ for completing the reduction.

Finally the essential points in the above derivation are summarized as follows:

1. We may take some other class of trajectories in place of trajectories 0, as long as they are equivalent in time scale τ_1.

2. Also, trajectories I may be replaced with trajectories II, etc., if these classes are equivalent in time scale τ_2.

3. X_i is an independent variable, and $F_i^{(1)}(X_i; t)$ is a discontinuous function to be represented by a δ-function. But $\overline{F^{(1)}(X_a; t)}$ is a continous function, if N/V and ΔX_a are sufficiently large. The situation is similar with respect to $F_{ij}^{(2)}(X_i, X_j; t)$, etc.

4. Although

$$\frac{d}{ds} F_{ij}^{(2)}(X_i(s), X_j(s); t+s) = 0$$

in eq. (5), yet

$$\left[\frac{d}{ds}\right]_{ab} \overline{F^{(2)}(X_a(s), X_b(s); t+s)} \neq 0$$

in eq. (8).

5. The domain of integration $\int d\mathbf{r}_b$ considered in eq. (12) is finite in the direction of $\mathbf{p}_b - \mathbf{p}_a$. This is necessary, after replacing $F_{ij}^{(2)}$ $(X_i, X_j; t)$ with $\overline{F^{(2)}(X_a, X_b; t)}$, for taking into account the fact that a particle with its finite velocity is localized in a narrow domain of the configuration space during a short period of time τ. Note that $F_{ij}^{(2)}(X_i, X_j; t)$ is discontinuously localized by itself, but that $\overline{F^{(2)}(X_a, X_b; t)}$ is a continous function. If $D^{(N)}$ were symmetric in the microscopic sense, the above limitation of the integration with respect to $d\mathbf{b}_b$ would not be justified. Then the value of the collision integral would always be indefinitely large.

4.4. Physical implications of the Boltzmann equation

The Boltzmann equation written in terms of f, as given by eq. (4.1-1),

$$\left(\frac{\partial}{\partial t} + \mathbf{c} \cdot \frac{\partial}{\partial \mathbf{r}} + \frac{\boldsymbol{\mathcal{F}}}{m} \cdot \frac{\partial}{\partial \mathbf{c}}\right) f = -J \tag{4.4-1}$$

with

$$-J = \int\int\int [f(\mathbf{c}')f(\mathbf{c}_1') - f(\mathbf{c})f(\mathbf{c}_1)] \, hv \, dh \, d\varphi \, d^3c_1 \tag{4.4-2}$$

$$v = |\mathbf{c}_1 - \mathbf{c}| \tag{4.4-3}$$

$\boldsymbol{\mathcal{F}}$: external force exerted on each of the particles, $\qquad$ (4.4-4)

is an integral-differential equation governing the evolution of $f(\mathbf{c}, \mathbf{r}, t)$;

$$f(\mathbf{c}, \mathbf{r}, t) \, d^3c \, d^3r$$

is the number of particles which have velocities between $\mathbf{c}$ and $\mathbf{c} + d\mathbf{c}$ and are located in an elementary space d^3r at time t.

4.4-1. f ALONG A TRAJECTORY

Regarding eq. (1) as a partial differential equation which is linear with respect to f, we write the characteristic equations as follows:

$$\frac{df}{dt} = -J \qquad (4.4\text{-}5)$$

$$\frac{dc}{dt} = \frac{\mathcal{F}}{m} \qquad (4.4\text{-}6)$$

$$\frac{d\mathbf{r}}{dt} = \mathbf{c} \qquad (4.4\text{-}7)$$

These equations mean that f along a trajectory, a solution of eqs. (6) and (7), is given by

$$f(\mathbf{c}, \mathbf{r}, t) = f(\mathbf{c}_0, \mathbf{r}_0, t_0) - \int_{t_0}^{t} J \, dt, \qquad (4.4\text{-}5)'$$

where

$$\mathbf{c} = \mathbf{c}_0 + \int_{t_0}^{t} \frac{\mathcal{F}}{m} \, dt \qquad (4.4\text{-}6)'$$

$$\mathbf{r} = \mathbf{r}_0 + \int_{t_0}^{t} \mathbf{c} \, dt. \qquad (4.4\text{-}7)'$$

Of course, J is a function of $\mathbf{c}$ and $\mathbf{r}$ as given by eqs. (6)′ and (7)′ which are the solutions of eqs. (6) and (7). f given by eq. (5)′ is a particular solution of the Boltzmann equation. In eq. (5)′, $\mathbf{c}_0$, $\mathbf{r}_0$, and t_0 are given, and $\mathbf{c}$ and $\mathbf{r}$ vary as functions of time t. It is possible to obtain a solution where $\mathbf{c}$, $\mathbf{r}$, and t are independent variables. When $\mathbf{c}$, $\mathbf{r}$, and t_0 are given, we may chose $\mathbf{c}_0$ and $\mathbf{r}_0$ so that eqs. (6)′ and (7)′ are satisfied at *time t*.

$$\mathbf{c}_0 = \mathbf{c} - \mathbf{c}', \quad \mathbf{r}_0 = \mathbf{r} - \mathbf{r}'$$

in accordance with

$$m \frac{d\mathbf{c}'}{dt} = \mathcal{F}(t, \mathbf{r}), \qquad \mathbf{r}: \text{invariant}$$

$$\frac{d\mathbf{r}'}{dt} = \mathbf{c}, \qquad \mathbf{c}: \text{invariant.}$$

On substitution of these in eq. (5)′, we have

$$f(\mathbf{c}, \mathbf{r}; t) = f(\mathbf{c}-\mathbf{c}', \mathbf{r}-\mathbf{r}'; t_0) - \int_{t_0}^{t} J \, dt. \qquad (4.4\text{-}5)''$$

The integration of J with respect to time must be done under the condition that $\mathbf{r}$ and $\mathbf{c}$ are invariant. f given by eq. (5)″ may be called a general solution. See Subsection 2.3-2.

If J vanishes, f is invariant along a trajectory, as seen from eq. (5)′. Because of J, f changes from one point to another on the trajectory. In a heuristic analogy, a trajectory determined by eqs. (6) and (7) is similar to a highway, on each point of which the velocity is specified. To an observer moving on the highway, the number density of automobiles, which corresponds to f, changes as a function of time, because some automobiles come into and some come out from the highway. Such exits and entrances correspond to the effect of J, the effect of collisions.

4.4-2. COLLISION INTEGRAL

We investigate the collision integral

$$-J = \int\int\int [f(\mathbf{c}')f(\mathbf{c}_1') - f(\mathbf{c})f(\mathbf{c}_1)] \, hv \, dh \, d\varphi \, d^3c_1 \qquad (4.4\text{-}2)$$

in detail. According to the definitions which we considered in the last section, $\mathbf{c}'$ and $\mathbf{c}_1'$ are the asymptotic velocities of two particles before their collision, and $\mathbf{c}$ and $\mathbf{c}'$ are the asymptotic velocities after the same collision. Therefore $\mathbf{c}$ and $\mathbf{c}_1$ are functions of $\mathbf{c}'$ and $\mathbf{c}_1'$, and conversely $\mathbf{c}'$ and $\mathbf{c}_1'$ are functions of $\mathbf{c}$ and $\mathbf{c}_1$. Furthermore, as shown below, if c and c_1 are the asymptotic velocities before a collision $\mathbf{c}'$ and $\mathbf{c}_1'$ are the asymoptotic velocities after the same collision.

Let us investigate the dynamical behaviors of two particles during their collision with the force law given by eq. (1.2-1). The equation of motion of particle 1 with mass m_1 is

$$m_1\ddot{\mathbf{r}}_1 = \mathcal{F}_{12} \qquad (4.4\text{-}8)$$

and the equation of particle 2 with mass m_2 is

$$m_2\ddot{\mathbf{r}}_2 = -\mathcal{F}_{12} \tag{4.4-9}$$

$$\mathcal{F}_{12} = \varkappa \frac{\mathbf{r}_2 - \mathbf{r}_1}{|\mathbf{r}_2 - \mathbf{r}_1|^{s+1}} = -m_1 m_2 K \frac{\mathbf{R}_{12}}{R_{12}^{s+1}}. \tag{4.4-10}$$

If K is positive, the inter-particle force is repulsive; if K is negative the force is attractive. Here

$$\mathbf{R}_{12} = \mathbf{r}_2 - \mathbf{r}_1. \tag{4.4-11}$$

It is easily shown that eqs. (8) and (9) yield

$$\frac{m_1 m_2}{m_1 + m_2}(\ddot{\mathbf{r}}_2 - \ddot{\mathbf{r}}_1) = -\mathcal{F}_{12} \tag{4.4-12}$$

which by definition of

$$M_{12} = \frac{m_1 m_2}{m_1 + m_2} \quad \text{(reduced mass)} \tag{4.4-13}$$

is reduced to

$$M_{12}\ddot{\mathbf{R}}_{12} = -\mathcal{F}_{12}. \tag{4.4-14}$$

By making the vector product of each member of eq. (14) with $\mathbf{R}_{12}$, we obtain

$$M_{12}\mathbf{R}_{12} \times \ddot{\mathbf{R}}_{12} = -\mathbf{R}_{12} \times \mathcal{F}_{12} \tag{4.4-15}$$

which, according to eq. (10), yields

$$\mathbf{R}_{12} \times \ddot{\mathbf{R}}_{12} = 0$$

or

$$\mathbf{R}_{12} \times \dot{\mathbf{R}}_{12} = \mathbf{\eta} \quad \text{(invariant)} \tag{4.4-16}$$

after integration. $M_{12}\,\mathbf{\eta}$ is the angular momentum of the system.

The center of gravity $\mathbf{R}_g$ of the system is given by

$$\mathbf{R}_g = \frac{m_1 \mathbf{r}_1 + m_2 \mathbf{r}_2}{m_1 + m_2}. \tag{4.4-17}$$

If we consider a plane which is perpendicular to $\mathbf{\eta}$ and carries $\mathbf{R}_g$ on it, the two particles are always on the plane. See Fig. 4.4-1.

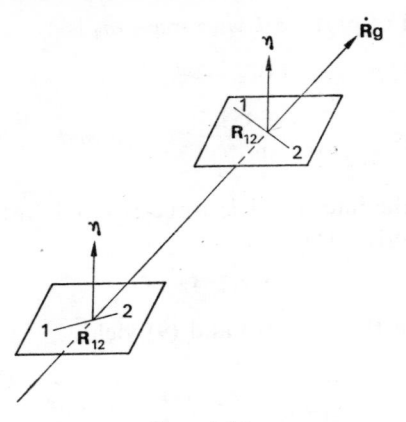

FIG. 4.4-1.

The center of gravity $\mathbf{R}_g$ of two colliding particles, 1 and 2, moves on a straight line with a uniform velocity $\dot{\mathbf{R}}_g$. The two particles are always on a plane which is perpendicular to $\boldsymbol{\eta}$ (invariant) and which carries the center of gravity on it.

Hence, if an observer stays on the plane, he may see the two particles remain on the same plane. As a result, he may treat eq. (14) in the plane with the origin of $\mathbf{R}_{12}$ at particle 1. (See Appendix A.)

The solution of eq. (14) had been completed many years ago, and only main results are mentioned in the following: The initial conditions are

$$\left.\begin{aligned}
\dot{\mathbf{r}}_1 &= \mathbf{c}_1 \\
\dot{\mathbf{r}}_2 &= \mathbf{c}_2 \\
\boldsymbol{\eta} &= h\mathbf{v}_{12} \\
\dot{\mathbf{R}}_{12} &= \mathbf{v}_{12} = \mathbf{c}_2 - \mathbf{c}_1
\end{aligned}\right\} \qquad (4.4\text{-}17)'$$

(asymptotic initial conditions at $t = -\infty$).

The asymptotic conditions after the collision are given by

$$\left.\begin{aligned}
\dot{\mathbf{r}}_1 &= \mathbf{c}_1' \\
\dot{\mathbf{r}}_2 &= \mathbf{c}_2' \\
\boldsymbol{\eta} &= h'\mathbf{v}_{12}' \\
\mathbf{v}_{12}' &= \mathbf{c}_2' - \mathbf{c}_1'
\end{aligned}\right\} \qquad (4.4\text{-}18)$$

(asymptotic final conditions, at $t = +\infty$).

The solution gives

$$h' = h \tag{4.4-19}$$

$$|\mathbf{v}'_{12}| = |\mathbf{v}_{12}| = \mathbf{v}_{12} \tag{4.4-20}$$

$$\left.\begin{array}{l} (\mathbf{v}'_{12})_\| = v_{12} \cos{(\pi - 2\theta_\infty)} \\ (\mathbf{v}'_{12})_\perp = v_{12} \sin{(\pi - 2\theta_\infty)}, \end{array}\right\} \tag{4.4-21}$$

where $(\ )_\|$ means component in the direction of $\mathbf{v}_{12}$ and $(\ )_\perp$ in the direction perpendicular to $\mathbf{v}_{12}$, as is shown in Fig. 4.4-2.

$$\theta_\infty = \int_0^{\xi_0} \frac{d\xi}{\left[1 - \xi^2 - \dfrac{2}{s-1}\left(\dfrac{\xi}{\alpha}\right)^{s-1}\right]^{1/2}} \tag{4.4-22}$$

ξ_0 is the solution of

$$1 - \xi_0^2 - \frac{2}{s-1}\left(\frac{\xi_0}{\alpha}\right)^{s-1} = 0 \tag{4.4-23}$$

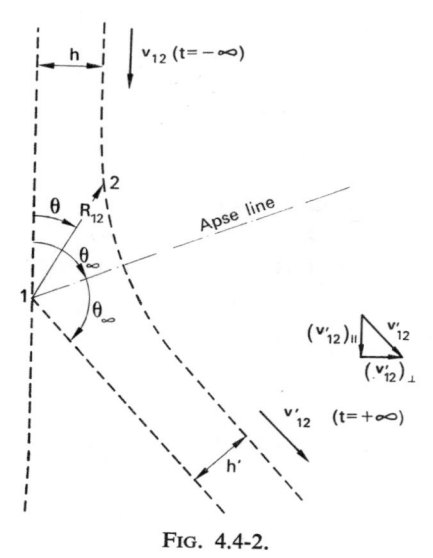

FIG. 4.4-2.

The trajectory of particle 2 relative to the position of particle 1 on the plane illustrated in Fig. 4-4.1. This illustrates a case of repulsive force.

and

$$\alpha = h \left[\frac{\mathbf{v}_{12}^2}{(m_1+m_2)K} \right]^{1/(s-1)}.$$ (4.4-24)

Besides, we have

$$(m_1+m_2)\dot{\mathbf{R}}_g = m_1\mathbf{c}_1+m_2\mathbf{c}_2 = m_1\mathbf{c}_1'+m_2\mathbf{c}_2'$$ (4.4-25)

$$m_1c_1^2+m_2c_2^2 = m_1c_1'^2+m_2c_2'^2.$$ (4.4-26)

From these, we obtain

$$\left. \begin{array}{l} \mathbf{c}_1' = \dot{\mathbf{R}}_g - \dfrac{m_2}{m_1+m_2}\,\mathbf{v}_{12}' \\[2mm] \mathbf{c}_2' = \dot{\mathbf{R}}_g + \dfrac{m_1}{m_1+m_2}\,\mathbf{v}_{12}' \\[2mm] \mathbf{c}_1 = \dot{\mathbf{R}}_g - \dfrac{m_2}{m_1+m_2}\,\mathbf{v}_{12} \\[2mm] \mathbf{c}_2 = \dot{\mathbf{R}}_g + \dfrac{m_1}{m_1+m_2}\,\mathbf{v}_{12}. \end{array} \right\}$$ (4.4-27)

From relations (19), (20), and (21), we may conclude the following:

1. If the initial condition of a collision is $(\mathbf{c}_1, \mathbf{c}_2, h)$, then the resultant condition after the collision is $(\mathbf{c}_1', \mathbf{c}_2', h)$.

2. If the initial condition is $(\mathbf{c}_1', \mathbf{c}_2', h)$, then the resultant condition is $(\mathbf{c}_1, \mathbf{c}_2, h)$.

3. A collision is time reversible:

$$(-\mathbf{c}_1', -\mathbf{c}_2', h) \quad \text{results in} \quad (-\mathbf{c}_1, -\mathbf{c}_2, h), \text{ etc.}$$

4. If we apply the Liouville theorem to the two-particle system, we obtain

$$m_1m_2\,d^3\mathbf{c}_1\,d^3\mathbf{c}_2\,d^3\mathbf{r}_1\,d^3\mathbf{r}_2 = m_1m_2\,d^3\mathbf{c}_1'\,d^3\mathbf{c}_2'\,d^3\mathbf{r}_1'\,d^3\mathbf{r}_2'.$$ (4.4-28)

Here $d^3\mathbf{c}$, etc., mean the displacements operated on those initial conditions and $d^3\mathbf{c}'$, etc., are the resultant displacements.

Special case: $s = 5$. In this case, we may solve eq. (23) obtaining easily

$$\xi_0^2 = -\alpha^4 + (\alpha^8 + 2\alpha^4)^{1/2}. \tag{4.4-29}$$

Those molecules are called Maxwellian.

Special case: $s = \infty$. By writing for eq. (10)

$$\mathcal{F}_{12} = m_1 m_2 K' \left(\frac{\sigma}{R_{12}}\right)^\infty R_{12}, \ K' > 0 \tag{4.4-30}$$

with constant σ, we see that

$$\left.\begin{array}{ll} \mathcal{F}_{12} = 0, & \text{if } R_{12} > \sigma \\ \mathcal{F}_{12} = \infty \times R_{12}, & \text{if } R_{12} < \sigma \end{array}\right\} \tag{4.4-31}$$

The particles collide as if they are solid elastic spheres.

4.4-3. BOLTZMANN'S H-THEOREM AND THE MAXWELL DISTRIBUTION

According to Boltzmann, we define

$$H = \int f \log f \, d^3c. \tag{4.4-32}$$

If we assume that f is spatially uniform, but varies with time, we have

$$\frac{\partial H}{\partial t} = \int \frac{\partial}{\partial t} (f \log f) \, d^3c$$

$$= \int (1 + \log f) \frac{\partial f}{\partial t} \, d^3c$$

$$= \int (1 + \log f)(f' f_1' - f f_1) |c_1 - c| \, 2\pi h \, dh \, d^3c \, d^3c_1,$$

where $f_1' = f(c_1')$, etc. By the help of

$$\int \phi_1 (f' f_1' - f f_1) |c_1 - c| \, 2\pi h \, dh \, d^3c \, d^3c_1$$

$$= \frac{1}{4} \int (\phi + \phi_1 - \phi' - \phi_1')(f' f_1' - f f_1)|c_1 - c| 2\pi h \, dh \, d^3c \, d^3c_1, \tag{4.4-33}$$

which may be proved by the consideration of the symmetry existing in the left-hand side with respect to $\mathbf{c}$, $\mathbf{c}_1$, etc., we obtain

$$\frac{\partial H}{\partial t} = \frac{1}{4} \int \log \left[\frac{ff_1}{f'f_1'} \right] (f'f_1' - ff_1) |\mathbf{c}_1 - \mathbf{c}| 2\pi h \, dh \, d^3\mathbf{c} \, d^3\mathbf{c}_1. \quad (4.4\text{-}34)$$

If $ff_1 > f'f_1'$, we see that $\partial H / \partial t < 0$ according to eq. (34). If $ff_1 < f'f_1'$, we also see that $\partial H / \partial t < 0$. In any case, H decreases as time passes. The process is irreversible. Finally, at the time when $\partial H / \partial t = 0$, we have

$$ff_1 = f'f_1' \quad (4.4\text{-}35)$$

or

$$\log f + \log f_1 = \log f' + \log f_1'.$$

Considering the conditions of a collision

$$m\mathbf{c} + m\mathbf{c}_1 = m\mathbf{c}' + m\mathbf{c}_1'$$

$$\frac{1}{2} mc^2 + \frac{1}{2} mc_1^2 = \frac{1}{2} mc'^2 + \frac{1}{2} mc_1'^2$$

we may conclude that

$$\left. \begin{array}{l} \log f = \alpha + \boldsymbol{\beta} \cdot m\mathbf{c} + \gamma \dfrac{1}{2} mc^2 \\[2mm] \qquad = \dfrac{a}{2} m(\mathbf{c} - \mathbf{u})^2 + b, \end{array} \right\} \quad (4.4\text{-}36)$$

where a, b, and $\mathbf{u}$ are constants. By replacing the constants a and b with n and kT, we may write

$$f = n \left(\frac{m}{2\pi kT} \right)^{3/2} \exp \left[-\frac{m}{2kT} (\mathbf{c} - \mathbf{u})^2 \right]. \quad (4.4\text{-}37)$$

According to the definition of f, it may be shown that the physical meaning of n is the number density of particles, $nm\mathbf{u}$ is the momentum density, and $\left(\frac{3}{2} kT + \frac{1}{2} m\mathbf{u}^2 \right) n$ is the energy density:

$$\left. \begin{array}{l} nm = \int mf \, d^3\mathbf{c} \\[2mm] nm\mathbf{u} = \int m\mathbf{c}f \, d^3\mathbf{c} \\[2mm] \dfrac{3}{2} nkT + \dfrac{1}{2} nmu^2 = \int \dfrac{1}{2} mc^2 f \, d^3\mathbf{c}. \end{array} \right\} \quad (4.4\text{-}38)$$

The detail will be discussed in Chapter 5. f given by eq. (37) is called the Maxwell distribution function, k is the Boltzmann constant, and T is the temperature.

Exercises

1. It is obvious that

$$\int \sum_{i=1}^{N} \delta(\mathbf{r} - \mathbf{r}_i^*) \, d\mathbf{r} = N,$$

where the domain of integration covers the entire configuration space. Assuming that the $\mathbf{r}^*$'s are distributed almost uniformly in domain V of the configuration space, show that

$$\int_{\Delta \mathbf{r}} \sum_{i=1}^{N} \delta(\mathbf{r} - \mathbf{r}_i^*) \, d\mathbf{r} = 0 \left[\frac{N \Delta \mathbf{r}}{V} \right].$$

2. There are N similar events, 1, 2, $\ldots$, i, $\ldots$, N. Event i occurs with probability $w_i \, \Delta t$ during the time between t and $t + \Delta t$. The probability of only one event o ccurring in Δt is given by

$$S(1) = \sum_{i=1}^{N} s_i = \sum_{i=1}^{N} w_i \, \Delta t \prod_{j \neq i} (1 - w_j \, \Delta t).$$

What is the probability of n events occurring in Δt? The answer:

$$S(n) = \sum_{i < j <} \sum_{\ldots < k} \sum s_{i, j, \ldots, k}$$

$$s_{i, j, \ldots, k} = w_i w_j \ldots w_k \, (\Delta t)^n \prod (1 - w_l \, \Delta t) \qquad l \neq i, j, \ldots, k.$$

3. Assuming that $w_i \, \Delta t \ll 1$ in question 2, show that

$$S(1) = \sum_{i=1} w_i \, \Delta t$$

$$S(n) = 0 \qquad n > 1.$$

4. Suppose that event i in question 2 is the one that a particle in Brownian motion gains momentum $\mathbf{p}_i$. The total gain of momentum of the particle in Δt is denoted by $\Delta \mathbf{p}$.

$$\Delta \mathbf{p} = \sum s_i \mathbf{p}_i$$

Assuming $w_i \, \Delta t \ll 1$, show that

$$\Delta \mathbf{p} \, \Delta \mathbf{p} = \sum s_i \mathbf{p}_i \mathbf{p}_i.$$

CHAPTER 5

The Derivation of the Navier–Stokes Equations

5.1. Equations of moments

We cannot observe f directly, but we can measure macroscopic quantities derived from f.

5.1-1. MOMENTS

Since $f\,d^3c$ is the number density of molecules in the states between $\mathbf{c}$ and $\mathbf{c}+d\mathbf{c}$ in a unit volume at $\mathbf{r}$ and t, the mass density of the gas is given by

$$\varrho = nm = m \int\int\int_{-\infty}^{+\infty} f\,dc_x\,dc_y\,dc_z. \qquad (5.1\text{-}1)$$

Here n is the number density of molecules. The gross momentum density is

$$\varrho\mathbf{u} = \int\int\int m\mathbf{c}f\,d^3c, \quad d^3c = dc_x\,dc_y\,dc_z. \qquad (5.1\text{-}2)$$

The energy density:

$$E = \int\int\int {}^{1}/_{2}mc^2f\,d^3c. \qquad (5.1\text{-}3)$$

The stress (flux of momentum):

$$\mathbf{P} = \int\int\int m\mathbf{cc}f\,d^3c, \qquad (5.1\text{-}4)$$

where

$$\mathbf{cc} = \begin{pmatrix} c_xc_x & c_xc_y & c_xc_z \\ c_yc_x & c_yc_y & c_yc_z \\ c_zc_x & c_zc_y & c_zc_z \end{pmatrix}. \qquad (5.1\text{-}4)'$$

The flux of energy:

$$\mathbf{Q} = \iiint {}^1\!/_2 mc^2 \mathbf{c} f\, d^3c. \qquad (5.1\text{-}5)$$

We may define similarly higher order moments.

By writing

$$\mathbf{C} = \mathbf{c} - \mathbf{u}$$

we have

$$d^3C = d^3c \qquad (5.1\text{-}6)$$

and we may perform integrations by parts. For eq. (2) we have

$$\varrho\mathbf{u} = \iiint m(\mathbf{C}+\mathbf{u})f\, d^3C = \iiint m\mathbf{C}f\, d^3C + \varrho\mathbf{u}.$$

Hence

$$\iiint m\mathbf{C}f\, d^3C = 0. \qquad (5.1\text{-}7)$$

For eq. (3),

$$E = \iiint \frac{1}{2} m(\mathbf{C}+\mathbf{u})^2 f\, d^3C$$

$$= \iiint \frac{1}{2} mC^2 f\, d^3C + \iiint m\mathbf{u}\cdot\mathbf{C}f\, d^3C + \iiint \frac{1}{2} mu^2 f\, d^3C.$$

The second member vanishes according to eq. (7); hence

$$\left.\begin{aligned}
E &= \mathcal{E} + \frac{1}{2}\,\varrho u^2 \\
\mathcal{E} &= \iiint \frac{1}{2} mC^2 f\, d^3C,
\end{aligned}\right\} \qquad (5.1\text{-}8)$$

where $\mathcal{E}$ is the internal energy or heat energy. Similarly

$$\mathbf{P} = \iiint m\mathbf{c}\mathbf{c}f\, d^3c = \iiint m(\mathbf{C}+\mathbf{u})\,(\mathbf{C}+\mathbf{u})f\, d^3C = \mathbf{p}+\varrho\mathbf{u}\mathbf{u}, \quad (5.1\text{-}9)$$

where

$$\mathbf{p} = \iiint m\mathbf{C}\mathbf{C}f\, d^3C \qquad (5.1\text{-}10)$$

is the stress which is usual in fluid dynamics. Obviously

$$p_{xx}+p_{yy}+p_{zz} = 2\mathcal{E}. \qquad (5.1\text{-}11)$$

Similarly we obtain

$$\mathbf{Q} = \mathbf{q} + \mathcal{E}\mathbf{u} + \frac{1}{2}\,\varrho u^2\mathbf{u} + \mathbf{p}\cdot\mathbf{u}, \qquad (5.1\text{-}12)$$

89

where

$$\mathbf{q} = \int\int\int \frac{1}{2} mC^2 \mathbf{C} f \, d^3C \qquad (5.1\text{-}13)$$

is the rate of heat-energy conduction. Further we may define higher order moments by

$$\mathbf{R}^{(\nu)} = \int\int\int m\mathbf{C}\ldots\mathbf{C} f \, d^3C. \qquad (5.1\text{-}14)$$

5.1-2. EQUATIONS OF MOMENTS

With respect to d^3c, we integrate, term by term, the Boltzmann equation

$$\left(\frac{\partial}{\partial t} + \mathbf{c} \cdot \frac{\partial}{\partial \mathbf{r}} + \frac{\mathcal{F}}{m} \cdot \frac{\partial}{\partial \mathbf{c}}\right) f = -J \qquad (5.1\text{-}15)$$

multiplied by m, and obtain

$$\frac{\partial \varrho}{\partial t} + \frac{\partial}{\partial \mathbf{r}} \cdot (\varrho \mathbf{u}) = 0. \qquad (5.1\text{-}16)$$

Here the mass conservation by collision is taken into account. Secondly, eq. (15) is multiplied by $m\mathbf{c}$, from the left, and is integrated with respect to d^3c to yield

$$\frac{\partial}{\partial t}(\varrho \mathbf{u}) + \frac{\partial}{\partial \mathbf{r}} \cdot (\varrho \mathbf{u}\mathbf{u} + \mathbf{p}) - n\mathcal{F}_0 - n\mathbf{u} \times \mathfrak{A} = 0, \qquad (5.1\text{-}17)$$

where we have assumed

$$\mathcal{F} = \mathcal{F}_0 + \mathbf{c} \times \mathfrak{A} \qquad (5.1\text{-}18)$$

and the momentum conservation by collision is considered. Equation (16) is the equation of continuity of fluid dynamics and eq. (18) is the equation of momentum which will yield the Navier–Stokes equation later on.[†] The equation of energy is obtained by integrating similarly the Boltzmann equation multiplied by $1/2 mc^2$:

$$\left.\begin{aligned}
\frac{\partial}{\partial t}\left(\mathcal{E} + \frac{1}{2}\varrho u^2\right) + \frac{\partial}{\partial \mathbf{r}} \cdot \left(\mathbf{q} + \mathbf{p}\cdot\mathbf{u} + \mathcal{E}\mathbf{u} + \frac{1}{2}\varrho u^2\mathbf{u}\right) \\
-\mathbf{u}\cdot(n\mathcal{F}_0 + n\mathbf{u}\times\mathfrak{A}) = 0.
\end{aligned}\right\} \qquad (5.1\text{-}19)$$

[†] Regarding a gas of molecules of more than one species, see treatments by Chapman and Cowling (1952).

90

Similarly we may derive equations of higher order moments. The moment equations derived above are never closed. In eq. (16), not only ϱ but also **u** are involved. **u** may be determined by eq. (17), but the equation involves **p** which will be determined by eq. (19); eq. (19) involves **q**, and so forth. The method of closing the equations by a finite number is not one.[†] In the following section, the Chapman–Enskog theory leading to the usual basic equations of fluid dynamics will be outlined.

5.2. The Chapman–Enskog theory

The distribution of molecules in a gas contained in a vessel and protected from the disturbance of any external cause tends to be Maxwellian[‡]

$$f^{(0)} = n\left(\frac{m}{2\pi kT}\right)^{3/2} \exp\left[-\frac{m}{2kT}(\mathbf{c}-\mathbf{u})^2\right]. \qquad (5.2\text{-}1)$$

Since $f^{(0)}$ yields[§]

$$\left.\begin{aligned} n &= \iiint_{-\infty}^{+\infty} f^{(0)}\, d^3c \\ \mathbf{u} &= \frac{1}{n}\iiint \mathbf{c} f^{(0)}\, d^3c \\ \frac{\mathscr{E}}{n} &= \frac{1}{n}\iiint \frac{1}{2} m(\mathbf{c}-\mathbf{u})^2 f^{(0)}\, d^3c = \frac{3}{2} kT, \end{aligned}\right\} \qquad (5.2\text{-}2)$$

T is the temperature and k the Boltzmann constant. The collision integral vanishes when $f^{(0)}$ is the distribution function, as is easily shown by a consideration of mass, momentum, and energy con-

[†] See Section 7.4.

[‡] This is the solution of the Boltzmann equation under the condition that the distribution is uniform and stationary.

[§]
$$\int_0^\infty x^{2n} \exp(-\lambda x^2)\, dx = \frac{1\times3\times\,\cdots\,\times(2n-1)}{2^{(n+1)}}\left(\frac{\pi}{\lambda^{2n+1}}\right)^{1/2}$$
$$\int_0^\infty x^{2n+1} \exp(-\lambda x^2)\, dx = \frac{n!}{2\lambda^{n+1}}.$$

servation laws in collisions.

$$-J[f^{(0)}(\mathbf{c}),\ f^{(0)}(\mathbf{c}_1)] = 0. \tag{5.2-3}$$

We now assume that the distribution function f of molecules in a gas is almost Maxwellian:

$$f = f^{(0)} + f^{(1)} + \ldots + f^{(r)} + \ldots. \tag{5.2-4}$$

Here n, $\mathbf{u}$, and T of which $f^{(0)}$ is composed are determined by

$$\left.\begin{aligned}
n &= \iiint f\, d^3c = \iiint f^{(0)}\, d^3c \\
\mathbf{u} &= \frac{1}{n}\iiint \mathbf{c}f\, d^3c = \frac{1}{n}\iiint \mathbf{c}f^{(0)}\, d^3c \\
\frac{3}{2}kT &= \frac{1}{n}\iiint \frac{1}{2}m(\mathbf{c}-\mathbf{u})^2 f\, d^3c \\
&= \frac{1}{n}\iiint \frac{1}{2}m(\mathbf{c}-\mathbf{u})^2 f^{(0)}\, d^3c
\end{aligned}\right\} \tag{5.2-5}$$

and hence it is possible to set conditions

$$\left.\begin{aligned}
\iiint f^{(r)}\, d^3c &= 0 \\
\iiint \mathbf{c}f^{(r)}\, d^3c &= 0 \\
\iiint (\mathbf{c}-\mathbf{u})^2 f^{(r)}\, d^3c &= 0
\end{aligned}\right\} \tag{5.2-6}$$

$$r = 1, 2, \ldots.$$

On substitution of f given by eq. (4) in the Boltzmann equation, we have

$$\left.\begin{aligned}
\left(\frac{\partial}{\partial f} + \mathbf{c}\cdot\frac{\partial}{\partial \mathbf{r}} + \frac{\mathcal{F}}{m}\cdot\frac{\partial}{\partial \mathbf{c}}\right)(f^{(0)}+f^{(1)}+f^{(2)}+ \ldots) \\
+ J^{(0)}+J^{(1)}+J^{(2)}+ \ldots = 0,
\end{aligned}\right\} \tag{5.2-7}$$

where

$$\left.\begin{aligned}
J^{(0)} &= J[f^{(0)}(\mathbf{c})f^{(0)}(\mathbf{c}_1)] \\
&= -\iint [f^{(0)}(\mathbf{c}')f^{(0)}(\mathbf{c}_1') - f^{(0)}(\mathbf{c})f^{(0)}(\mathbf{c}_1)]\, 2\pi h\, dh v\, d^3c_1 \\
&= 0. \\
J^{(1)} &= J[f^{(0)}(\mathbf{c})f^{(1)}(\mathbf{c}_1)] + J[f^{(1)}(\mathbf{c})f^{(0)}(\mathbf{c}_1)] \\
J^{(2)} &= J[f^{(0)}(\mathbf{c})f^{(2)}(\mathbf{c}_1)] + J[f^{(1)}(\mathbf{c})f^{(1)}(\mathbf{c}_1)] \\
&\quad + J[f^{(2)}(\mathbf{c})f^{(0)}(\mathbf{c}_1)], \quad \text{etc.}
\end{aligned}\right\} \tag{5.2-8}$$

We now assume that n, $\mathbf{u}$, and T in $f^{(0)}$ are functions of t, $\mathbf{r}$ and divide eq. (7) into

$$\left.\begin{array}{l}\left(\dfrac{\partial}{\partial t}+\mathbf{c}\cdot\dfrac{\partial}{\partial \mathbf{r}}+\dfrac{\mathcal{F}}{m}\cdot\dfrac{\partial}{\partial \mathbf{c}}\right)f^{(0)}+J^{(1)}=0 \\[3mm] \left(\dfrac{\partial}{\partial t}+\mathbf{c}\cdot\dfrac{\partial}{\partial \mathbf{r}}+\dfrac{\mathcal{F}}{m}\cdot\dfrac{\partial}{\partial \mathbf{c}}\right)f^{(1)}+J^{(2)}=0. \end{array}\right\} \quad (5.2\text{-}9)$$

Mathematical precision is one of the characteristics of the Chapman–Enskog theory. But the main part of the detailed analysis is concerned with the first member of eq. (9). If we take for $\partial/\partial t$ in the first member

$$\frac{\partial}{\partial t}=\frac{\partial_0 n}{\partial t}\frac{d}{dn}+\frac{\partial_0 \mathbf{u}}{\partial t}\frac{d}{d\mathbf{u}}+\frac{\partial_0 T}{\partial t}\frac{d}{dT},$$

$$\frac{\partial_0 n}{\partial t}=-\frac{\partial}{\partial \mathbf{r}}\cdot(n\mathbf{u}) \qquad\qquad \text{from eq. (5.1-16)}$$

$$\frac{\partial_0 \mathbf{u}}{\partial t}=-\mathbf{u}\cdot\frac{\partial}{\partial \mathbf{r}}\mathbf{u}-\frac{1}{\varrho}\frac{\partial}{\partial \mathbf{r}}\cdot\mathbf{p}^{(0)}+\frac{\mathcal{F}_0}{m}+\frac{1}{m}\mathbf{u}\times\mathfrak{A}$$

$$\text{from eq. (5.1-17) with } \mathbf{p}=\mathbf{p}^{(0)}=nkT\,\delta$$
$$(\delta=\text{unit tensor}),$$

$$\frac{\partial_0 T}{\partial t}=-\mathbf{u}\cdot\frac{\partial T}{\partial \mathbf{r}}-\frac{2T}{3}\frac{\partial}{\partial \mathbf{r}}\cdot\mathbf{u}$$

$$\text{from eq. (5.1-19) with } \mathbf{p}=nkT\,\delta$$
$$\text{and } \mathbf{q}=\mathbf{q}^{(0)}=0,$$

then the first member yields

$$\left.\begin{array}{l}f^{(0)}\left\{\left[\left(\dfrac{m}{2kT}\right)C^2-\dfrac{5}{2}\right]\mathbf{C}\cdot\dfrac{\partial\log T}{\partial \mathbf{r}}+2\left(\dfrac{m}{2kT}\right)\right. \\[3mm] \left.+2\left(\dfrac{m}{2kT}\right)\left(\mathbf{CC}-\dfrac{1}{3}C^2\delta\right):\dfrac{\partial}{\partial \mathbf{r}}\mathbf{u}+J^{(1)}=0.\right.\end{array}\right\} \quad (5.2\text{-}10)$$

Equation (10) is an integral equation where $f^{(1)}$ in $J^{(1)}$ is the unknown function. If we obtain $f^{(1)}$ explicitly as a function $\mathbf{C}$, we may calculate $\mathbf{p}^{(1)}$ and $\mathbf{q}^{(1)}$. $\mathbf{p}^{(1)}$ is the shearing stress to the first approximation by which viscosity coefficient μ is defined, and $\mathbf{q}^{(1)}$ is the heat conduction by which heat conductivity λ is defined. By putting

$$f^{(1)}=f^{(0)}\Phi^{(1)} \qquad\qquad (5.2\text{-}11)$$

and considering eqs. (6) and (10) and general characteristics of vector quantities, we have

$$\Phi^{(1)} = -\frac{1}{n}\left(\frac{2kT}{m}\right)^{1/2}\mathbf{A}\cdot\frac{\partial \log T}{\partial \mathbf{r}} - \frac{1}{n}\mathbf{B}:\frac{\partial \mathbf{u}}{\partial \mathbf{r}}. \quad (5.2\text{-}12)$$

Substitution of $\Phi^{(1)}$ in eq. (5.2-10) leads to

$$nI(\mathbf{A}) = f^{(0)}\left[\left(\frac{m}{2kT}\right)C^2 - \frac{5}{2}\right]\left(\frac{m}{2kT}\right)^{1/2}\mathbf{C} \quad (5.2\text{-}13)$$

$$nI(\mathbf{B}) = 2f^{(0)}\frac{m}{2kT}\left(\mathbf{CC} - \frac{1}{3}C^2\,\delta\right), \quad (5.2\text{-}14)$$

where

$$\left.\begin{array}{c} I(\mathbf{A}) = \dfrac{1}{n^2}\displaystyle\int\int f^{(0)}(\mathbf{c})f^{(0)}(\mathbf{c}_1)[\mathbf{A}(\mathbf{c}') + \mathbf{A}(\mathbf{c}_1') - \mathbf{A}(\mathbf{c}) - \mathbf{A}(\mathbf{c}_1)] \\[2mm] \times 2\pi hv \; dh \; d^3c_1, \quad \text{etc.} \end{array}\right\} \quad (5.2\text{-}15)$$

In terms of $\Phi^{(1)}$, we have

$$\left.\begin{array}{l} \mathbf{p}^{(1)} = \displaystyle\int m\mathbf{CC}f^{(0)}\Phi^{(1)}\,d^3C \\[2mm] \qquad = -\mu\left[\dfrac{\partial \mathbf{u}}{\partial \mathbf{r}} + \overline{\dfrac{\partial \mathbf{u}}{\partial \mathbf{r}}} - \dfrac{1}{3}(\text{div } \mathbf{u})\,\delta\right], \end{array}\right\} \quad (5.2\text{-}16)$$

where $\overline{\partial \mathbf{u}/\partial \mathbf{r}}$ is a tensor conjugate to $\partial \mathbf{u}/\partial \mathbf{r}$, and

$$\mu = \frac{1}{10}kT\int \mathbf{B}:\mathbf{I}(\mathbf{B})\,d^3C \quad (5.2\text{-}17)$$

is the viscosity coefficient. Similarly

$$\mathbf{q}^{(1)} = \int \frac{1}{2}mC^2\mathbf{C}f^{(0)}\Phi^{(1)}\,d^3C = -\lambda\frac{\partial T}{\partial \mathbf{r}}, \quad (5.2\text{-}18)$$

where

$$\lambda = \frac{2k^2T}{3m}\int \mathbf{I}(\mathbf{A})\cdot\mathbf{A}\,d^3C \quad (5.2\text{-}19)$$

is the heat conductivity. In order to calculate μ and λ we have to solve eqs. (13) and (14). The solutions were given by Chapman and

Enskog expanding **A** and **B** in terms of certain polynomials. In the case of

$$|\mathcal{F}_{12}| = \varkappa \frac{1}{R_{12}^5} \quad \text{(Maxwellian)}$$

they obtained

$$\left.\begin{aligned}
\mu &= \frac{1}{3\pi}\left(\frac{2m}{\varkappa}\right)^{1/2}\frac{kT}{0.436} \\
\lambda &= \frac{5}{2}\mu c_v, \quad c_v = \frac{3}{2}\frac{k}{m}.
\end{aligned}\right\} \tag{5.2-20}$$

In the case of

$$|\mathcal{F}_{12}| = \varkappa'\left(\frac{\sigma}{R_{12}}\right)^{\infty} \quad \text{(solid spherical model)}$$

the results are

$$\left.\begin{aligned}
\mu &= \frac{5}{16}\frac{(kmT)^{1/2}}{\pi^{1/2}\sigma^2} \\
\lambda &= \frac{5}{2}\mu c_v = \frac{75}{64}\frac{(k^3 T)^{1/2}}{\sigma^2(\pi m)^{1/2}}.
\end{aligned}\right\} \tag{5.2-21}$$

The characteristics of those solutions will be investigated in the next part. One simple but important consequence of the solution is that

$$f^{(1)} \propto \frac{f^{(0)}}{n} \tag{5.2-22}$$

in view of eqs. (8) and (10). Further investigations will show that

$$f^{(2)} \propto \frac{f^{(0)}}{n^2}$$

$$f^{(r)} \propto \frac{f^{(0)}}{n^r}.$$

Hence, it is necessary for the convergency of the solution that n is sufficiently large.

5.3. An integral equation equivalent to the Boltzmann equation and its application

We define Θ by

$$\left.\begin{array}{l} \Theta = \int\int\int f(\mathbf{c}_1) h v \, dh \, d\varphi \, d^3 c_1 \\ v = |\mathbf{c}_1 - \mathbf{c}|. \end{array}\right\} \tag{5.3-1}$$

Through v which is a function of $\mathbf{c}$, Θ is a function of $\mathbf{c}$. $f\Theta$ is one part of the Boltzmann collision integral. Since

$$f\Theta \, d^3 c$$

is the number of collisions which occur on particles in the states between $\mathbf{c}$ and $\mathbf{c} + d\mathbf{c}$ in unit time and unit volume, Θ itself is the probability of occurrence of a collision on a particle with velocity $\mathbf{c}$ in unit time. For the other part of the Boltzmann collision integral, we define

$$[f\Theta]' = \int\int\int f(\mathbf{c}') f(\mathbf{c}_1') h v \, dh \, d\varphi \, d^3 c_1. \tag{5.3-2}$$

Then we have

$$-J = [f\Theta]' - f\Theta. \tag{5.3-3}$$

We define a function $f(\mathbf{c}, \mathbf{r}, t)$ by

$$f(\mathbf{c}, \mathbf{r}, t) = \int_0^\infty [f_s \Theta_s]' \exp\left(-\int_0^s \Theta_s \, ds\right) ds, \tag{5.3-4}$$

where

$$f_s = f(\mathbf{c} + \mathbf{c}(s), \mathbf{r} + \mathbf{r}(s), t - s) \tag{5.3-5}$$

and

$$\left.\begin{array}{l} -\dfrac{d\mathbf{r}(s)}{ds} = \mathbf{c}, \quad \mathbf{r}(0) = 0, \\[2mm] -\dfrac{d\mathbf{c}(s)}{ds} = \dfrac{\mathcal{F}}{m}, \quad \mathbf{c}(0) = 0. \end{array}\right\} \tag{5.3-6}$$

Note that $\mathbf{c}$ and $\mathcal{F}$ in eq. (6) are independent of s. Then, it is shown that f satisfies the Boltzmann equation

$$\frac{\partial f}{\partial t} + \mathbf{c} \cdot \frac{\partial f}{\partial \mathbf{r}} + \frac{\mathcal{F}}{m} \cdot \frac{\partial f}{\partial \mathbf{c}} = -J$$

as follows. With respect to a function ψ, we have in general

$$\left.\begin{aligned}
\psi(s) &= \psi(\mathbf{c}+\mathbf{c}(s),\ \mathbf{r}+\mathbf{r}(s),\ t-s) \\
\frac{\partial\psi(s)}{\partial t} &= -\frac{\partial\psi(s)}{\partial s}, \quad \mathbf{c}\cdot\frac{\partial\psi(s)}{\partial\mathbf{r}} = -\frac{d\mathbf{r}(s)}{ds}\cdot\frac{\partial\psi(s)}{\partial\mathbf{r}(s)} \\
\frac{\mathcal{F}}{m}\cdot\frac{\partial\psi(s)}{\partial\mathbf{c}} &= -\frac{d\mathbf{c}(s)}{ds}\cdot\frac{\partial\psi(s)}{\partial\mathbf{c}(s)},
\end{aligned}\right\} \quad (5.3\text{-}7)$$

where

$$\frac{d}{ds} \equiv \frac{\partial}{\partial s} - \mathbf{c}\cdot\frac{\partial}{\partial\mathbf{r}(s)} - \frac{\mathcal{F}}{m}\cdot\frac{\partial}{\partial\mathbf{c}(s)}.$$

On consideration of eq. (7), it is shown that

$$\frac{\partial f}{\partial t} = -\int_0^\infty \left\{ \frac{\partial}{\partial s}[f_s\Theta_s]' \right.$$
$$\left. +[f_s\Theta_s]'\left(-\int_0^s \frac{\partial\Theta_s}{\partial s}\,ds\right) \right\} \exp\left(-\int_0^s \Theta_s\,ds\right)\,ds,\ \text{etc.}$$

Hence, the proof is completed as follows:

$$\left.\begin{aligned}
&\frac{\partial f}{\partial t} + \mathbf{c}\cdot\frac{\partial f}{\partial\mathbf{r}} + \frac{\mathcal{F}}{m}\cdot\frac{\partial f}{\partial\mathbf{c}} \\
&= -\int_0^\infty \left\{ \frac{d}{ds}[f_s\Theta_s]' + [f_s\Theta_s]'(-\Theta_s) \right\} \exp\left(-\int_0^s \Theta_s\,ds\right)\,ds \\
&\quad -\Theta_{s=0}\int_0^\infty \left\{ [f_s\Theta_s]'\exp\left(-\int_0^s \Theta_s\,ds\right) \right\}\,ds \\
&= -\left|[f_s\Theta_s]'\exp\left(-\int_0^s \Theta_s\,ds\right)\right|_0^\infty -\Theta f(\mathbf{c},\ \mathbf{r},\ t) \\
&= [f\Theta]'_{s=0} - \Theta_{s=0}f(\mathbf{c},\ \mathbf{r},\ t).
\end{aligned}\right\} \quad (5.3\text{-}8)$$

In spite of its simple appearance, eq. (4) is not simple. But it is possible to obtain f by an iteration method. We take for f to the zeroth approximation

$$f^{\langle 0\rangle} = n^{\langle 0\rangle}\left(\frac{m}{2\pi kT^{\langle 0\rangle}}\right)^{3/2} \exp\left[-\frac{m}{2kT^{\langle 0\rangle}}(\mathbf{c}-\mathbf{u}^{\langle 0\rangle})^2\right] \quad (5.3\text{-}9)$$

Thermal equilibrium. If a gas is in thermal equilibrium and uniform, $n^{\langle 0 \rangle}$, $\mathbf{u}^{\langle 0 \rangle}$, $T^{\langle 0 \rangle}$ are independent of t and $\mathbf{r}$. Then it is shown that $f^{\langle 0 \rangle}$ is the exact solution of the integral equation (4).

Since

$$f^{\langle 0 \rangle} = f^{\langle 0 \rangle}(s)$$

and

$$f^{\langle 0 \rangle}(\mathbf{c}')f^{\langle 0 \rangle}(\mathbf{c}_1') = f^{\langle 0 \rangle}(\mathbf{c})f^{\langle 0 \rangle}(\mathbf{c}_1),$$

we have

$$[f^{\langle 0 \rangle}\Theta^{\langle 0 \rangle}]' = f^{\langle 0 \rangle}(\mathbf{c})\Theta^{\langle 0 \rangle}.$$

Consideration of these leads to

$$\left.\begin{aligned}
\int_0^\infty [f_s^{\langle 0 \rangle}\Theta_s^{\langle 0 \rangle}]' \exp\left(-\int_0^s \Theta_s\, ds\right) ds \\
= \int_0^\infty f_s^{\langle 0 \rangle}\Theta_s^{\langle 0 \rangle} \exp\left(-\int_0^s \Theta_s\, ds\right) ds \\
= f^{\langle 0 \rangle}\int_0^\infty \Theta^{\langle 0 \rangle} \exp\left(-\int_0^s \Theta^{\langle 0 \rangle}\, ds\right) ds \\
= f^{\langle 0 \rangle}\left| -\exp\left(-\int_0^s \Theta_s^{\langle 0 \rangle}\, ds\right)\right|_0^\infty = f^{\langle 0 \rangle}.
\end{aligned}\right\} \quad (5.3\text{-}10)$$

Non-uniform state. Let us write for f

$$\left.\begin{aligned}
f &= f^{\langle 0 \rangle}+\varphi \\
n &= \int f\, d^3c \\
\mathbf{u} &= \frac{1}{n}\int \mathbf{c}f\, d^3c \\
\frac{3}{2} kT &= \frac{1}{n}\int \frac{1}{2} m(\mathbf{c}-\mathbf{u})^2 f\, d^3c
\end{aligned}\right\} \quad (5.3\text{-}11)$$

$$f^{\langle 0 \rangle} = n^{\langle 0 \rangle}\left(\frac{m}{2\pi kT^{\langle 0 \rangle}}\right)^{3/2} \exp\left[-\frac{m}{2kT^{\langle 0 \rangle}}(\mathbf{c}-\mathbf{u}^{\langle 0 \rangle})^2\right]. \quad (5.3\text{-}12)$$

It should be emphasized, in general,

$$\begin{aligned}
n &\neq n^{\langle 0 \rangle} \\
\mathbf{u} &\neq \mathbf{u}^{\langle 0 \rangle} \\
T &\neq T^{\langle 0 \rangle}
\end{aligned} \quad (5.3\text{-}13)$$

and $n^{\langle 0 \rangle}$, $\mathbf{u}^{\langle 0 \rangle}$, $T^{\langle 0 \rangle}$ are functions of t and $\mathbf{r}$.

1. To the zeroth approximation, it will be shown that $n^{\langle 0 \rangle}$, $\mathbf{u}^{\langle 0 \rangle}$, and $T^{\langle 0 \rangle}$ satisfy the equation of continuity, the Euler equation and the adiabatic equation. On substitution of $f^{\langle 0 \rangle}$ in $[f\Theta]'_s$, we obtain

$$[f\Theta]'_s \rightarrow [f^{\langle 0 \rangle}\Theta^{\langle 0 \rangle}]'_s = f_s^{\langle 0 \rangle}\Theta_s^{\langle 0 \rangle} \tag{5.3-14}$$

due to the characteristics of $f^{\langle 0 \rangle}$. By expanding each function in the integrand of eq. (4) to a power series of $-s$, we obtain

$$\left.\begin{aligned}
f_s^{\langle 0 \rangle} &= f^{\langle 0 \rangle} + \frac{df^{\langle 0 \rangle}}{dt}(-s) + \ \cdots \\[2mm]
\Theta_s^{\langle 0 \rangle} &= \Theta^{\langle 0 \rangle} + \frac{d\Theta^{\langle 0 \rangle}}{dt}(-s) + \ \cdots \\[2mm]
\exp\left(-\int_0^s \Theta_s^{\langle 0 \rangle}\, ds\right) &= \exp\left(-\Theta^{\langle 0 \rangle}s\right)\left(1 + 1/2\,\frac{d\Theta^{\langle 0 \rangle}}{dt}s^2 + \cdots\right),
\end{aligned}\right\} \tag{5.3-15}$$

where

$$\frac{d}{dt} = \frac{\partial}{\partial t} + \mathbf{c}\cdot\frac{\partial}{\partial \mathbf{r}} + \frac{\mathscr{F}}{m}\cdot\frac{\partial}{\partial \mathbf{c}}. \tag{5.3-16}$$

On substitution of the above in the integrand, we have for eq. (4)

$$\left.\begin{aligned}
f &= \int_0^\infty f^{\langle 0 \rangle}\Theta^{\langle 0 \rangle}\exp_{\_}(-\Theta^{\langle 0 \rangle}s)\left[1 + \frac{1}{f^{\langle 0 \rangle}}\frac{df^{\langle 0 \rangle}}{dt}(-s)\right.\\[2mm]
&\qquad \left. + \frac{1}{\Theta^{\langle 0 \rangle}}\frac{d\Theta^{\langle 0 \rangle}}{dt}(-s) + \frac{1}{2}\frac{d^2\Theta^{\langle 0 \rangle}}{dt^2}s^2 + \ \cdots\right]ds\\[2mm]
&= f^{\langle 0 \rangle}\left(1 - \frac{1}{\Theta^{\langle 0 \rangle}}\frac{d\log f^{\langle 0 \rangle}}{dt}\right).
\end{aligned}\right\} \tag{5.3-17}$$

Here the following definite integrals have been taken into account:

$$\int_0^\infty \exp(-\Theta^{\langle 0 \rangle}s)\, ds = \frac{1}{\Theta^{\langle 0 \rangle}}$$

$$\int_0^\infty s\exp(-\Theta^{\langle 0 \rangle}s)\, ds = \frac{1}{\Theta^{\langle 0 \rangle 2}}$$

$$\int_0^\infty s^2\exp(-\Theta^{\langle 0 \rangle}s)\, ds = \frac{1}{\Theta^{\langle 0 \rangle 3}}$$

By rewriting eq. (17), we obtain

$$\frac{df^{\langle 0\rangle}}{dt} = \Theta^{\langle 0\rangle}(f^{\langle 0\rangle} - f).$$ (5.3-18)

If, to the zeroth approximation, we write

$$f = f^{\langle 0\rangle},$$ (5.3-19)

we obtain

$$\frac{df^{\langle 0\rangle}}{dt} = 0.$$ (5.3-20)

By considering $n^{\langle 0\rangle}$, $\mathbf{u}^{\langle 0\rangle}$, $T^{\langle 0\rangle}$ as functions of $\mathbf{r}$ and t, it is a simple matter to derive from eq. (20) the equation of continuity, the Euler equation and the adiabatic condition as we did in Section 5.1.

2. To the first approximation, we have for f

$$f^{\langle 1\rangle} = f^{\langle 0\rangle} + \varphi^{\langle 1\rangle}$$ (5.3-21)

which is to replace f in the left-hand side of eq. (4) when the right-hand side is given in terms of $f^{\langle 0\rangle}$ in place of f. The treatment has been completed by eq. (17):

$$f^{\langle 1\rangle} = f^{\langle 0\rangle}\left(1 - \frac{1}{\Theta^{\langle 0\rangle}}\frac{d \log f^{\langle 0\rangle}}{dt}\right).$$ (5.3-22)

In the present case, it is assumed that $f^{\langle 1\rangle} \neq f^{\langle 0\rangle}$. By rewriting the above, we obtain[†]

$$\left.\begin{aligned}
f^{\langle 1\rangle} &= f^{\langle 0\rangle} + \varphi^{\langle 1\rangle}\\
&= f^{\langle 0\rangle} - \frac{f^{\langle 0\rangle}}{\Theta^{\langle 0\rangle}}\left[\left(\frac{m}{2kT^{\langle 0\rangle}}\,C^{\langle 0\rangle 2} - \frac{5}{2}\right)C^{\langle 0\rangle} \cdot \frac{\partial \log T}{\partial \mathbf{r}}\right.\\
&\qquad \left. + \frac{m}{kT^{\langle 0\rangle}}\left(\mathbf{C}^{\langle 0\rangle}\mathbf{C}^{\langle 0\rangle} - \frac{1}{3}\,C^{\langle 0\rangle 2}\,\delta\right):\frac{\partial \mathbf{u}^{\langle 0\rangle}}{\partial \mathbf{r}}\right],
\end{aligned}\right\}$$ (5.3-23)

[†] The calculation is the same as of the similar case in the Chapman–Enskog theory. See the derivation of eq. (5.2-10)

$$\frac{\partial}{\partial t} = \frac{\partial n^{\langle 0\rangle}}{\partial t}\frac{d}{dn^{\langle 0\rangle}} + \frac{\partial \mathbf{u}^{\langle 0\rangle}}{\partial t}\cdot\frac{d}{d\mathbf{u}^{\langle 0\rangle}} + \frac{\partial T^{\langle 0\rangle}}{\partial t}\cdot\frac{d}{dT^{\langle 0\rangle}},$$

where $\dfrac{\partial n^{\langle 0\rangle}}{\partial t}$, $\dfrac{\partial \mathbf{u}^{\langle 0\rangle}}{\partial t}$, etc., are obtained from moment equations derived from eq. (20).

where

$$\mathbf{C}^{\langle 0 \rangle} = \mathbf{c} - \mathbf{u}^{\langle 0 \rangle}. \tag{5.3-24}$$

From the above, we obtain moments of $f^{\langle 1 \rangle}$

$$\varrho^{\langle 1 \rangle} = \int m f^{\langle 1 \rangle} d^3 c = \varrho^{\langle 0 \rangle} \tag{5.3-25}$$

$$\left.\begin{array}{r} \varrho^{\langle 1 \rangle} \mathbf{u}_\xi^{\langle 1 \rangle} = \int m c_\xi f^{\langle 1 \rangle}\, d^3 c = \varrho^{\langle 0 \rangle} \left(u_\xi^{\langle 0 \rangle} - \dfrac{1}{3}\, \dfrac{A}{\varrho^{\langle 0 \rangle}}\, \dfrac{\partial \log T}{\partial \xi} \right) \\[2mm] \xi = x,\, y,\, z, \end{array}\right\} \tag{5.3-26}$$

where

$$A = \frac{m^2}{2kT} \int \frac{f^{\langle 0 \rangle}}{\Theta^{\langle 0 \rangle}}\, C^{\langle 0 \rangle 2} C^{\langle 0 \rangle 2}\, d^3 c - \frac{5m}{2} \int \frac{f^{\langle 0 \rangle}}{\Theta^{\langle 0 \rangle}}\, C^{\langle 0 \rangle 2}\, d^3 c. \tag{5.3-27}$$

We obtain for stress

$$\left.\begin{array}{l} P_{\xi\xi}^{\langle 1 \rangle} = \int m c_\xi c_\xi f^{\langle 1 \rangle}\, d^3 c \\[2mm] \qquad = p^{\langle 0 \rangle} + \varrho^{\langle 0 \rangle} u_\xi^{\langle 0 \rangle 2} - 2\mu^{\langle 0 \rangle} \left(\dfrac{\partial u_\xi^{\langle 0 \rangle}}{\partial \xi} - \dfrac{1}{3}\, \mathrm{div}\ \mathbf{u}^{\langle 0 \rangle} \right) \\[3mm] \qquad - \dfrac{2}{3}\, \varrho^{\langle 0 \rangle} u_\xi^{\langle 0 \rangle} A\, \dfrac{\partial \log T^{\langle 0 \rangle}}{\partial \xi} \end{array}\right\} \tag{5.3-28}$$

$$\left.\begin{array}{l} P_{\xi\eta}^{\langle 1 \rangle} = \int m c_\xi c_\eta f^{\langle 1 \rangle}\, d^3 c \\[2mm] \qquad = \varrho^{\langle 0 \rangle} u_\xi^{\langle 0 \rangle} u_\eta^{\langle 0 \rangle} - \dfrac{1}{3} A \left(u_\xi^{\langle 0 \rangle} \dfrac{\partial \log T^{\langle 0 \rangle}}{\partial \eta} + u_\eta^{\langle 0 \rangle} \dfrac{\partial \log T^{\langle 0 \rangle}}{\partial \xi} \right) \\[3mm] \qquad - \mu^{\langle 0 \rangle} \left(\dfrac{\partial u_\xi^{\langle 0 \rangle}}{\partial \eta} + \dfrac{\partial u_\eta^{\langle 0 \rangle}}{\partial \xi} \right), \end{array}\right\} \tag{5.3-29}$$

where

$$\left.\begin{array}{l} p^{\langle 0 \rangle} = \int \dfrac{m}{3}\, C^{\langle 0 \rangle 2} f^{\langle 0 \rangle}\, d^3 c = n^{\langle 0 \rangle} k T^{\langle 0 \rangle} \\[3mm] \mu^{\langle 0 \rangle} = \int \dfrac{m^2}{kT^{\langle 0 \rangle}}\, C_\xi^{\langle 0 \rangle 2} C_\eta^{\langle 0 \rangle 2}\, \dfrac{f^{\langle 0 \rangle}}{\Theta^{\langle 0 \rangle}}\, d^3 c. \end{array}\right\} \tag{5.3-30}$$

101

With respect to energy, we obtain

$$
\left.\begin{aligned}
E^{\langle 1 \rangle} &= \int \frac{m}{2}(c_x^2 + c_y^2 + c_z^2)f^{\langle 1 \rangle}\, d^3c \\
&= \frac{1}{2}(P_{xx}^{\langle 1 \rangle} + P_{yy}^{\langle 1 \rangle} + P_{zz}^{\langle 1 \rangle}) \\
&= \frac{3}{2}p^{\langle 0 \rangle} + \frac{1}{2}\varrho^{\langle 0 \rangle}u^{\langle 0 \rangle 2} - \frac{2}{3}\varrho^{\langle 0 \rangle}A\mathbf{u}^{\langle 0 \rangle} \cdot \frac{\log T^{\langle 0 \rangle}}{\partial \mathbf{r}}
\end{aligned}\right\} \quad (5.3\text{-}31)
$$

$$
\left.\begin{aligned}
Q_x^{\langle 1 \rangle} &= \int \frac{m}{2}c^2 c_x f^{\langle 1 \rangle}\, d^3c \\
&= \frac{3}{2}p^{\langle 0 \rangle}u_x^{\langle 0 \rangle} + \frac{1}{2}\varrho^{\langle 0 \rangle}u^{\langle 0 \rangle 2}u_x^{\langle 0 \rangle} \\
&\quad + u_x^{\langle 0 \rangle}\left[p^{\langle 0 \rangle} - 2\mu^{\langle 0 \rangle}\left(\frac{\partial u_x^{\langle 0 \rangle}}{\partial x} - \frac{1}{3}\operatorname{div}\mathbf{u}^{\langle 0 \rangle}\right)\right] \\
&\quad + u_y^{\langle 0 \rangle}\left[-\mu^{\langle 0 \rangle}\left(\frac{\partial u_y^{\langle 0 \rangle}}{\partial x} + \frac{\partial u_x^{\langle 0 \rangle}}{\partial y}\right)\right] \\
&\quad + u_z^{\langle 0 \rangle}\left[-\mu^{\langle 0 \rangle}\left(\frac{\partial u_x^{\langle 0 \rangle}}{\partial z} + \frac{\partial u_z^{\langle 0 \rangle}}{\partial x}\right)\right] \\
&\quad - \frac{A}{3}u_x^{\langle 0 \rangle}\mathbf{u}^{\langle 0 \rangle} \cdot \frac{\partial \log T^{\langle 0 \rangle}}{\partial \mathbf{r}} - \frac{1}{6}(A' + Au^{\langle 0 \rangle 2})\frac{\partial \log T^{\langle 0 \rangle}}{\partial x},
\end{aligned}\right\} \quad (5.3\text{-}32)
$$

in which

$$
A' = \int mC^{\langle 0 \rangle 2}C^{\langle 0 \rangle 2}\left(\frac{m}{2kT^{\langle 0 \rangle}}C^{\langle 0 \rangle 2} - \frac{5}{2}\right)\frac{f^{\langle 0 \rangle}}{\Theta^{\langle 0 \rangle}}\, d^3c. \quad (5.3\text{-}33)
$$

Those moments appear as different from those obtained by the Chapman–Enskog theory. However, if we rewrite these in terms of

$$
\left.\begin{aligned}
\varrho^{\langle 1 \rangle} &= \varrho^{\langle 0 \rangle} \\
u_\xi^{\langle 1 \rangle} &= u_\xi^{\langle 0 \rangle} - \frac{1}{3}\frac{A}{\varrho^{\langle 0 \rangle}}\frac{\partial \log T^{\langle 0 \rangle}}{\partial \xi} \\
T^{\langle 1 \rangle} &= T^{\langle 0 \rangle},
\end{aligned}\right\} \quad (5.3\text{-}34)
$$

they become the same as obtained in the Chapman–Enskog theory. The difference between the present iteration method and the

Chapman–Enskog theory is that at each step of iteration of this method, ϱ, $\mathbf{u}$, T are to be given to the relevant approximation.[†] After replacing variables, we have

$$P^{\langle 1\rangle}_{\xi\xi} = p^{\langle 1\rangle} + \varrho^{\langle 1\rangle} u^{\langle 1\rangle^2}_\xi - 2\mu^{\langle 1\rangle}\left(\frac{\partial u^{\langle 1\rangle}_\xi}{\partial \xi} - \frac{1}{3}\,\mathrm{div}\,\mathbf{u}^{\langle 1\rangle}\right)$$

$$P^{\langle 1\rangle}_{\xi\eta} = \varrho^{\langle 1\rangle} u^{\langle 1\rangle}_\xi u^{\langle 1\rangle}_\eta - \mu^{\langle 1\rangle}\left(\frac{\partial u^{\langle 1\rangle}_\xi}{\partial \eta} + \frac{\partial u^{\langle 1\rangle}_\eta}{\partial \xi}\right)$$

$$E^{\langle 1\rangle} = \frac{1}{2}\,(3p^{\langle 1\rangle} + \varrho^{\langle 1\rangle} u^{\langle 1\rangle^2})$$

$$Q^{\langle 1\rangle}_\xi = u^{\langle 1\rangle}_x(P^{\langle 1\rangle}_{x\xi} - \varrho^{\langle 1\rangle} u^{\langle 1\rangle}_x u^{\langle 1\rangle}_\xi) + u^{\langle 1\rangle}_y(P^{\langle 1\rangle}_{y\xi} - \varrho^{\langle 1\rangle} u^{\langle 1\rangle}_y u^{\langle 1\rangle}_\xi)$$

$$\qquad + u^{\langle 1\rangle}_z(P^{\langle 1\rangle}_{z\xi} - \varrho^{\langle 1\rangle} u^{\langle 1\rangle}_z u^{\langle 1\rangle}_\xi) + E^{\langle 1\rangle} u^{\langle 1\rangle}_\xi + \lambda^{\langle 1\rangle}\frac{\partial \log T^{\langle 1\rangle}}{\partial \xi}$$

$$p^{\langle 1\rangle}\varrho^{\langle 1\rangle^{-1}} = \frac{k}{m}\,T^{\langle 1\rangle} \tag{5.3-35}$$

$$\mu^{\langle 1\rangle} = \mu^{\langle 0\rangle} = \frac{m^2}{kT^{\langle 0\rangle}}\int C^{\langle 0\rangle^2}_\xi C^{\langle 0\rangle^2}_\eta \frac{f^{\langle 0\rangle}}{\Theta^{\langle 0\rangle}}\,d^3c$$

$$\lambda^{\langle 1\rangle} = \frac{1}{6}\left(5A\,\frac{p^{\langle 0\rangle}}{\varrho^{\langle 0\rangle}} - A'\right)$$

$$\qquad = \frac{1}{6}\left[-\frac{25}{2}\,kT^{\langle 0\rangle}\int C^{\langle 0\rangle^2}\frac{f^{\langle 0\rangle}}{\Theta^{\langle 0\rangle}}\,d^3c\right.$$

$$\qquad + 5m\int C^{\langle 0\rangle^2}C^{\langle 0\rangle^2}\frac{f^{\langle 0\rangle}}{\Theta^{\langle 0\rangle}}\,d^3c$$

$$\qquad \left. - \frac{m^2}{2kT^{\langle 0\rangle}}\int C^{\langle 0\rangle^2}C^{\langle 0\rangle^2}C^{\langle 0\rangle^2}\frac{f^{\langle 0\rangle}}{\Theta^{\langle 0\rangle}}\,d^3c\right].$$

It should be noted that $\varrho^{\langle 1\rangle}$, $\mathbf{u}^{\langle 1\rangle}$ and $T^{\langle 1\rangle}$ are equal to ϱ, $\mathbf{u}$ and T which appear in the Chapman–Enskog theory, only to the first

[†] The present theory has been developed by the author (1954) and his co-worker Taketa from Clausius–Meyer's method of calculating heat conduction which was popular in the last century. At that time, many authors were confused since they did not realize the difference, for example, between $u^{\langle 0\rangle}_\xi$ and $u^{\langle 1\rangle}_\xi$, etc. Finally Boltzmann (1896) said, "This is therefore a clear proof of the inaccuracy of all these calculations".

approximation. Remember, however, that ϱ, $\mathbf{u}$, T obtained by solving the Navier–Stokes as derived by Enskog and Chapman are, after all, the first approximations.

3. To the second approximation, we have for f

$$f^{\langle 2 \rangle} = f^{\langle 0 \rangle} + \varphi^{\langle 2 \rangle}, \tag{5.3-36}$$

which will be obtained as f in the left-hand side of eq. (4) when $f^{\langle 1 \rangle}$ is substituted in the right-hand side:

$$f^{\langle 2 \rangle} = \int_0^\infty [f_s^{\langle 1 \rangle} \Theta_s^{\langle 1 \rangle}]' \exp\left(-\int_0^s \Theta_s^{\langle 1 \rangle} \, ds\right) ds. \tag{5.3-37}$$

The procedure of manipulation is to be similar to the derivation of $f^{\langle 1 \rangle}$. In interpreting the results, it is necessary to define $\varrho^{\langle 2 \rangle}$, $\mathbf{u}^{\langle 2 \rangle}$, $T^{\langle 2 \rangle}$ by

$$\left.\begin{array}{c} \varrho^{\langle 2 \rangle} = \int m f^{\langle 2 \rangle} \, d^3 c \\[2mm] \varrho^{\langle 2 \rangle} \mathbf{u}^{\langle 2 \rangle} = \int m \mathbf{c} f^{\langle 2 \rangle} \, d^3 c \\[2mm] \dfrac{3}{2} \dfrac{\varrho^{\langle 2 \rangle}}{m} kT^{\langle 2 \rangle} + \dfrac{1}{2} \varrho^{\langle 2 \rangle} u^{\langle 2 \rangle 2} = \int \dfrac{1}{2} m c^2 f^{\langle 2 \rangle} \, d^3 c. \end{array}\right\} \tag{5.3-38}$$

We may repeat the method of iteration to obtain higher order approximations. Finally it is noted that the procedure (14) cannot be applied to $[f^{\langle 1 \rangle} \Theta^{\langle 1 \rangle}]_s$, $[f^{\langle 2 \rangle} \Theta^{\langle 2 \rangle}]_s$, etc., since $f^{\langle 1 \rangle}$, $f^{\langle 2 \rangle}$, etc., are not Maxwellian. It is necessary to consider some expansion method in view of

$$|\varphi^{\langle 1 \rangle}| < f^{\langle 0 \rangle}$$

$$|\varphi^{\langle 2 \rangle}| < f^{\langle 0 \rangle}, \text{ etc.}$$

If the iteration converges, we may claim that f is given by $f^{\langle 0 \rangle} + \varphi^{\langle 1 \rangle}$ to the first approximation. In view of eq. (26), there is no difference between the dynamical characteristics of the present results and those of Enskog and Chapman. It should be noted that $n^{\langle 1 \rangle}$, $\mathbf{u}^{\langle 1 \rangle}$, and $T^{\langle 1 \rangle}$ are equal to n, $\mathbf{u}$, T, which appear in the Chapman–

Enskog theory only to the first approximation. There is no essential difference between the present method and the Chapman–Enskog method, if we interpret the results properly. An advantage of the present method is that $f^{(1)} = f^{(0)} + \varphi^{(1)}$ is given as an explicit function of variables.

5.4. The macroscopic variables of a gas on the surface of a wall

A container is made of walls. In Chapter 2, we took into account the effect of a wall by considering the forces $\mathcal{F}_{iw}$ in the Liouville equation. Since Chapter 3, however, we have ignored those forces on the assumption that the molecules under consideration were remote from any wall. Finally in Sections 5.2 and 5.3 we obtained equations governing the macroscopic behaviors of a gas; these equations are valid only in the inner domain remote from the walls. In order to solve these equations, we have to have boundary conditions which are set conveniently on the surface of walls. Unfortunately, however, the equations are not valid there. We investigate the difficult situation and find the solution in the following:

The surface of a wall is supposed to have some roughness with characteristic dimension l_r. The distance from the wall over which $\mathcal{F}_{iw}$ is negligible is denoted by $l_{\mathcal{F}}$. The mean free path l_m is defined by

$$l_m = \frac{\int |c| f \, d^3c}{\int \Theta f \, d^3c},$$
(5.4-1)

where Θ is given by eq. (5.3-1). If the molecules are electrically neutral, it may be safe to assume that

$$l_{\mathcal{F}} < 10^6 \text{ cm}$$
(5.4-2)

and hence it is feasible to assume that

$$l_{\mathcal{F}} < l_r, l_m.$$
(5.4-3)

105

In Fig. 5.4-1, we imagine a plane which is parallel to the surface (average) of the wall and at a distance δy from the surface. The imaginary plane is named the equivalent surface of the wall. Suppose that

$$\delta_y > l_r, l_m. \tag{5.4-4}$$

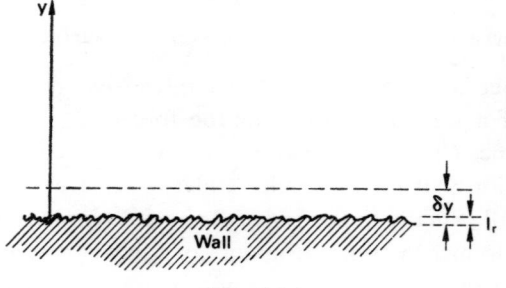

FIG. 5.4-1.

The surface of a wall is more or less rough. The scale of roughness is denoted by l_r and the mean free path length of particles of the gas by l_m. We consider an imaginary plane which is parallel to the wall and at distance δy:

$$\delta y > l_r, l_m$$

Beyond this imaginary plane, the Navier–Stokes equations are valid.

Due to the above condition, the Navier–Stokes equations are valid on the equivalent surface. The conditions (variables) on the equivalent surface are denoted with subscript δ attached to ordinary symbols:

$$\left.\begin{aligned}
\varrho &= \varrho_\delta, \ \mathbf{u} = \mathbf{u}_\delta, \ T = T_\delta \\
\frac{\partial \varrho}{\delta y} &= \left(\frac{\partial \varrho}{\delta y}\right)_\delta, \frac{\partial \mathbf{u}}{\partial y} = \left(\frac{\partial \mathbf{u}}{\partial y}\right)_\delta \\
\frac{\partial T}{\partial y} &= \left(\frac{\partial T}{\partial y}\right)_\delta, \quad \text{etc.}
\end{aligned}\right\} \tag{5.4-5}$$

106

We assume that the variables on the surface of the wall and those on the equivalent surface are connected by the following equations.

$$
\left.
\begin{aligned}
\varrho_\delta &= \varrho_w + \left(\frac{\partial \varrho}{\partial y}\right)_\delta \delta y \alpha_1, \\[2mm]
\mathbf{u}_\delta &= \mathbf{u}_w + \left(\frac{\partial \mathbf{u}}{\partial y}\right)_\delta \delta y \alpha_2, \\[2mm]
T_\delta &= T_w + \left(\frac{\partial T}{\partial y}\right)_\delta \delta y \alpha_3, \ \text{etc.},
\end{aligned}
\right\}
\tag{5.4-6}
$$

where variables on the surface are given by ordinary symbols with subscript w; $\alpha_1, \alpha_2, \alpha_3, \ldots$ are numbers which are not so much remote from unity. This condition is assumed, because we consider that the state of the gas between the surface of the wall and the equivalent surface is in a state which does not significantly deviate from thermal equilibrium due to frequent collisions among particles there. See condition (4).

We now assume the following relations

$$
\left.
\begin{aligned}
\left(\frac{\partial \varrho}{\partial y}\right)_\delta \delta y \alpha_1 / \varrho_w &\ll 1, \\[2mm]
\left(\frac{\partial \mathbf{u}}{\partial y}\right)_\delta \delta y \alpha_2 / U &\ll 1, \\[2mm]
\left(\frac{\partial T}{\partial y}\right)_\delta \delta y \alpha_3 / T_w &\ll 1,
\end{aligned}
\right\}
\tag{5.4-7}
$$

where U is the characteristic velocity of the gas flow. Thereby it follows that

$$
\left.
\begin{aligned}
\varrho_\delta &= \varrho_w, \\
\mathbf{u}_\delta &= \mathbf{u}_w = 0, \\
T_\delta &= T_w. \\
\left(\frac{\partial T}{\partial y}\right)_\delta &= \left(\frac{\partial T}{\partial y}\right)_w, \ \text{etc.}
\end{aligned}
\right\}
\tag{5.4-8}
$$

107

Thus we can set boundary conditions for the Navier–Stokes equations within the domain where the validity of the equations is assured. The necessary conditions for doing so are (4) and (7). Those are satisfied by (1) sufficiently small values of l_m and l_r, and (2) sufficiently small values of derivatives of ϱ, $\mathbf{u}$, T.

Those conditions will be discussed again in Part II. Meanwhile, we think that for a gas in a moderate state, it is possible to consider the equivalent surface which satisfies the above conditions.

Exercises

1. Show that

$$f^{(0)} = n\left(\frac{m}{2\pi kT}\right)^{3/2} \exp\left[-\frac{m}{2kT}(\mathbf{c}-\mathbf{u})^2\right]$$

is a solution of the Boltzmann equation, when n, $\mathbf{u}$, and T are invariants and $\mathcal{F} = 0$. Hints: $m\mathbf{c} + m\mathbf{c}_1 = m\mathbf{c}' + m\mathbf{c}_1'$, $1/2mc^2 + 1/2mc_1^2 = 1/2mc'^2 + 1/2mc_1'^2$.

2. Show that

$$\int J\, d^3\mathbf{c} = 0$$
$$\int m\mathbf{c}J\, d^3\mathbf{c} = 0$$
$$\int mc^2 J\, d^3\mathbf{c} = 0.$$

3. If ψ, F and G are functions of velocity, it is shown that

$$\int \psi(\mathbf{c})F(\mathbf{c}')G(\mathbf{c}_1')\,|\mathbf{c}_1-\mathbf{c}|\,d\varphi\, dh\, d^3\mathbf{c}\, d^3\mathbf{c}_1$$
$$= \int \psi(\mathbf{c}')F(\mathbf{c})G(\mathbf{c}_1)\,|\mathbf{c}_1-\mathbf{c}|\,d\varphi\, dh\, d^3\mathbf{c}\, d^3\mathbf{c}_1.$$

4. f is a function of two independent variables $\mathbf{c}$ and t.

$$f(\mathbf{c};t) = \psi(\mathbf{c}-\mathbf{u}(t);t)$$

and

$$\int f\, d^3c = n(t), \quad \int \mathbf{c}f\, d^3c = n(t)\mathbf{u}(t).$$

We may take for the independent variables t and $\mathbf{C}$

$$\mathbf{C} = \mathbf{c} - \mathbf{u}(t).$$

Show that

$$\frac{\partial\psi(\mathbf{C})}{\partial t} = \frac{\partial f(\mathbf{c})}{\partial t} - \frac{d\mathbf{u}}{dt}\cdot\frac{df(\mathbf{c})}{d\mathbf{u}}$$

and that

$$\int (\mathbf{C}+\mathbf{u})\frac{\partial\psi(\mathbf{C})}{\partial t}\, d^3C = \int \mathbf{c}\left[\frac{\partial f(\mathbf{c})}{\partial t} - \frac{d\mathbf{u}}{dt}\cdot\frac{df(\mathbf{c})}{d\mathbf{u}}\right] d^3c.$$

PART II

Rarefied Gases

CHAPTER 6

Assumption Necessary for the Derivation of the Navier–Stokes Equations

6.1. Introductory remarks

It has been our strong conviction that there is neither shearing stress nor energy conduction if there is no spatial gradient of the state of a gas. This conviction is feasible only when the state of a gas is close to thermal equilibrium so that the Chapman–Enskog theory is valid. As is discussed in Appendix G the Chapman–Enskog theory is an elaboration of the dynamical theory of gases proposed by Maxwell in 1866. There Maxwell solved equations of transfer,[†] similar to the equations of moment derived from the Boltzmann equation, by an iteration method obtaining higher order approximations in collision integral terms at each step of iteration, beginning with the condition of local thermal equilibrium for the first approximation. The approach of obtaining higher order approximations in collision

---

† An infinite number of equations of transfer is equivalent to the Boltzmann equation. If one were able to treat all of them properly, the result would predict feasibly rarefied gas-dynamical phenomena. But only a few of the equations of lower ranks can be treated because of the limit of one's mathematical ability. These equations of a limited number are not closed by themselves; i.e. the number of equations is always smaller than the number of the unknown variables. Thus the characteristics of the solution are already determined when giving equations of transfer and choosing a limited number of them to be solved. From this consideration, the difficulty in Ikenbery–Truesdell's theory based on equations of transfer is obvious. See Section 7.4. A similar, but not the same, cause of difficulty is seen in Grad's theory as cited in the same section.

111

integrals is justified if the average collision frequency is sufficiently high, as discussed in detail in the following section. Maxwell himself was aware of the particular meaning of his dynamical theory of gases and supplemented it with another theory (1879) dealing with stresses in rarefied gases. Being rather impressed by the mathematical perfection of the Chapman–Enskog theory, we often tend to forget the additional theory of Maxwell stressing the particular situation of dynamics of rarefied gases. In an extreme case, as will be demonsrated in Section 7.3, it is possible that there is a uniform flow field where shearing stresses appear significantly.

The Boltzmann equation is applicable to a gas which is rarefied so that the assumption of binary collision is feasible.[†] The validity of the Navier–Stokes equations, which are derived from the Boltzmann equation, is restricted by another condition. In Chapter 6, we investigate the condition necessary for the convergence of the Chapman–Enskog expansion of the distribution function. The criterion of the convergence which is the criterion of the validity of the Navier–Stokes equation, provides us a way of sorting gas-dynamical phenomena into the following three regimes: (1) the ordinary gas-dynamics regime, (2) the transition regime, (3) the free molecule flow regime. The criterion proposed here is more specific than the ordinary criterion given in terms of the Knudsen number alone. The result of the investigation in Chapter 6 is applied to various flow flelds in Chapter 7. Special attention is paid to the effect of walls. But no attempt is made to solve any specific boundary (or initial) value problem.

In fact, the significance of rarefied gas dynamics is found in the mode of interaction between a gas flow and a wall and/or between two different flows connected by a sharp gradient of state. Such a flow is characterized by a strong deviation of the gas state from thermal equilibrium in a macroscopic scale and is of great interest from the kinetic-theoretical viewpoint. But no general theory treating

---

[†] The Boltzmann equation is a statistical equation; if the density of a gas is too rare, fluctuations even in a macroscopic sense may be observed. In this case, the feasibility of the Boltzmann equation is conditional, as once suggested by the present author (1955). See also p. 71.

such states has been developed thus far. Therefore, at least at this moment, the description of rarefied gas-dynamical phenomena is *ad hoc*. Without solving any particular boundary (or initial) value problem, rarefied gas dynamics appears vain. Yet there are some basic problems which may be considered in general.

6.2. The criterion of the convergence of the Chapman–Enskog series

According to the Chapman–Enskog theory of solving the Boltzmann equation, the distribution function f is expanded in a series

$$f = f^{(0)} + f^{(1)} + f^{(2)} + \dots \qquad (6.2\text{-}1)$$
$$\Phi^{(1)} = f^{(1)}/f^{(0)} \propto 1/n \qquad (6.2\text{-}2)$$
$$f^{(2)}/f^{(0)} \propto 1/n^2,$$

where $f^{(0)}$ is the Maxwell distribution function which gives the same mass density, momentum density, and energy density as those of f itself. The Navier–Stokes equations are derived from $f^{(0)} + f^{(1)}$. The validity of the equation is secured by the condition

$$|f^{(2)}/f^{(0)}| \ll 1$$
$$|f^{(3)}/f^{(0)}| \ll 1$$

or, as a pratical interpretation of the condition, by

$$|f^{(1)}/f^{(0)}| < 1. \qquad (6.2\text{-}3)$$

In the Chapman–Enskog theory, $f^{(1)}$ is not obtained explicitly. In the theory given in Section 5.3, however, we have $\varphi^{(1)}$ which is equivalent to $f^{(1)}$ in the Chapman–Enskog theory if we give proper interpretations to parameters (macroscopic variables) $n^{(0)}$, $\mathbf{u}^{(0)}$ and $T^{(0)}$ involved in function $\varphi^{(1)}$. Hence, condition (3) yields

$$|\Phi^{(1)}| = |\varphi^{(1)}/f^{(0)}| < 1 \qquad (6.2\text{-}3)'$$

with

$$\left.\begin{array}{l} \Phi^{(1)} = -\dfrac{f^{(0)}}{\Theta^{(0)}} \left[\left(\dfrac{m}{2kT^{(0)}} C^{(0)^2} - \dfrac{5}{2} \right) \mathbf{C}^{(0)} \cdot \dfrac{\partial \log T}{\partial \mathbf{r}} \right. \\[3mm] \left. + \dfrac{m}{kT^{(0)}} \overline{\mathbf{C}^{(0)}\mathbf{C}^{(0)}} : \dfrac{\partial \mathbf{u}^{(0)}}{\partial \mathbf{r}} \right] \end{array}\right\} \quad (6.2\text{-}4)$$

[previously given by eq. (5.3-23)]

113

and

$$\mathbf{C}^{\langle 0 \rangle} = \mathbf{c} - \mathbf{u}^{\langle 0 \rangle}$$

$$\overline{\mathbf{C}^{\langle 0 \rangle}\mathbf{C}^{\langle 0 \rangle}} = \mathbf{C}^{\langle 0 \rangle}\mathbf{C}^{\langle 0 \rangle} - \frac{1}{3}\mathbf{C}^{\langle 0 \rangle 2}\,\boldsymbol{\delta}.$$

As shown by eq. (5.3-34) the parameters $n^{\langle 0 \rangle}$, $\mathbf{u}^{\langle 0 \rangle}$, $T^{\langle 0 \rangle}$ are equivalent to n, $\mathbf{u}$, T to the approximation of neglecting their derivatives. Thereby, it is concluded that we may substitute n, $\mathbf{u}$, T respectively for $n^{\langle 0 \rangle}$, $\mathbf{u}^{\langle 0 \rangle}$, $T^{\langle 0 \rangle}$ in $\varphi^{\langle 1 \rangle}$ to the approximation that the second and/or higher powers of the first order derivatives of those parameters and also the second and/or higher order derivatives of those parameters are ignored. To this approximation, condition (3) is shown to be equivalent to

$$\left| \Phi^{\langle 1 \rangle} \right| = \left| \frac{1}{\Theta^{\langle 0 \rangle}} \left[\left(\frac{m}{2kT}C^2 - \frac{5}{2} \right) \mathbf{C} \cdot \frac{\partial \log T}{\partial \mathbf{r}} \right. \right. \\ \left. \left. + \frac{m}{kT} \overline{\mathbf{CC}} : \frac{\partial \mathbf{u}}{\partial \mathbf{r}} \right] \right| < 1 \qquad (6.2\text{-}5)$$

on substitution of (4) in (3)′. Here

$$\Theta^{\langle 0 \rangle} = \int \int_{h=0}^{h'} f^{\langle 0 \rangle}(c_1) 2\pi h v \, dh \, d^3 c_1$$

$$v = |\mathbf{c} - \mathbf{c}_1|, \qquad (6.2\text{-}6)$$

and h' is the length of impact parameter at which

$$f^{\langle 0 \rangle}(\mathbf{c}_1') \eqcirc f^{\langle 0 \rangle}(\mathbf{c}_1).$$

$\Theta^{\langle 0 \rangle}$ is a function of $\mathbf{c}$ and is the average number of collisions which occur on one particle with velocity $\mathbf{c}$ in a unit time. Hence the following is the average number of collisions which occur on any one particle in a unit time:

$$\frac{1}{n} \int f^{\langle 0 \rangle}\Theta^{\langle 0 \rangle} \, d^3 c = \frac{1}{n} \int f^{\langle 0 \rangle}(\mathbf{c}_1) f^{\langle 0 \rangle}(\mathbf{c}) 2\pi h v \, dh \, d^3 c = 2nh'^2 \left(\frac{kT}{m} \right)^{1/2}.$$

$$(6.2\text{-}7)$$

If we then consider for a molecule an elastic sphere with diameter σ, then

$$h' = \sigma. \tag{6.2-8}$$

If we define the average of $|C|$ by

$$
\left.
\begin{aligned}
\langle |C| \rangle &= \int |c-u| f^{(0)} \, d^3c/n \\
&= \left(\frac{m}{2\pi kT} \right)^{3/2} \int 4\pi C^3 \exp\left(\frac{m}{2kT} C^2 \right) dC \\
&= 4\pi \left(\frac{m}{2\pi kT} \right)^{3/2} \frac{1}{2} \left(\frac{2kT}{m} \right)^2 \\
&= \frac{2}{\pi^{1/2}} \left(\frac{2kT}{m} \right)^{1/2}
\end{aligned}
\right\} \tag{6.2-9}
$$

the Maxwell mean free path is given by eq. (5.4-1) with $f^{(0)}$ for f:

$$
\left.
\begin{aligned}
l_m &= \frac{C}{\int f^{(0)} \Theta^{(0)} \, d^3c/n} \\
&= \frac{1}{2^{1/2} \pi n \sigma^2}
\end{aligned}
\right\} \tag{6.2-10}
$$

We may define for the average of $\Theta^{(0)}$

$$\langle \Theta^{(0)} \rangle = \frac{\langle |C| \rangle}{l_m}. \tag{6.2-11}$$

On substitution of $\langle \Theta^{(0)} \rangle$ in place of $\Theta^{(0)}$ in eq. (5) and consideration of

$$\left| \frac{\partial \log T}{\partial \mathbf{r}} \right| \to \frac{\Delta T}{L_T} \frac{1}{T}, \quad \left| \frac{\partial \mathbf{u}}{\partial \mathbf{r}} \right| \to \frac{\Delta U}{L_U},$$

we obtain[†] for the average value of $|\Phi^{(1)}|$

$$\langle |\Phi^{(1)}| \rangle = a \frac{l_m}{L_T} \frac{\Delta T}{T} + b \frac{l_m}{L_U} \frac{\Delta U}{(2kT/m)^{1/2}}. \tag{6.2-12}$$

[†] $\langle C^2 \rangle = \int C^2 f^{(0)} \, d^3c/n$
$\qquad = 4\pi \int C^4 f^{(0)} \, dC/n$
$\qquad = \frac{3}{2} \left(\frac{2kT}{m} \right)$

Here a and b are numbers of the order of unity, $\Delta\tau$ is the change of temperature over the typical distance denoted by L_T, and ΔU the change of velocity over the typical distance L_U. It is noted[†] that ΔT is not necessarily smaller than T, and ΔU is not necessarily smaller than $(2kT/m)^{1/2}$. In general $\Delta T/T$ and $\Delta U/(2kT/m)^{1/2}$ are independent of l_m/L_T and/or of l_m/L_U.

6.3. Simple application of the criterion

Let us observe a gas in a container which is divided into two parts by a wall made of a good insulator of heat. The temperature T_1 in one part is higher than the temperature T_2 in the other part (Fig. 6.3-1).

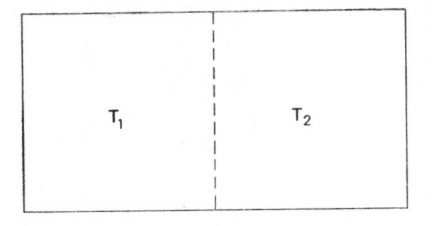

Fig. 6.3-1.

The gas in the container is divided by a wall. Temperature $T_1 >$ temperature T_2; the pressures are the same in both parts.

Suppose that we take out the dividing wall all at once at $t = 0$. For a while after that moment, it holds that

$$l_m/L_T \gg 1. \tag{6.3-1}$$

We may take for $\Delta T/T$ either

$$\Delta T/T = (T_1 - T_2)/T_1$$

[†] Pioneering investigations of rarefied gas dynamics were made by Zahm (1934), Tsien (1946), Schaaf and Chambre (1958), and others. Earlier, authors paid attention to the Knudsen number l_m/L_T and/or l_m/L_U only. See the account given by Schaaf (1963).

or
$$\Delta T/T = (T_1 - T_2)/T_2.$$

In any case
$$\Delta T/T \gtrsim 1$$

if
$$T_1 \gg T_2. \left. \right\} \tag{6.3-2}$$

But
$$\Delta T/T < 1$$

if
$$T_1 \simeq T_2. \left. \right\} \tag{6.3-3}$$

In case of eq. (2), it is obvious that

$$\langle |\Phi^{(1)}| \rangle = \frac{l_m}{L_T} \frac{\Delta T}{T} \gg 1, \tag{6.3-4}$$

and hence there is no hope that the Chapman–Enskog theory is valid. But in case of relation (3), it is possible that

$$\langle |\Phi^{(1)}| \rangle < 1 \tag{6.3-5}$$

in spite of relation (1), and hence the Navier–Stokes equations are valid.

Exercises

1. Assuming that the pressure of a gas is 5×10^4 dyn/cm^2 and the viscosity coefficient $\mu = 2 \times 10^{-4}$ cgs units, calculate the velocity gradient du/dy which causes the same value of shearing stress as the value of pressure, according to

$$\text{shearing stress} = \mu \frac{du}{dy}.$$

2. What is the altitude where the pressure of the atmosphere reaches 5×10^4 dyn/cm^2.

CHAPTER 7

Kinetic-theoretical Characteristics
of Dynamics of Rarefied Gases

7.1. Distribution function near a wall

Figure 7.1-1 illustrates the behaviors of particles near a wall. The roughness of the surface is of the order of l_r. Unlike the case illustrated by Fig. 5.7-1, we assume

$$l_m \gg l_r. \tag{7.1-1}$$

In the domain $l_m > y > l_r$, the chance is small of a particle (molecule),

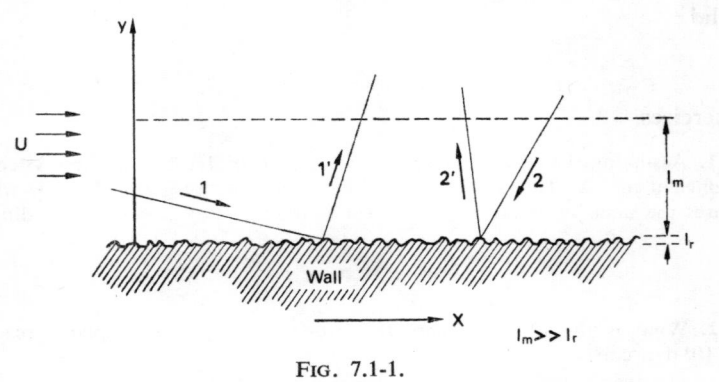

FIG. 7.1-1.

The mean free path length l_m is much larger than the dimension of roughness of the wall l_r. If the order of l_m is macroscopic, it is possible that, in the domain of y where $l_m > y > l_r$, the state of the gas near the wall deviates considerably from thermal equilibrium.

coming into the domain from the outside, colliding with another molecule and hence the molecule flies freely to the surface of the wall. The molecule is reflected from the wall and goes out of the domain. The trajectory is illustrated by line $1-1'$. The reflection is not necessarily specular. The trajectory of another molecule is depicted by line $2-2'$. On the surface the distribution is given by

$$f = f^{(-)} + f^{(+)}, \tag{7.1-2}$$

where $f^{(-)}$ is the distribution of the molecules with $c_y < 0$ and $f^{(+)}$ is of the molecules with $c_y > 0$. At $c_y = 0$, f may be arbitrary as long as f is finite there. If there is no accumulation of molecules on the surface of the wall, the consideration of mass conservation law gives

$$\int_{c_x=-\infty}^{+\infty} \int_{c_y=-\infty}^{0} \int_{c_z=-\infty}^{+\infty} c_y f^{(-)} \, d^3c = \int_{c_x=-\infty}^{+\infty} \int_{c_y=0}^{-\infty} \int_{c_z=-\infty}^{+\infty} c_y f^{(+)} \, d^3c \tag{7.1-3}$$

We define the reflection probability factor φ of a wall as follows:

$$f^{(+)}(\mathbf{c}) = \int \varphi(\mathbf{c}; \mathbf{c}') f^{(-)}(\mathbf{c}') \, d^3c. \tag{7.1-4}$$

Here the domain of integration is

$$c_x': \text{from } -\infty \text{ to } +\infty,$$
$$c_y': \text{from } -\infty \text{ to } \quad 0,$$
$$c_z': \text{from } -\infty \text{ to } +\infty.$$

Special case 1. When the reflections are all specular, φ is given in terms of δ-function:

$$\varphi_1 = \delta(c_x - c_x') \, \delta(-c_y - c_y') \, \delta(c_z - c_z') \tag{7.1-5}$$

and hence

$$f^{(+)}(c_x, -c_y, c_z) = f^{(-)}(c_x, c_y, c_z). \tag{7.1-6}$$

119

Special case 2. If all the reflections are at random and the distribution of the particles after the reflections is Maxwellian according to the temperature of the wall, φ is φ_2 which satisfies

$$f^{(+)} = n^{(+)} \left(\frac{m}{2\pi k T_w} \right)^{3/2} \exp \left(-\frac{m}{2kT_w} c^2 \right)$$

$$= \int \varphi_2 f^{(-)}(c') \, d^3c' \qquad (T_w: \text{wall temperature})$$

and hence consideration[†] of eq. (3) leads to

$$\left. \begin{array}{l} \varphi_2 = \left[n^{(+)} \left(\frac{m}{2\pi k T_w} \right)^{3/2} \exp \left(-\frac{m}{2kT_w} c^2 \right) \right] c_y' \\[2mm] \qquad \times \left[\frac{n^{(+)}}{2\pi^{1/2}} \left(\frac{2kT_w}{m} \right)^{1/2} \right]^{-1} . \end{array} \right\} \qquad (7.1\text{-}7)$$

Here $n^{(+)}/2$ is the density of the molecules of which $c_y > 0$.

Special case 3. If the wall is a perfect insulator of energy, there is no exchange of energy between the wall and the colliding molecules. Hence[‡]

$$\int_{c_y > 0} \frac{1}{2} mc^2 c_y f^{(+)} \, d^3c = \int_{c_y < 0} \frac{1}{2} mc^2 c_y f^{(-)} \, d^3c. \qquad (7.1\text{-}8)$$

The reflection of a molecule may occur at random, and $f^{(+)}$ may be a function which is even with respect to c_x and c_z. It is not inconsistent to assume that

$$\left. \begin{array}{l} f^{(+)} = n^{(+)} \left(\frac{m}{2\pi k T} \right)^{3/2} \exp \left(-\frac{m}{2kT} c^2 \right) \\[2mm] \qquad = \int_{c_y' < 0} \varphi_3 f^{(-)}(c') \, d^3c'. \end{array} \right\} \qquad (7.1\text{-}9)$$

[†] $\displaystyle \int_{c_y > 0} c_y f^{(+)} \, d^3c = n^{(+)} \left(\frac{m}{2\pi k T_w} \right)^{1/2} \int_0^\infty c_y \exp \left(-\frac{m}{2kT_w} c_y^2 \right) dc_y$

$\displaystyle \qquad\qquad = \frac{n^{(+)}}{2\pi^{1/2}} \left(\frac{2kT_w}{m} \right)^{1/2}$

[‡] $\displaystyle \int_{c_y > 0} d^3c \equiv \int_{c_x = -\infty}^{+\infty} \int_{c_y = 0}^{+\infty} \int_{c_z = -\infty}^{+\infty} d^3c, \quad \text{etc.}$

Besides, condition (3) still holds. Since[†]

$$\int_{c_y > 0} \frac{1}{2} mc^2 c_y f^{(+)} \, d^3c = \frac{1}{2\pi^{1/2}} n^{(+)} m \left(\frac{2kT}{m} \right)^{3/2},$$

T is determined by

$$T = \frac{m}{2k} \left[\frac{\pi^{1/2}}{n^{(+)}} \int_{c_y < 0} c^2 c_y f^{(-)} \, d^3c \right]^{3/2} \tag{7.1-10}$$

in accordance with eq. (8). Hence

$$\left. \begin{aligned} \varphi_3 &= \left[n^{(+)} \left(\frac{m}{2\pi kT} \right)^{3/2} \exp \left(-\frac{m}{2kT} c^2 \right) \right] c_y' \\ &\times \left[\frac{n^{(+)}}{2\pi^{1/2}} \left(\frac{2kT}{m} \right)^{1/2} \right]^{-1}. \end{aligned} \right\} \tag{7.1-11}$$

As regards a real wall, it is feasible to consider for φ

$$\varphi = \alpha_1 \varphi_1 + \alpha_2 \varphi_2 + \alpha_3 \varphi_3, \tag{7.1-12}$$

where the α's are positive and

$$\alpha_1 + \alpha_2 + \alpha_3 = 1. \tag{7.1-13}$$

In the domain $l_m > y > l_r$, both $f^{(-)}$ and $f^{(+)}$ are almost uniform, because there are few collisions which cause the change of those functions. More specifically, $f^{(+)}$ and/or $f^{(-)}$ are invariant along trajectories determined by

$$\left. \begin{aligned} \frac{d\mathbf{r}}{dt} &= \mathbf{c}, \\ \frac{d\mathbf{c}}{dt} &= \frac{\mathcal{F}_o}{m}. \end{aligned} \right\} \tag{7.1-14}$$

[†]
$$\int_{c_y > 0} \frac{1}{2} mc_x^2 c_y f^{(+)} \, d^3c = \frac{mn^{(+)}}{8\pi^{1/2}} \left(\frac{2kT}{m} \right)^{3/2}$$
$$\int_{c_y > 0} \frac{1}{2} mc_y^3 f^{(+)} \, d^3c = \frac{mn^{(+)}}{4\pi^{1/2}} \left(\frac{2kT}{m} \right)^{3/2}.$$

121

Here $\mathcal{F}_o$ is the external force acting on each particle and the effect may be ignored depending on the circumstance. From function f given by eq. (2), we derive gross density, gross momentum density, etc., in the vicinity of the surface of a wall.

$$
\left.\begin{aligned}
\varrho &= \int mf^{(+)}\, d^3c + \int mf^{(-)}\, d^3c, \\
\varrho\mathbf{u} &= \int m\mathbf{c}f^{(+)}\, d^3c + \int m\mathbf{c}f^{(-)}\, d^3c, \\
E &= \int 1/2mc^2 f^{(+)}\, d^3c + \int 1/2mc^2 f^{(-)}\, d^3c, \\
\mathbf{P} &= \int m\mathbf{c}\mathbf{c}f^{(+)}\, d^3c + \int m\mathbf{c}\mathbf{c}f^{(-)}\, d^3c, \\
\mathbf{Q} &= \int 1/2mc^2\mathbf{c}f^{(+)}\, d^3c + \int 1/2mc^2\mathbf{c}f^{(-)}\, d^3c,
\end{aligned}\right\} \qquad (7.1\text{-}15)
$$

where the domain of c_y is from 0 to $+\infty$ for $f^{(+)}$ and from $-\infty$ to 0 for $f^{(-)}$. The domains of the other variables are from $-\infty$ to $+\infty$. Those macroscopic variables were once defined in Section 5.1. A significant feature of the field under consideration is that, in general, there appear shearing stress and/or heat conduction, etc., in spite of the condition that the state is almost uniform and collisions are rare in the domain. In the Chapman–Enskog theory, on the other hand, shearing stress and heat conduction occur due to collisions among particles on the existence of non-uniformity of the field under consideration. The apparent contradiction is explained as follows: In the Chapman–Enskog theory it is assumed that a gas is almost in thermal equilibrium. In the present case, the assumption is not always relevant, and the distribution function even to the zeroth approximation may deviate considerably from the Maxwell function. Of course the Chapman–Enskog series does not converge, if the deviation is large. Let us investigate the situation in detail.

Regarding the gas field illustrated in Fig. 7.1-1 we assume that the velocity of the gas in the direction of the x-axis at $y = l_m$ is given by u_{lm}. According to eq. (10), we obtain[†]

$$
\langle \Phi^{(1)} \rangle = b\, \frac{u_{lm}}{(2kT/m)^{1/2}} \qquad (7.1\text{-}16)
$$

[†] Here T is determined by

$$
\frac{3}{2}\, nkT = \int \frac{1}{2}\, m(c - u)^2 f\, d^3c.
$$

If

or

$$\left.\begin{array}{c} \langle \Phi^{(1)} \rangle < 1 \\[12pt] u_{lm} < (2kT/m)^{1/2} \end{array}\right\} \tag{7.1-17}$$

the Navier–Stokes equations are yet valid in the domain. If, on the other hand,

or

$$\left.\begin{array}{c} \langle \Phi^{(1)} \rangle \gtrsim 1 \\[12pt] u_{lm} \gtrsim (2kT/m)^{1/2}, \end{array}\right\} \tag{7.1-18}$$

the Navier–Stokes equations are not valid.

A similar argument may hold regarding the distribution of energy (temperature).

7.2. Boundary conditions of moments

As explained in Section 7.1, we usually assume

$$\mathbf{u} = 0 \tag{7.2-1}$$

on the surface of a wall when we apply the Navier–Stokes equations to the flow field bounded by the wall. We have seen, however, that, so far as

$$\frac{bu_{lm}}{(2kT/m)^{1/2}} < 1,$$

the Navier–Stokes equation is applicable, even if $\mathbf{u}$ does not vanish on the wall. Then, condition (1) is not an *a priori* condition. In general, it is necessary to investigate boundary conditions not only for the Navier–Stokes equations but also for the Boltzmann equation itself which has to be considered directly when the Navier–Stokes equations are not valid.

7.2-1. KINETIC-THEORETICAL BOUNDARY CONDITIONS

We have to prepare boundary conditions, necessary for solving the relevant differential and/or integral equations governing a field, by means of certain experimental measurements of the field near the wall. This is the eventual principle of giving boundary conditions. The mass velocity is one of those quantities to be measured on the wall. Besides, there are several observable quantities which are given by eq. (7.1-15). If we measure one of them, for example,

$$\mathbf{P} = \int m\mathbf{cc}f^{(+)}\,d^3c + \int m\mathbf{cc}f^{(-)}\,d^3c, \qquad (7.2\text{-}2)$$

then this will be combined with eq. (7.1-4)

$$f^{(+)}(\mathbf{c}) = \int \varphi(\mathbf{c}, \mathbf{c}')f^{(-)}(\mathbf{c}')\,d^3c', \qquad (7.2\text{-}3)$$

If φ, a characteristic of the wall, is known, we may substitute $f^{(+)}$ from eq. (7.1-4) in (2) to obtain an integral equation by which $f^{(-)}$ is determined. If it is necessary[†] to do so, we may consider other quantities among those given by eq. (7.1-15).

As a matter of principle, the above consideration is sufficient for setting suitable boundary conditions necessary for solving the Boltzmann equation and, needless to say, the Navier–Stokes equations derived from the Boltzmann equation.

There are possibilities, however, of reducing these general boundary conditions to some which are convenient specifically for the Navier–Stokes equations. These are derived by generalizing the slip condition proposed initially by Maxwell (1879).

[†] If the state of a gas deviates significantly from thermal equilibrium, as is the case of rarefied gas dynamics, gross momentum density and gross energy density are not sufficient for specifying the state; we have to consider other gross variables (moments of f) at the same time. At this moment it seems that there is no general rule. Depending on a given situation, we have to take into account a sufficient number of gross variables.

7.2-2. MAXWELL'S BOUNDARY CONDITIONS OF VELOCITY

As noted previously, condition $u_x = 0$ is not an *a priori* condition on a wall, even when the Navier–Stokes equations are feasibly applicable to the flow adjacent to the wall. In order to give a convenient boundary condition, general boundary conditions considered in the last sub-section are modified in the following, according to Maxwell (1879), Millikan (1923), Epstein (1924), Kramers (1949), Koga (1957),

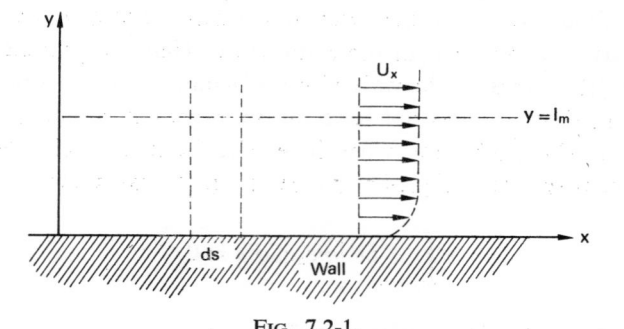

FIG. 7.2-1.

Maxwell assumed that the shearing stress force on an elementary area dS on the wall is balanced with the stress force on dS at $y = l_m$.

and others. Let us consider an elementary area dS on the surface of the wall. We imagine an elementary cylinder extending to the y-direction from the elementary area dS as illustrated in Fig. 7.2-1. The cylinder reaches the imaginary plane set at $y = l_m$. It is assumed that the shearing stress force on dS at $y = 0$ is balanced by the stress force on dS at $y = l_m$. The shearing stress force at $y = m$ is given by

$$(P_{xy})_{y=l_m} dS = \int m c_x c_y (f^{(0)} + f^{(1)}) \, d^3c \, dS = \left[\varrho u_x u_y - \mu \left(\frac{\partial u_x}{\partial y} \right) \right]_{y=l_m} dS$$

(7.2-4)

because the Chapman–Enskog theory is assumed to be valid there.

125

The shearing stress at $y = 0$, that is the momentum component in the x direction given to a unit area of the wall, is

$$
\left.
\begin{aligned}
(P_{xy})_{y=0}\, dS = (1-\alpha_1) &\left[\int_{c_y < 0} (f^{(0)}+f^{(1)}) m c_x c_y \, d^3c \right. \\
&\left. + \int_{c_y > 0} f^{(+)} m c_x c_y \, d^3c \right] dS.
\end{aligned}
\right\} \quad (7.2\text{-}5)
$$

Here the following has been taken into account: a particle which reflects from the wall in the specular sense does not give the wall any momentum component in the x-direction. Hence a particle contributes to the stress on the wall with probability $(1-\alpha_1)$. A particle of random reflection does not have, on average, any momentum component in the x-direction when it recedes from the wall. Hence the third member in the right-hand side of eq. (5) vanishes:

$$
\int_{c_y > 0} f^{(+)} m c_x c_y \, d^3c = 0.
$$

The first member is calculated as follows:

$$
\begin{aligned}
(P_{xy})'_{y=0} &= (1-\alpha_1) \int_{c_y < 0} m c_x c_y f^{(0)} \, d^3c \\
&= (1-\alpha_1) \int_{c_y < 0} m c_x c_y n \left(\frac{m}{2\pi kT} \right)^{3/2} \exp\left\{ -\frac{m}{2kT} [(c_x - u_x)^2 \right. \\
&\qquad \left. + c_y^2 + c_z^2] \right\} d^3c \\
&= -(1-\alpha_1) \frac{nm}{2\pi^{1/2}} \left(\frac{2kT}{m} \right)^{1/2} u_x.
\end{aligned}
$$

Here u_x is the gas velocity on the wall. Consideration of

$$
\langle C \rangle = \frac{\int C f^{(0)} \, d^3c}{\int f^{(0)} \, d^3c} = \frac{2}{\pi^{1/2}} \left(\frac{2kT}{m} \right)^{1/2},
$$

$$
C = |\mathbf{c} - \mathbf{u}|,
$$

leads to

$$(P_{xy})'_{y=0} = -\frac{1}{4}(1-\alpha_1)nu_x\langle C\rangle. \qquad (7.2\text{-}6)$$

The second member in the right-hand side of eq. (5) is

$$(P_{xy})''_{y=0} = (1-\alpha_1)\int_{c_y<0} mc_xc_yf^{(1)}\,d^3c. \qquad (7.2\text{-}7)$$

It is known that

$$\int mc_xc_yf^{(1)}\,d^3c = -\mu\left(\frac{\partial u_x}{\partial y}+\frac{\partial u_y}{\partial x}\right).$$

Considering

$$\partial u_y/\partial x = 0, \quad u_y = 0$$

and assuming† that

$$-\frac{1}{2}\mu\frac{\partial u_x}{\partial y} = \int_{c_y<0}f^{(1)}mc_xc_y\,d^3c = \int_{c_y>0}f^{(1)}mc_xc_y\,d^3c, \quad (7.2\text{-}8)$$

we obtain

$$(P_{xy})''_{y=0} = -\frac{1}{2}(1-\alpha_1)\mu\frac{\partial u_x}{\partial y}. \qquad (7.2\text{-}9)$$

According to the initial consideration that the stress force at $y = l_m$ and the stress force at $y = 0$ are balanced against each other, we obtain

$$(P_{xy})_{y=l_m} = (P_{xy})_{y=0}$$

or

$$\mu\left(\frac{\partial u_x}{\partial y}\right)_{y=l_m} = (\alpha_1-1)\left[\frac{1}{2}\mu\left(\frac{\partial u_x}{\partial y}\right)+\frac{n}{4}u_x\langle C\rangle\right]_{y=0}. \quad (7.2\text{-}10)$$

On consideration of

$$(\partial u_x/\partial y)_{y=l_m} = (\partial u_x/\partial y)_{y=0},$$

eq. (10) yields

$$u_{x(y=0)} = \frac{2(1+\alpha_1)}{1-\alpha_1}\cdot\frac{\mu}{\varrho\langle C\rangle}\frac{\partial u_x}{\partial y}. \qquad (7.2\text{-}11)$$

† This must be the most ambiguous point in the Maxwell slip theory.

In the procedure deriving eq. (11), the feasibility of assumption (8) is most doubtful: $f^{(1)}$ is not an even function regarding c_y. However, we may accept eq. (11) as a semi-empirical formula.

By writing

$$\frac{\partial u_x}{\partial y} \rightarrow \frac{U}{L}$$

with L which is, for example, the dimension of the thickness of a boundary layer, eq. (11) yields

$$u_x = \frac{2(1+\alpha_1)}{1-\alpha_1} \frac{\mu U}{\varrho \langle C \rangle L}. \tag{7.2-12}$$

Since $\varrho \langle C \rangle L/\mu$ (a number similar to Reynolds' number) is usually much larger than unity, u_x is much smaller than U. As density ϱ and the average thermal speed $\langle C \rangle$ decrease, however, u_x may become significant. It is noted that condition (11) by itself does not give any criterion regarding its feasible applicability. The feasible application is limited to the domain where

$$\langle \Phi^{(1)} \rangle < 1 \tag{7.2-13}$$

as discussed previously.

7.2-3. BOUNDARY CONDITION FOR TEMPERATURE

Let us consider the boundary condition for temperature in the same way as we have done with respect to velocity. We consider the balance of energy flux regarding the elementary cylinder illustrated in Fig. 7.2-1.

Among the three modes of molecular reflection on a wall investigated in Section 7.1 only the second mode represented by φ_2, eq. (7.1-7) contributes to the exchange of energy between the wall and molecules. The energy transferred from the wall to the gas through unit area of the surface is

$$(Q_y)_{y=0} = \alpha_2 \left[\int_{c_y > 0} \frac{1}{2} mc^2 c_y f^{(+)} \, d^3c + \int_{c_y < 0} \frac{1}{2} mc^2 c_y (f^{(0)} + f^{(1)}) \, d^3c \right] \tag{7.2-14}$$

in the Chapman–Enskog approximation. Here $f^{(+)}$ is, in accordance with eq. (7.1-7),

$$f^{(+)} = n^{(+)}\left(\frac{m}{2\pi kT_w}\right)^{3/2} \exp\left(-\frac{m}{2kT_w}c^2\right) \qquad (7.2\text{-}15)$$

where T_w is the temperature of the wall. In $f^{(+)}$, $n^{(+)}$ is determined by the mass conservation law:

$$\int_{c_y > 0} mc_y f^{(+)}\, d^3c + \int_{c_y < 0} mc_y(f^{(0)}+f^{(1)})\, d^3c = 0. \quad (7.2\text{-}16)$$

In the same sense[†] as of eq. (8), we put

$$\int_{c_y < 0} c_y f^{(1)}\, d^3c = \frac{1}{2}\int_{-\infty < c_y < +\infty} c_y f^{(1)}\, d^3c = 0.$$

Thereby eq. (16) yields

$$n = n^{(+)}. \qquad (7.2\text{-}16)'$$

On substitution of eq. (15) we obtain

$$\left.\begin{aligned}
\int \frac{1}{2} mc^2 c_y f^{(+)}\, d^3c &= \frac{1}{2}m\int_{c_y > 0}(c_x^2 c_y + c_y^3 + c_z^2 c_y)n\left(\frac{m}{2\pi kT}\right)^{3/2} \\
&\times \exp\left(-\frac{m}{2kT_w}c^2\right)d^3c = \frac{nm}{2\pi^{1/2}}\left(\frac{2kT_w}{m}\right)^{3/2}.
\end{aligned}\right\} \quad (7.2\text{-}17)$$

As regards the second term of eq. (14) it is shown that

$$\left.\begin{aligned}
\int_{c_y < 0}\frac{1}{2}mc^2 c_y f^{(0)}d^3c &= \int_{c_y < 0}\frac{1}{2}m[(C_x+u_x)^2 c_y + c_y^3 + c_z^2 c_y] \\
\times n\left(\frac{m}{2\pi kT}\right)^{3/2}&\exp\left[-\frac{m}{2kT}(C_x^2+c_y^2+c_z^2)\right]dC_x\, dc_y\, dc_z \\
&= -nm\left(\frac{2kT}{m}\right)^{3/2}\left(\frac{1}{2\pi^{1/2}}+\frac{\pi^{1/2}}{2}u_x^2\frac{m}{2kT}\right),
\end{aligned}\right\} \quad (7.2\text{-}18)$$

[†] In this sense, the boundary condition obtained in the present section, as well as Maxwell's boundary condition, is an assumption.

and, again in the same sense as of eq. (8), we write

$$\int_{c_y < 0} \frac{1}{2} mc^2 c_y f^{(1)} \, d^3c = \frac{1}{2} \int_{-\infty}^{+\infty} \frac{1}{2} mc^2 \, c_y f^{(1)} d^3c = -\frac{1}{2} \lambda \frac{\partial T}{\partial y}. \quad (7.2\text{-}19)$$

To sum up those calculated above, we have for eq. (14)

$$\left. (Q_y)_{y=0} = \left\{ \frac{nm}{2\pi^{1/2}} \left(\frac{2kT_w}{m} \right)^{3/2} - nm \left(\frac{2kT}{m} \right)^{3/2} \right. \\ \times \left(\frac{1}{2\pi^{1/2}} + \frac{\pi^{1/2}}{2} \frac{mu_x^2}{2kT} \right) - \frac{1}{2} \lambda \left(\frac{\partial T}{\partial y} \right)_{y=0} \right\} \alpha_2. \right\} \quad (7.2\text{-}20)$$

To compensate the energy flux given by eq. (20) the energy flux at $y = l_m$ is

$$(Q_y)_{y=l_m} = \int_{-\infty}^{+\infty} \frac{1}{2} mc^2 c_y (f^{(0)} + f^{(1)}) \, d^3c = -\lambda \left(\frac{\partial T}{\partial y} \right)_{y=l_m}. \quad (7.2\text{-}21)$$

Hence consideration of

$$\left. \begin{aligned} (Q_y)_{y=l_m} &= (Q_y)_{y=0} \\ \left(\frac{\partial T}{\partial y} \right)_{y=0} &= \left(\frac{\partial T}{\partial y} \right)_{y=l_m} = \frac{\partial T}{\partial y} \end{aligned} \right\} \quad (7.2\text{-}22)$$

and

leads to

$$\left. \begin{aligned} \frac{nm}{2\pi^{1/2}} \left(\frac{2kT_w}{m} \right)^{3/2} &- nm \left(\frac{1}{2\pi^{1/2}} + \frac{\pi^{1/2}}{2} \frac{mu_x^2}{2kT} \right) \left(\frac{2kT}{m} \right)^{3/2} \\ &= \left(-\frac{1}{\alpha_2} + \frac{1}{2} \right) \lambda \frac{\partial T}{\partial y}. \end{aligned} \right\} \quad (7.2\text{-}23)$$

In conclusion, a boundary condition for the Navier–Stokes equations is given by eq. (23). In general, u_x on the wall is much smaller than $(2kT/m)^{1/2}$, and condition eq. (23) yields

$$\frac{nm}{2\pi^{1/2}} \left[\left(\frac{2kT_w}{m} \right)^{3/2} - \left(\frac{2kT}{m} \right)^{3/2} \right] = \left(-\frac{1}{\alpha_2} + \frac{1}{2} \right) \lambda \frac{\partial T}{\partial y}. \quad (7.2\text{-}24)$$

7.3. Usage of boundary condition of moments

Two examples of rarefied gas flows adjacent to walls are qualitatively investigated, in order to see typical modes of appearance of flow regimes defined previously.

7.3-1. FLOW PARALLEL TO A FLAT PLATE

Let us suppose that there is a uniform gas flow with velocity U. A semi-infinite flat plate with a sharp leading edge is submerged in the flow so that the leading edge is perpendicular to the flow direction and the plate is parallel to the flow, as illustrated in Fig. 7.3-1.

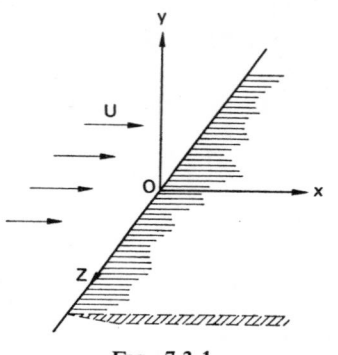

Fig. 7.3-1.

The leading edge of a plate is parallel to the z-axis at the origin of the coordinate system. The main flow U and the plate are both parallel to the x-axis.

After a while, the flow will be steady. By setting the origin at the leading edge, we consider the x-axis in the flow direction and the y-axis perpendicular to the plate. The gas is rarefied so that

$$l_m \gg l_r \qquad (7.3\text{-}1)$$

where l_r is the characteristic dimension of the roughness of the plate

surface. We investigate the state of the flow along the plate between the surface of the plate, $y = 0$, and the imaginary plane set at $y = l_m$. We assume that the velocity U of the main flow is larger than the average thermal velocity of particles (See eq. (6.2–12):

$$bU/(2kT/m)^{1/2} > 1. \tag{7.3-2}$$

The distribution function of molecules before they are disturbed by the flat plate is given by

$$f = n\left(\frac{m}{2\pi kT}\right)^{3/2} \exp\left\{-\frac{m}{2kT}[(c_x - U)^2 + c_y^2 + c_z^2]\right\}. \tag{7.3-3}$$

Because of condition (2), the x-component of the velocity of a particle is U with a predominantly large probability. At a moment of time we consider the molecules in an elementary volume ΔV at the leading edge somewhere near $y = l_m/2$. The number of these molecules is denoted by $n\Delta V$. Each of these molecules has velocity

$$(U, O, O) \tag{7.3-4}$$

with a small thermal fluctuation

$$\mathbf{C} = (c_x - U, c_y, c_z). \tag{7.3-5}$$

Since $\langle|\mathbf{C}|\rangle$ is much smaller than U, these molecules, as if they were molecules in a molecular beam, move almost in the x-direction, parallel to the wall. However, there is another group of molecules which have been reflected from the wall after colliding on the surface. They have large components of velocity in the y and z directions according to φ given by eq. (7.1-12). Molecules of the first group collide with those of the latter group. Hence at x the number of molecules in the first group which have had no experience of collision since leaving the leading edge is given in an approximation by

$$(\Delta Vn)' = \Delta Vn \exp\left(-\frac{1}{\langle C \rangle}\int_0^x \langle \Theta \rangle' \, dx\right),$$

with[†]

$$\langle\Theta\rangle' = \langle C\rangle'/l_m$$

or

$$(\Delta Vn)' = \Delta Vn \exp(-x/l_m). \tag{7.3-6}$$

Suppose that a molecule with velocity U in the x-direction loses the velocity by its collision. If the density of the gas at x is not very different from the density at the leading edge, those molecules in V which have experienced collisions are replaced with molecules whose velocities are mostly random and contribute nothing to the mass velocity. Then the average mass velocity of the molecules in ΔV at x is given by

$$u = \frac{(\Delta Vn)'U}{\Delta Vn} = U \exp(-x/l_m). \tag{7.3-7}$$

Since u does not change much from $y = l_r$ to $y = l_m$, we may take for u at $y = l_m$

$$u_{l_m} = U \exp(-x/l_m). \tag{7.3-7'}$$

In the table the values of u_{l_m}/U corresponding to various values of x/l_m are given in Table 7.3-1.

TABLE 7.3-1

x/l_m	u_{l_m}/U
0	1
0.5	0.606
1	0.367
1.5	0.223
2	0.135
2.5	0.082
3	0.050
3.5	0.030
4	0.018
4.5	0.011
5	0.007
6	0.002

[†] Particles which have been reflected from the wall have large thermal velocities, and hence $\langle C'\rangle$ is larger than $\langle C\rangle$.

133

Example: if $\dfrac{U}{(2kT/m)^{1/2}} = 20$ (Mach number = 10),

then

$$b\,\frac{u_{l_m}}{(2kT/m)^{1/2}} = 1 \qquad (b = 1 \text{ is assumed})$$

at

$$x = 3l_m.$$

According to eq. (7.1-17), this is the critical condition of the validity of the Navier–Stokes equations. If x increases further, it follows that

$$b\,\frac{u_{l_m}}{(2kT/m)^{1/2}} < 1 \tag{7.3-8}$$

and the Navier–Stokes equations are applicable. But here, either u_{l_m} or u at $y = l_r$ does not vanish. If x increases further, they vanish eventually. Of course the above is simply a qualitative presentation of the main character of the flow near the flat plate.[†]

According to the rather simple investigation stated above, we illustrate, in Fig. 7.3-2 schematically the various conditions in the flow field near the leading edge of the flat plate. In the domain between $x = 0$ and $x = x_1$, $f^{(-)}$ is almost the same as the distribution function of molecules in the main flow:

$$f^{(-)} = n\left(\frac{m}{2\pi kT}\right)^{3/2} \exp\left\{ -\frac{m}{2kT}\,[(c_x-U)^2+c_y^2+c_z^2] \right\}, \ c_y < 0,$$

and

$$f^{(+)} = \int \varphi(\mathbf{c};\mathbf{c}')f^{(-)}(\mathbf{c}')\,d^3c'. \tag{7.3-9}$$

In the domain from $x = x_1$ to ∞, the distribution function is given by the Chapman–Enskog theory. However, in the domain from

---

[†] If the flow is supersonic, as is well known, the domain is surrounded by a shock surface to which the application of the Chapman–Enskog theory is not necessarily feasible. Eventually the separation of such domains is a kind of technique for solving the Boltzmann equation for the entire domain of flow.

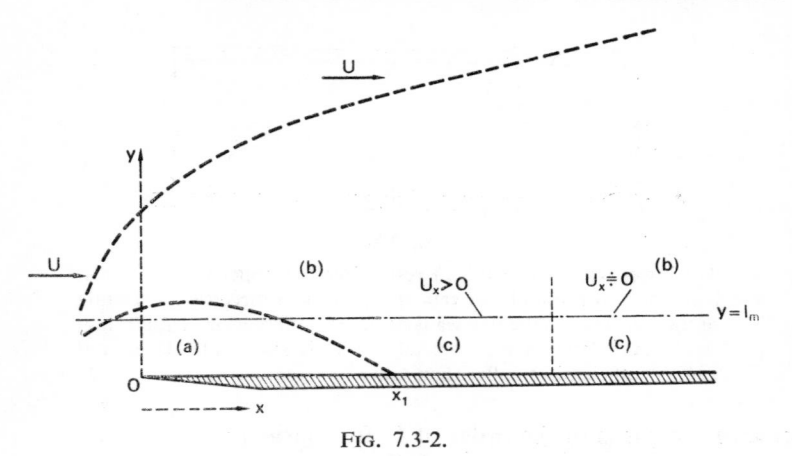

FIG. 7.3-2.

The flow near the leading edge of a semi-infinite plate set in the same way as illustrated in Fig. 7.3-1. In domain (a) the Navier–Stokes equations are not valid; in domain (b) the equations may be valid as combined with Maxwell's slip condition applied for the domain (c). It is possible that a shock front surrounds the domain (b). In a radical sense, the entire domain must be treated as a whole based on the Boltzmann equation. Separation of the domain in parts is a matter of technique of solution.

$x = 0$ to x_1, the situation is very complicated. It is obvious, however, that the distribution function satisfies the Boltzmann equation. Therefore if the boundary condition is given by the distribution function on the surface of the plate there is a possibility of solution.

7.3-2. COUETTE FLOW

We investigate a steady flow between two infinitely wide and flat plates. The plates are parallel and one moves with a uniform speed in the x-direction relative to the other plate, as illustrated in Fig. 7.3-3. The distance between the two plates is denoted by L. The temperatures of the plates are kept at T by means of some cooling device. Suppose that the mean free path length l_m of a mole-

135

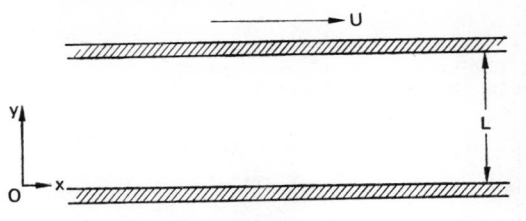

FIG. 7.3-3.

The lower wall at $y = 0$ is at rest, while the upper wall at $y = L$ is moving with a uniform velocity U in the x direction. The state of the gas between the two walls deviates from thermal equilibrium significantly and macroscopically, if U is sufficiently large and L/l_m is sufficiently smaller than unity.

cule of the gas is of the order of L. By considering

$$\langle \Phi^{(1)} \rangle = a \frac{l_m \Delta T}{LT} + b \frac{l_m U}{L(2kT/m)^{1/2}}, \quad \Delta T = 0, \qquad (7.3\text{-}10)$$

we notice that the mode of the flow depends on $U/(2kT/m)^{1/2}$. If

$$U/(2kT/m)^{1/2} < 1$$

the flow may be treated by means of the Navier–Stokes equations with boundary conditions considered in Section 7.2. If U becomes larger, the Navier–Stokes equations are not valid, and we have to solve directly the Boltzmann equation; the boundary condition is also given in Section 7.2.

At the extreme condition where $l_m \gg L$, there is no substantial probability of collisions among particles. Suppose that the molecules colliding on a wall rebound from the wall according to the Maxwell distribution with the same temperature of the wall. In other words, the molecules receding from the wall have no mass velocity relative to the wall. Suppose further that these molecules interact with the other wall in the same way. By repeating reflection from one wall to the other, these molecules transport momentum from the x-direction from the upper wall to the lower wall; that is the upper wall is pulled back to the opposite direction of its motion and the lower wall is pulled to the direction of the motion of the

upper wall. Therefore there appears a uniform shearing stress p_{xy} inside the flow.[†] The magnitude of p_{xy} is calculated as follows: the distribution of the particles of which $c_y > 0$ is

$$f^{(+)} = n\left(\frac{m}{2\pi kT}\right)^{3/2} \exp\left(-\frac{m}{2kT}c^2\right), \quad c^2 = c_x^2 + c_y^2 + c_z^2, \quad (7.3\text{-}11)$$

while the distribution of the particles of which $c_y < 0$ is

$$f^{(-)} = n\left(\frac{m}{2\pi kT}\right)^{3/2} \exp\left\{-\frac{m}{2kT}[(c_x - U)^2 + c_y^2 + c_z^2]\right\}. \quad (7.3\text{-}12)$$

Here T is the temperature of the two walls assumed common to both. Hence interesting moments of the distributions are as follows: The mass velocity:

$$\left.\begin{array}{l} u_x = \dfrac{1}{n}\left(\displaystyle\int c_x f^{(+)} d^3c + \int c_x f^{(-)} d^3c\right) = \dfrac{1}{2}U \\[2ex] u_y = u_z = 0. \end{array}\right\} \quad (7.3\text{-}13)$$

The stress:

$$\left.\begin{array}{l} p_{xx} = m\int c_x^2 f^{(+)} d^3c + m\int c_x^2 f^{(-)} d^3c = nkT + 1/2\,nmU^2 \\[1ex] p_{yy} = p_{zz} = nkT \\[1ex] p_{xy} = m\displaystyle\int c_x c_y f^{(+)} d^3c + m\int c_x c_y f^{(-)} d^3c \\[2ex] \qquad = \dfrac{nm}{2\pi^{1/2}}\left(\dfrac{2kT}{m}\right)^{1/2} U \\[2ex] p_{xz} = p_{yz} = 0. \\[2ex] E \text{ (the total energy density)} = \dfrac{3}{2}nkT + \dfrac{1}{4}nmU^2 \\[2ex] \text{The energy density due to mass motion} = \dfrac{1}{8}nmU^2 \\[2ex] \mathcal{E} \text{ (the energy density due to random motion)} \\[2ex] \qquad = \dfrac{3}{2}nkT + \dfrac{1}{8}nmU^2. \end{array}\right\} \quad (7.3\text{-}14)$$

[†] This conclusion appears paradoxical in view of our usual interpretation of gas dynamics by means of the Navier–Stokes equations. Note that the Navier–Stokes equations are not feasible in this case, see the next section.

137

It is noted that there is a uniform shearing stress given by eq. (14) in the uniform flow field.

7.3-3. SHOCK WAVE

We consider a one-dimensional (normal) shock wave (Fig. 7.3-4). According to Rankine and Hugoniot, the relations between the

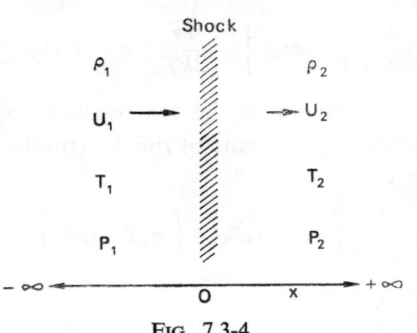

FIG. 7.3-4.

A stationary and plane shock wave: The condition of the flow before the shock is designated with quantities with subscript 1 and the condition after the shock with those with subscript 2.

state of the gas upstream from a shock wave and the state downstream from the same shock wave are given by

$$\left.\begin{array}{l} \varrho_1 U_1 = \varrho_2 U_2 \qquad \text{(mass conservation)}, \\ \varrho_1 U_1^2 + n_1 kT_1 = \varrho_2 U_2^2 + n_2 kT_2 \text{ (momentum conservation)}, \\ U_1\left(\dfrac{5}{2}\, n_1 kT_1 + \dfrac{1}{2}\, \varrho_1 U_1^2\right) = U_2\left(\dfrac{5}{2}\, n_2 kT_2 + \dfrac{1}{2}\, \varrho_2 U_2^2\right) \\ \qquad\qquad\qquad\qquad\text{(energy conservation)}, \end{array}\right\} \quad (7.3\text{-}15)$$

where subscript 1 is for the state upstream from the shock wave and subscript 2 is for the state downstream from the shock. Defining

$$\left.\begin{array}{l} M_1 = \dfrac{U_1}{(\gamma p_1/\varrho_1)^{1/2}} = \dfrac{U_1}{(\gamma/2)^{1/2}(2kT/m)^{1/2}} \\ \qquad\qquad\qquad\qquad \text{(Mach number)} \\ \gamma = \dfrac{c_p}{c_v} = \dfrac{5}{3} \qquad \text{(monatomic gas)} \end{array}\right\} \quad (7.3\text{-}16)$$

and considering

$$p = nkT$$

relations (15) yield

$$
\left.
\begin{aligned}
\frac{\varrho_2}{\varrho_1} &= \frac{(\gamma+1)M_1^2}{2+(\gamma-1)M_1^2} \\[2mm]
\frac{U_2}{U_1} &= \frac{2+(\gamma-1)M_1^2}{(\gamma+1)M_1^2} \\[2mm]
\frac{T_2}{T_1} &= \left(\frac{2\gamma M_1^2-\gamma+1}{\gamma+1}\right)\left(\frac{2+(\gamma-1)M_1^2}{(\gamma+1)M_1^2}\right).
\end{aligned}
\right\}
\qquad (7.3\text{-}17)
$$

Since $(\gamma/2)^{1/2} = 0.92$, M_1 is almost equal to $U_1/(2kT_1/m)^{1/2}$. It is known that the ratio of the mean free path length in the gas upstream from the shock wave to the thickness of the shock wave is 0.1 at $M_1 = 1.5$. But the ratio does not significantly increase as M_1 increases. At $M_1 = 6$, the ratio is of the order of 0.2.

$$l_1/L = 0.1 \sim 0.2, \qquad (7.3\text{-}18)$$

where L denotes the thickness of the shock wave. However, the degree of non-uniformity represented by

$$
\left.
\begin{aligned}
\frac{\Delta T}{T} &= \frac{T_2-T_1}{T_1} \\[2mm]
\frac{\Delta U}{2kT/m} &= \frac{U_1-U_2}{2kT_1/m}
\end{aligned}
\right\}
\qquad (7.3\text{-}19)
$$

increases rapidly as M_1 increases, as shown by the numerical values of $\Delta T/T$ given in Table 7.3-2.

TABLE 7.3-2

M_1	$\Delta T/T$
1	0
1.5	0.5
2	1.1
3	2.7
4	4.8
5	7.8
6	11.1

The validity of the Navier–Stokes equations applied to a shock wave is to be judged not only by l_1/L given by eq. (18) but also by those given by eq. (19). It is known that the results of calculations based on the Navier–Stokes equation agree with experimental results for shock waves of Mach number up to 1.7. As M_1 increases further, however, the Navier–Stokes equations become unreliable. One has to integrate directly the Boltzmann equation by considering the proper boundary conditions for a shock wave.

One who attempts to calculate the structure of a shock wave by integrating the Boltzmann equation realizes that one of the difficulties in the treatment is that the boundary conditions are asymptotic conditions. In other words, when the x-axis is parallel to the flow and the origin is located somewhere within the shock wave, boundary conditions are given in terms of the values of the variables at

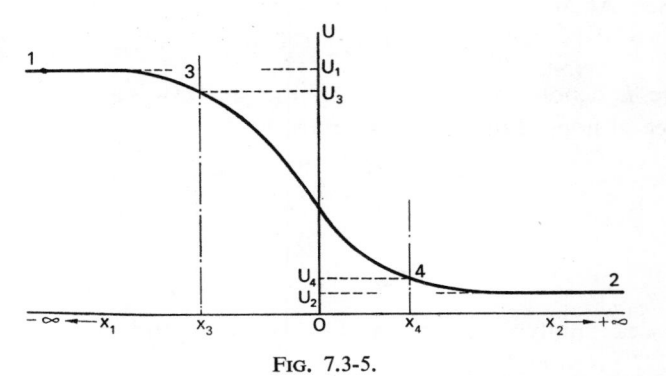

Fig. 7.3-5.

The distribution of flow velocity within a shock wave: Between x_1 and x_3 the Navier–Stokes equations are valid. Also between x_4 and x_2 the equations are valid. It is convenient for the treatment of a shock wave if conditions are given at x_3 and x_4.

$x \to \pm \infty$. In Fig. 7.3-5, the distribution of mass velocity U inside a shock wave is schematically illustrated. In the following, it is shown that there is a method of setting conditions at $x = x_3$ and x_4 within finite distances from the center of a shock wave.

140

The asymptotic distribution function upstream from a shock wave is given by

$$f_1 = n_1\left(\frac{m}{2\pi kT_1}\right)^{3/2} \exp\left\{-\frac{m}{2kT_1}[(c_x-U_1)^2+c_y^2+c_z^2]\right\}, \quad (7.3\text{-}20)$$

and for the function downstream from the shock

$$f_2 = n_2\left(\frac{m}{2\pi kT_2}\right)^{3/2} \exp\left\{-\frac{m}{2kT_2}[(c_x-U_2)^2+c_y^2+c_z^2]\right\}. \quad (7.3\text{-}21)$$

Suppose that the point $x = x_3$ is located near the beginning of the shock and the deviation of the state from thermal equilibrium is slight. Then the Chapman–Enskog theory is valid between $x = -\infty$ and x_3. The distribution function at $x = x_3$ is given by

$$f_3 = f_3^{(0)}+f_3^{(1)}. \quad (7.3\text{-}22)$$

According to the mass conservation law in the steady and one-dimensional flow, we have

or

$$\left.\begin{array}{c} \int mc_x f_1\, d^3c = \int mc_x f_3\, d^3c \\[2mm] \varrho_1 U_1 = \varrho_3 U_3. \end{array}\right\} \quad (7.3\text{-}23)$$

The momentum conservation law is represented by

$$\int mc_x^2 f_1\, d^3c = \int mc_x^2 f_3\, d^3c$$

(by substitution of eq. (22))

$$= \int mc_x^2(f_3^{(0)}+f_3^{(1)})\, d^3c. \quad (7.3\text{-}24)$$

Here

$$\int mc_x^2 f_1\, d^3c = n_1 kT_1 + n_1 m U_1^2. \quad (7.3\text{-}25)$$

Since

$$f_3^{(0)} = n_3\left(\frac{m}{2\pi kT_3}\right)^{3/2} \exp\left\{-\frac{m}{2kT_3}[(c_x-U_3)^2+c_y^2+c_z^2]\right\}$$

we obtain

$$\int mc_x^2 f_3^{(0)}\, d^3c = n_3 kT_3 + mn_3 U_3^2. \quad (7.3\text{-}26)$$

141

As regards $f_3^{(1)}$, eq. (5.2-16) leads[†] to

$$\int mc_x^2 f_3^{(1)} \, d^3c = -\frac{4}{3} \mu_3 \left(\frac{du}{dx}\right)_3 . \qquad (7.3\text{-}27)$$

On substitution of eqs. (25), (26) and (27) in eq. (24), we obtain

$$n_1 k T_1 + \varrho_1 U_1^2 = n_3 k T_3 + \varrho_3 U_3^2 - \frac{4}{3} \mu_3 \left(\frac{du}{dx}\right)_3 , \qquad (7.3\text{-}28)$$

where μ_3 is the viscosity coefficient at $x = x_3$. Regarding energy flux, we have the similar relation

$$\int 1/2mc^2 c_x f_1 \, d^3c = \int 1/2mc^2 c_x f_3 \, d^3c. \qquad (7.3\text{-}29)$$

By performing the integrations, in accordance with treatments in Section 5.2, we obtain

$$U_1 \left(\frac{5}{2} n_1 k T_1 + \frac{1}{2} \varrho_1 U_1^2\right) = U_3 \left(\frac{5}{2} n_3 k T_3 + \frac{1}{2} \varrho_3 U_3^2\right)$$
$$-\frac{4}{3} \mu_3 \left(\frac{du}{dx}\right)_3 U_3 - \lambda_3 \left(\frac{dT}{dx}\right)_3 ,$$

or, on consideration of eq. (23)

$$\frac{1}{2} U_1^2 + \frac{5}{2} \frac{k T_1}{m} = \frac{1}{2} U_3^2 + \frac{5}{2} \frac{k T_3}{m}$$
$$-\frac{4}{3} \frac{\mu_3}{\varrho_3} \left(\frac{du}{dx}\right)_3 - \frac{\lambda_3}{\varrho_3 U_3} \left(\frac{dT}{dx}\right)_3 , \qquad (7.3\text{-}30)$$

where λ_3 is the heat conductivity at $x = x_3$. Relations (28) and (30) provide us with the convenience of checking the results of integration of the Boltzmann equation at $x = x_3$, instead of $-\infty$. In the same way we may consider the condition at $x = x_4$ which is related to the condition at $x = +\infty$. Of course, there is no simple relation which connects the condition at $x = x_3$ and the one at $x = x_4$. This

† $\quad \int f_3^{(1)} \, d^3c = 0, \quad \int c_x f_3^{(1)} \, d^3c = 0.$

must be obtained by integrating the Boltzmann equation. Also noted is that eqs. (23) (28) and (30) are not closed by themselves. In other words, they involve more than three unknown variables.

7.4. Approaches developed for rarefied gas dynamics

So far, we have discussed the feasibility of the Chapman–Enskog theory in view of rarefied gas dynamics and attempted to expand the domain of its applicability. Yet there is a limit over which we cannot proceed further with the Chapman–Enskog theory. The prototype of the Chapman–Enskog theory is found in Maxwell's equations of transfer and his treatment of the effects of the Boltzmann collision integral. His equations of transfer are the same as those equations of moments derived from the Boltzmann equation in Section 5.1.[†] Maxwell did not obtain the distribution functions, but he evaluated moments of the distributions function, for example stress, which is involved in the collision integral by assuming that the force of collision is proportional to the inverse fifth power of the distance between two colliding molecules and is repulsive. An important fact, from our viewpoint, is that he assumed that, for calculating derivatives of moments with respect to position vector, f is Maxwellian. This assumption is exactly the same as that of the Chapman–Enskog theory.

Thus it appears that shearing stresses exist only when a gas is spatially non-uniform; eventually his method has been elaborated on to the Chapman–Enskog theory by Boltzmann, Hilbert, Chapman, Enskog, et al.[‡]

The particular point of the Chapman–Enskog theory (or Maxwell's theory), when regarded as an iteration method, is that the unknown perturbation of the distribution function at each step of iteration is obtained in the collision integral. Therefore the solution is given by an inverse power series of the density of the gas. Note that the

---

[†] The above paper of Maxwell appeared in 1866, while the Boltzmann equation appeared in 1872.

[‡] According to S. Chapman and T. G. Cowling (1952).

collision integral is proportional to n^2 while the other members of the Boltzmann equation are proportional to n. The situation is obviously unfavorable for a rarefied gas. Grad (1949), in deriving his thirteen moments equations[†] with the intention of applying them to rarefied gas dynamics, did not *solve* the Boltzmann equation. He expanded the distribution function in Hermite polynomials in terms of powers of $c/(kT/m)^{1/2}$, of which the first member is the Maxwell function (a complete set of orthogonal functions). In this expansion, powers of the density are not involved. Therefore the theory appears favorable for a rarefied gas. The point which is not plausible in his theory seems to be that moments of higher orders are simply dropped so that the equations are closed. Of course it is quite unknown whether the "dropped" moments are trival or not. Ikenberry and Truesdell (1965) discussed equations of transfer, in a manner similar to that of Maxwell, including higher order moments.

The present author (1954) also derived a set of equations in which ϱ, $\mathbf{u}$, T, and $\mathbf{p}_{ij}$ are independent variables. The iteration method is similar to that of the Chapman–Enskog theory. None of those approaches seems to have enjoyed any substantial success.

The basic difficulty underlying these iteration methods is schematically described as follows: let us write for the Boltzmann equation

$$\frac{df}{dt} = \Theta F[f],$$

where the right-hand side member is the Boltzmann collision integral, Θ the collision frequency. If Θ is large and df/dt is moderate, then

$$F[f] = \frac{1}{\Theta}\frac{df}{dt} \to 0.$$

The solution of

$$F[f] = 0$$

is

$$f = f^{(0)}$$
$$\text{(Maxwellian).}$$

[†] The thirteen moments are ϱ, $\mathbf{u}$, T, $\mathbf{p}_{ij}$ (stress) and q_i (heat conduction). The number of the above variables are fourteen, but one variable loses its independence from the equation of state: $i, j = x, y, z$.

Thus, we may take $f^{(0)}$ for f to the zeroth approximation provided that Θ is sufficiently large.

As Θ decreases toward zero, as in the case of a rarefied gas, we obtain

$$F[f] = \frac{1}{\Theta} \frac{df}{dt} \to \infty$$

if df/dt is finite, even though small. In other words,

$$F[f] = 0$$

is not a proper means by which we may determine f to the zeroth approximation.[†] Instead, we may begin with

$$\frac{df}{dt} = 0. \tag{7.4-1}$$

Suppose that we have for d/dt

$$\frac{d}{dt} = \frac{\partial}{\partial t} + \mathbf{c} \cdot \frac{\partial}{\partial \mathbf{r}} + \frac{\mathcal{F}}{m} \cdot \frac{\partial}{\partial \mathbf{c}}, \tag{7.4-2}$$

where $\mathcal{F}$, external force, may be a function of $\mathbf{r}$, $\mathbf{c}$, and t:

$$\mathcal{F} = \mathcal{F}(\mathbf{r}, \mathbf{c}; t).$$

We suppose that $\mathbf{r}$, $\mathbf{c}$ are functions of t and are solutions of

$$d\mathbf{r}/dt = \mathbf{c}, \quad d\mathbf{c}/dt = \mathcal{F}/m \tag{7.4-3}$$

or

$$\mathbf{r} = \mathbf{r}_0 + \int_{t_0}^{t_c} \mathbf{c}\, dt, \quad \mathbf{c} = \mathbf{c}_0 + \int_{t_0}^{t} (\mathcal{F}/m)\, dt$$

where $\mathbf{r}_0$, $\mathbf{c}_0$, t_0 and t are independent variables.

[†] Of the state of a rarefied ionized gas in an external magnetic field, such a condition is also must emphatically realized. See Section 7.5.3.

Then it is easily shown that

$$f = f^{(0)}(\mathbf{c}, \mathbf{r}; t) = f^{(0)}(\mathbf{c_0}, \mathbf{r_0}; t_0) \tag{7.4-4}$$

is the solution of eq. (1). See section 4.4.

Then, to the next approximation, f is obtained by solving

$$\frac{df}{dt} = \{\Theta F[f]\}_{f=f^{(0)}}, \tag{7.4-5}$$

where the collision factor in the right-hand side is calculated by taking $f^{(0)}$ for f.

7.4-1. COUETTE FLOW

Let us consider again the steady Couette flow introduced in Section 7.3-2. Functions (7.1-11) and (7.3-12) serve for $f^{(0)}$ considered by eq. (4). According to eq. (5.3-3), we write for the Boltzmann equation

$$\frac{df}{dt} = [f\Theta]' - f\Theta. \tag{7.4-6}$$

In the present case, we have

$$\frac{d}{dt} = c_y \frac{d}{dy}, \tag{7.4-7}$$

by which eq. (6) yields

$$c_y \frac{df}{dy} = [f\Theta]' - f\Theta. \tag{7.4-8}$$

In general, Θ is a functional of f. According to the general consideration given above,

$$c_y \frac{df^{(1)}}{dy} = [f\Theta]'^{(0)} - f^{(1)}\Theta^{(0)} \tag{7.4-8)'}$$

146

is chosen for the equation by which $f^{(1)}$, f to the first approximation, is to be determined. Here $[f\Theta]'^{(0)}$ and $\Theta^{(0)}$ are respectively $[f\Theta]'$ and Θ in which $f^{(0)}$ has been substituted for f. By solving eq. (8) with respect to $f^{(1)}$ we obtain

$$f^{(1)(+)} = A \exp\left(-\frac{\Theta^{(0)}}{c_y}y\right) + \frac{[f\Theta]'^{(0)}}{\Theta^{(0)}}, \qquad (7.4\text{-}9)$$

in which A is a function of $\mathbf{c}$ and is determined by the boundary conditions as follows:

$$\left.\begin{array}{c} f^{(1)} = f^{(1)(+)} = n^{(1)}\left(\dfrac{m}{2\pi kT}\right)^{3/2} \exp\left(-\dfrac{m}{2kT}c^2\right) \\[2mm] (c_y > 0) \end{array}\right\} \qquad (7.4\text{-}10)$$

at

$$y = 0$$

and

$$\left.\begin{array}{c} f^{(1)} = f^{(1)(-)} = n^{(1)}\left(\dfrac{m}{2\pi kT}\right)^{3/2} \exp\left(-\dfrac{m}{2kT}c_U^2\right) \\[2mm] c_U^2 = (c_x - U)^2 + c_y^2 + c_z^2 \\[1mm] (c_y < 0) \end{array}\right\} \qquad (7.4\text{-}11)$$

at

$$y = L.$$

Substitution of eqs. (10) and (11) in the left-hand side of eq. (9) leads to

$$A^{(+)} = A_{(c_y > 0)} = n^{(1)}\left(\frac{m}{2\pi kT}\right)^{3/2} \exp\left(-\frac{m}{2kT}c^2\right) - \frac{[f\Theta]'^{(0)}}{\Theta^{(0)}} \qquad (7.4\text{-}12)$$

$$\left.\begin{array}{l} A^{(-)} = A_{(c_y < 0)} = \left[n^{(1)}\left(\dfrac{m}{2\pi kT}\right)^{3/2} \exp\left(-\dfrac{m}{2kT}c_U^2\right) - \dfrac{[f\Theta]'^{(0)}}{\Theta^{(0)}}\right] \\[3mm] \qquad\qquad \times \exp\left(\dfrac{\Theta^{(0)}L}{c_y}\right). \end{array}\right\}$$

$$(7.4\text{-}13)$$

In these results $n^{(1)}$ is as yet unknown, and is to be determined by considering the mass conservation law either at $y = 0$ or at $y = L$.

At $y = 0$, the law is given by

$$\left. \begin{aligned} &\int_{c_y > 0} c_y \left(A^{(+)} + \frac{[f\Theta]'^{(0)}}{\Theta^{(0)}} \right) d^3c \\ &+ \int_{c_y < 0} c_y \left(A^{(-)} + \frac{[f\Theta]'^{(0)}}{\Theta^{(0)}} \right) d^3c = 0. \end{aligned} \right\} \qquad (7.4\text{-}14)$$

(The condition at $y = L$ is shown to be equivalent to the above, of course.)

In the above example, the collision effect is assumed to be a minor factor in the result. (For $|c_y| < \Theta^{(0)} y$ it is not necessarily so. Therefore, a careful consideration is required for evaluating those results.) Between the above case and a Couette flow which may be treated by means of the Navier–Stokes equations, there is a broad regime of medium conditions.

7.4-2. WANG CHANG–UHLENBECK'S METHOD (1949–1958)

In treating a rarefied gas flow near a wall, they assume for the distribution function near the wall the superposition of the distribution function of impinging molecules ($c_y < 0$) and the distribution function of receding molecules ($c_y > 0$), by taking the y-axis as perpendicular to the wall outwards with its origin at the wall. The total distribution is discontinuous at $c_y = 0$ in the vicinity of the wall. The function should approach the ordinary Maxwell function, as y increases, according to the Boltzmann equation. The procedure is to consider a feasible function of y and $\mathbf{c}$ which is supposed to satisfy the Boltzmann equation and the above boundary condition.

It is necessary that the function is explicit with respect to $\mathbf{c}$ so that the collision integration may be carried out. Thus the Boltzmann equation yields an ordinary differential equation with y as the independent variable. Various variations of the method have been developed by Gross and Ziering (1959), Takao and Fujimoto (1956), and others. Details of these treatments are out of the scope of this book.

7.4-3. Mott–Smith's theory of shock waves[†] (1951)

Mott–Smith assumes that the distribution function within a shock wave is given by a superposition of the distribution function of the gas upstream and the distribution function of the gas downstream from the shock. Those functions are superposed after being multiplied by weights which are functions of position within the shock wave so that the total function will be continuously connected to the Maxwell distribution functions on both sides of the shock:

$$f = f_\alpha + f_\beta$$
$$f_\alpha = n_\alpha(x) \, (m/2\pi kT_\alpha)^{3/2} \exp[-(m/2kT_\alpha)(\mathbf{c} - u_\alpha)^2], \quad \text{etc.,}$$

in which subscript α denotes variables upstream from the shock and β variables downstream from the shock; except for $n_\alpha(x)$, $n_\beta(x)$, the variables T's, $\mathbf{u}$'s are constants. On substitution of f in the Boltzmann equation, equations of moments are obtained as purely differential equations where $n_\alpha(x)$ and $n_\beta(x)$ are unknown functions. In spite of its primitive appearance, the theory seems to retain the essential point of the problem in account.

7.5. Free molecule flow

Suppose that a solid body of dimension L is moving in a rarefied atmosphere where the molecular free path length satisfies the following condition

$$\frac{l_m}{L} \gg 1. \tag{7.5-1}$$

In other words, most of the molecules which collide with the solid body have had their last collisions with other molecules at distances of the order of l_m from the body. Also most of those molecules rebounding from the solid body will collide, for the first time after

---

[†] Recently Chu (1965) investigated the process of formation of a shock wave in a shock tube by a method of numerical integration of the Boltzmann equation.

reflection, with other molecules at a distance l_m from the body. Most of the interactions between those molecules receding from the body and those proceeding towards the body occur at a distance l_m from the body. There the distribution of those molecules which come to collision with the solid body is disturbed by those molecules which have collided with the body previously. In Fig. 7.5-1, geometrical relations are illustrated for those events. The origin of position

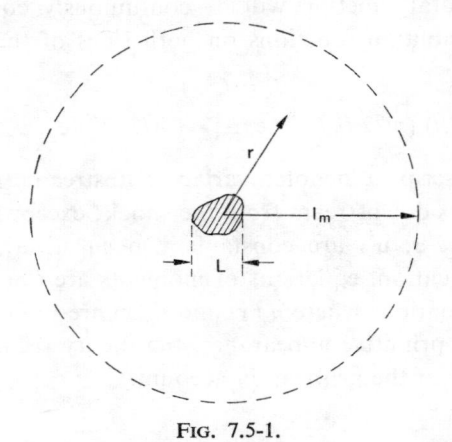

FIG. 7.5-1.

The body of dimension L is in a rarefied gas. L is macroscopic, but is much smaller than l_m. The "free molecule flow" approximation is valid in the domain $r < l_m$.

vector $\mathbf{r}$ is fixed at a point within the solid body. We investigate the possible degree of the effect of such interactions on the distribution of molecules at a distance $r = l_m$ from the body. The solid angle which the body makes at an observer at a distance m is the order of

$$\Delta\omega = \pi(L/2)^2/l_m^2. \tag{7.5-2}$$

Suppose that the number of molecules which impinge on the surface of the solid body in unit time is given by

$$\nu = 4\pi(L/2)^2 nU, \tag{7.5-3}$$

where U represents the average relative speed between a molecule and the solid body. Those molecules, after reflection from the surface of the body, pass with velocity U the surface of the imaginary sphere of radius l_m with its center at the center of the body. Hence the density of such molecules on the sphere is given by

$$\left.\begin{array}{l} n' = \dfrac{v}{4\pi l_m^2 U} = n(L/2)^2/l_m^2, \\[3mm] \dfrac{n'}{n} = \dfrac{L^2}{4l_m^2} . \end{array}\right\} \tag{7.5-4}$$

or

On consideration of eq. (1), this is a small value compared with unity

$$n'/n \ll 1. \tag{7.5-5}$$

Then we conclude that the distribution of molecules at that distance from the body is not significantly disturbed by the solid body.

7.5-1. THE DISTRIBUTION OF THE IMPINGING
MOLECULES IN THE ABSENCE OF EXTERNAL FORCES

If it is the case that the atmosphere is in thermal equilibrium with no external forces, the distribution of molecules at $r = l_m$ is given by

$$f_0 = n_0 \left(\frac{m}{2\pi kT_0} \right)^{3/2} \exp\left[-\frac{m}{2kT_0}(\mathbf{c} - \mathbf{u})^2 \right] \tag{7.5-6}$$

with respect to the coordinate system fixed at the solid body. Here $\mathbf{u}$ is the velocity of the solid body relative to the atmosphere. In the space between the imaginary sphere $\mathbf{r} = l_m$ and the surface on the solid body, we may write for the Boltzmann equation

$$\frac{\partial f}{\partial t} + \mathbf{c} \cdot \frac{\partial f}{\partial \mathbf{r}} = 0 \tag{7.5-7}$$

because collisions are rare. Then

$$df/dt = 0$$

along trajectories determined by

$$d\mathbf{r}/dt = \mathbf{c}, \quad d\mathbf{c}/dt = 0. \tag{7.5-8}$$

In other words, f is invariant along those trajectories which begin on the surface of the imaginary sphere of radius $\mathbf{r} = l_m$ and end on the surface of the solid body. Therefore the distribution of the impinging molecules is given by

$$f^{(-)} = n_0 \left(\frac{m}{2\pi kT_0} \right)^{3/2} \exp \left[-\frac{m}{2kT_0} (\mathbf{c} - \mathbf{u})^2 \right] \tag{7.5-9}$$

(the component of $\mathbf{c}$ normal to the surface of the body) < 0.

The distribution of the receding molecules is, according to eq. (7.1-4),

$$f^{(+)} = \int \varphi f^{(-)}(\mathbf{c}') \, d^3\mathbf{c}'. \tag{7.5-10}$$

If φ is known, we may calculate $f^{(+)}$ and hence the momentum, and energy exchanged between the atmosphere and the solid body. The calculation is not necessarily simple. However, if $|\mathbf{u}|$ is much larger than $\langle \mathbf{c} \rangle$ the calculation becomes simpler.

7.5-2. The Impinging Molecules in a Gravitational Force Field

If there is a uniform gravitational force $\mathbf{g}$, the Maxwell distribution function is given by[†]

$$\left. \begin{array}{l} f_0 = n_0 \left(\frac{m}{2\pi kT_0} \right)^{3/2} \exp \left[-\frac{m}{2kT_0} (\mathbf{c} - \mathbf{u})^2 \right. \\[2mm] \left. + \frac{m}{kT_0} \mathbf{g} \cdot \mathbf{r} - \frac{m}{kT_0} \mathbf{g} \cdot \mathbf{u} t \right]. \end{array} \right\} \tag{7.5-11}$$

Here n_0 is the number density of the gas molecules at $\mathbf{r} = 0$, the center of the solid body[‡] at time $t = 0$. Since the origin of $\mathbf{r}$ is fixed

[†] This function satisfies the Boltzmann equation.

[‡] In fact there is the solid body. But the definition of f_0 is made by ignoring the body. Therefore f_0 is valid in the space outside the sphere $\mathbf{r} = l_m$.

inside the solid body, we consider the impinging molecules on the surface of the body which is represented by $\mathbf{r} = \mathbf{R}$. Then the number density of impinging molecules is given by

$$f^{(-)} = n_0 \left(\frac{m}{2\pi k T_0} \right)^{3/2} \exp \left[-\frac{m}{2kT_0} (\mathbf{c} - \mathbf{u})^2 + \frac{m}{kT_0} \mathbf{g} \cdot \mathbf{R} - \frac{m}{kT_0} \mathbf{g} \cdot \mathbf{u} t \right]$$

(7.5-12)

(the component of $\mathbf{c}$ normal to the surface of the body) < 0,

because the distribution of the impinging molecules is independent of the disturbance of the body. If

$$\mathbf{g} \perp \mathbf{u},$$

then

$$n = n_0 \exp \left(\frac{m}{kT_0} \mathbf{g} \cdot \mathbf{R} \right). \tag{7.5-13}$$

But if

$$\mathbf{g} \mathbin{/\mkern-5mu/} \mathbf{u},$$

then

$$n = n_0 \exp \left(\frac{m}{kT_0} \mathbf{g} \cdot \mathbf{R} - \frac{m}{kT_0} gut \right). \tag{7.5-14}$$

In other words, if the solid body is climbing in the atmosphere, the gas velocity relative to the body is in the same direction as $\mathbf{g}$ and the number density decreases as time passes.

7.5-3. SOLUTION OF THE BOLTZMANN EQUATION

In the present case, the Boltzmann equation is

$$\frac{\partial f}{\partial t} + \mathbf{c} \cdot \frac{\partial f}{\partial \mathbf{r}} + \frac{\mathcal{F}}{m} \cdot \frac{\partial f}{\partial \mathbf{c}} = 0. \tag{7.5-15}$$

If the distribution function at time t_0 is given by

$$f_{t_0} = f(\mathbf{c}, \mathbf{r}), \tag{7.5-16}$$

153

then the distribution function at time t is given by

$$f_t = f(\mathbf{c} - \mathbf{c}', \mathbf{r} - \mathbf{r}'), \tag{7.5-17}$$

where $\mathbf{c}'$ and $\mathbf{r}'$ satisfy

$$\frac{d\mathbf{c}'}{dt} = \frac{\mathcal{F}(\mathbf{r}, \mathbf{c}; t)}{m}, \quad \frac{d\mathbf{r}'}{dt} = \mathbf{c} \tag{7.5-18}$$

$$\mathbf{c}'(t_0) = 0, \quad \mathbf{r}'(t_0) = 0.$$

Proof: It is easily shown that f_t satisfies eq. (15), and $f_t = f_{t_0}$, if $t = t_0$. For example, let us consider electrons in a strong and uniform magnetic field. If we ignore the effect of the mutual interactions among electrons, the distribution function of the electrons satisfies

$$\frac{\partial f}{\partial t} + \mathbf{c} \cdot \frac{\partial f}{\partial \mathbf{r}} - \frac{eB}{m} \left(c_y \frac{\partial f}{\partial c_x} - c_x \frac{\partial f}{\partial c_y} \right) = 0, \tag{7.5-19}$$

where B is the strength of the magnetic field which is supposed to be uniform and is in the z-direction, m the mass of the electron, and e the electronic charge. The general solution of eq. (19) is

$$f = f(\mathbf{c} - \mathbf{c}', \mathbf{r} - \mathbf{r}'), \tag{7.5-20}$$

where

$$\frac{d\mathbf{c}'}{dt} = \frac{e}{m} \mathbf{B} \times \mathbf{c}, \frac{d\mathbf{r}'}{dt} = \mathbf{c}. \tag{7.5-21}$$

Function $f(\mathbf{c}, \mathbf{r})$ is to be determined by the initial and/or boundary condition. For example, it depends on the manner of injecting electrons into the magnetic field. There is no particular reason for f to be Maxwellian, as was suggested by the author (1961).

Exercises

1. Show that

$$f = f\left[c_x^2 + c_y^2, \ x - y - \frac{m}{eB} (c_x + c_y), \ z - c_z t \right]$$

is a solution of eq. (7.5-19).

2. Show that

$$E = \int \frac{1}{2} mc^2(f^{(+)}+f^{(-)}) \, d^3c \ = \ \frac{3}{2} nkT + \frac{1}{4} nmU^2, \qquad (7.3\text{-}14)$$

where $f^{(+)}$ and $f^{(-)}$ are given respectively by eq. (7.3-11) and eq. (7.3-12).

3. In eq. (7.3-15), the equation of momentum conservation is derived by considering the balance between the force on surface 1 and the force on surface 2. Show the derivation.

4. Show the derivation of the third equation of (7.3-15).

5. Discuss the difference between stress and force.

PART III

Ionized Gases

CHAPTER 8

Difficulties in Kinetic Theory
Applied to Charged Particles

8.1. Introductory remarks

If constituent particles in a gas interact mutually with the Coulomb force, $\mathcal{F}_{ij}$ given by eq. (1.2-1) with $s = 2$, the Boltzmann collision integral diverges when the integration with respect to dh (impact parameter) is extended toward $h = \infty$. Hence, it is obvious that the assumption of binary collision, on which the Boltzmann collision integral is based, is not feasible for a gas consisting of charged particles. The BBGKY hierarchy itself is not generally suitable for ionized gases: Suppose that three electrons, 1, 2, and 3, are in interaction at the same time. Because of the long range Coulomb force, it is rather difficult to conceive that the time scale of interaction between electron 1 and electron 2 is much longer than the time scale of interaction between electron 1 and electron 3, etc. Instead, it is more likely that the two time scales are similar. This condition is not compatible with condition (3.3-13) under which the BBGKY hierarchy is derived in Section 3.3. If a gas consists of ions and electrons, where the mass of a single ion is much larger than the electronic mass, the time scale of ion–ion interaction may be much longer than the time scale of electron–electron and/or electron–ion interactions. Then, the BBGKY hierarchy may be applicable in part. In Chapter 8, these difficulties are investigated, and in Chapter 9, feasible kinetic-theoretical treatments of ionized gases are considered.

A special feature of dynamics of ionized gases is that there is no standard set of macroscopic equations which governs the entire regime of the dynamics. The validity of each equation may be conditionally local even within a single field of ionized-gas flow. In this sense, the approaches here are as *ad hoc* as in dynamics of rarefied gases.

8.2. The Fokker–Planck presentation of the Boltzmann integral for weak interactions

Before investigating the divergence of the Boltzmann collision integral for an ionized gas, we convert[†] the part of the Boltzmann collision integral representing weak interactions to the Fokker–Planck expression. We suppose that the gas under consideration consists of two species of particles. The distribution function of the first species is denoted by $f_1(c_1)$ and the distribution function of the second species by $f_2(c_2)$. The Boltzmann equations for these are given by

$$\frac{df_1}{dt} = -J_{11} - J_{12} \tag{8.2-1}$$

$$\frac{df_2}{dt} = -J_{22} - J_{21}. \tag{8.2-2}$$

$-J_{11}$ is the Boltzmann collision integral of particles of the first species, $-J_{12}$ is for the collisions between the different species, and so forth:

$$-J_{11} = \iint [f_1(c_1')f_1(c_1^{*\prime}) - f_1(c_1)f_1(c_1^*)] \, d\varphi h \, dh v_{11} \, d^3c_1^*$$
$$v_{11} = |\mathbf{c}_1 - \mathbf{c}_1^*| \tag{8.2-3}$$

$$-J_{12} = \iiint [f_1(c_1')f_2(c_2') - f_1(c_1)f_2(c_2)] \, d\, h dh v_{12} \, d^3c_2$$
$$v_{12} = |\mathbf{c}_1 - \mathbf{c}_2|, \text{ etc.} \tag{8.2-4}$$

[†] The conversion was first given by Landau. See the account given by Thompson (1962). Allis (1956) proposed a method of conversion by means of moment equations. These methods are fairly complex compared with the present method.

In the following, we treat $-J_{12}$ in detail. The others will be treated in the same way as the example.

We divide $-J_{12}$ into two parts: one is attributed to the range of h from 0 to h' and the other to the range from h' to ∞.

$$-J_{12} = \mathcal{J}_0(1, 2) + \mathcal{J}_\infty(1, 2) \tag{8.2-5}$$

$$\mathcal{J}_0(1, 2) = \iint\int_{h=0}^{h'} [f_1(c_1')f_2(c_2') - f_1(c_1)f_2(c_2)] \, d\varphi h \, dh v_{12} \, d^3c_2 \tag{8.2-6}$$

$$\mathcal{J}_\infty(1, 2) = \iint\int_{h=h'}^{\infty} [f_1(c_1')f_2(c_2') - f_1(c_1)f_2(c_2)] \, d\varphi h \, dh v_{12} \, d^3c_2. \tag{8.2-7}$$

Here h' is chosen so that $|c_1'-c_1|$ and $|c_2'-c_2|$ for $h > h'$ are sufficiently small and the expansions of functions in powers of $c_1'-c_1$ and/or of $c_2'-c_2$ are feasibly performed in the following treatments, by which $\mathcal{J}_\infty(1, 2)$ is reduced to the Fokker–Planck interaction presentation.

Instead of c_1 and c_2, we take momenta p_1 and p_2 for variables:

$$p_1 = m_1 c_1 \tag{8.2-8}$$

$$p_2 = m_2 c_2. \tag{8.2-9}$$

Then it follows that

$$\mathcal{J}_\infty(1, 2) = \iint\int_{h=h'}^{\infty} [f_1(p_1')f_2(p_2') - f_1(p_1)f_2(p_2)] \, d\varphi h \, dh v_{12} \, d^3p_2/m_2^3. \tag{8.2-10}$$

Defined by

$$\Delta p = p_2' - p_2 = -p_1' + p_1, \tag{8.2-11}$$

Δp is a function of p_1, p_2, h, φ, as shown in Section 4.4. Thereby we may take for the independent variables of collision

$$\Delta p, p_1, h, \varphi \tag{8.2-12}$$

instead of

$$p_2, p_1, h, \varphi. \tag{8.2-13}$$

Consequently $\mathbf{p}_2$ is a dependent variable:

$$\mathbf{p}_2 = \mathbf{p}_2(\varDelta\mathbf{p}, \mathbf{p}_1, h, \varphi). \qquad (8.2\text{-}14)$$

By considering the reversible relation (see Appendix A.1) between $(\mathbf{p}_1, \mathbf{p}_2)$ and $(\mathbf{p}_2', \mathbf{p}_1')$, we may say the following: If we define f_2^* by

$$f_2^*(\mathbf{p}_1; \varDelta\mathbf{p}) = f_2(\mathbf{p}_2) \qquad (8.2\text{-}15)$$

and substitute eq. (14) in f_2, then consideration of eqs. (11) and (14) leads to

$$f_2(\mathbf{p}_2') = f_2^*(\mathbf{p}_1'; \ -\varDelta\mathbf{p}) = f_2^*(\mathbf{p}_1 - \varDelta\mathbf{p}; \ -\varDelta\mathbf{p}) \qquad (8.2\text{-}16)$$

On expansion of the right-hand side of the above to Taylor's series, we obtain

$$\left. \begin{aligned} f_2(\mathbf{p}_2') &= f_2^*(\mathbf{p}_1; \ -\varDelta\mathbf{p}) - \varDelta\mathbf{p} \cdot \frac{\partial f_2^*(\mathbf{p}_1; \ -\varDelta\mathbf{p})}{\partial\mathbf{p}_1} \\ &\quad + \frac{1}{2!} \varDelta\mathbf{p}\,\varDelta\mathbf{p} : \frac{\partial^2 f_2^*}{\partial\mathbf{p}_1\partial\mathbf{p}_1} - \frac{1}{3!}[\ ] + \ldots \end{aligned} \right\} \qquad (8.2\text{-}17)$$

Besides, it holds that

$$\left. \begin{aligned} f_1(\mathbf{p}_1') &= f_1(\mathbf{p}_1 - \varDelta\mathbf{p}) \\ &= f_1(\mathbf{p}_1) - \varDelta\mathbf{p} \cdot \frac{\partial f_1}{\partial\mathbf{p}_1} + \frac{1}{2!} \varDelta\mathbf{p}\,\varDelta\mathbf{p} : \frac{\partial^2 f_1}{\partial\mathbf{p}_1\partial\mathbf{p}_1} - \ldots \end{aligned} \right\} \qquad (8.2\text{-}18)$$

Defining

$$B = \frac{1}{m_2^3} v_{12} \frac{\partial(p_{2x}, p_{2y}, p_{2z})}{\partial(\varDelta p_x, \varDelta p_y, \varDelta p_z)} \qquad (8.2\text{-}19)$$

we write

$$m_3^{-2} d\varphi h\, dh v_{12}\, d^3\mathbf{p}_2 = B\, d\varphi h\, dh\, d^3\varDelta\mathbf{p}. \qquad (8.2\text{-}20)$$

162

By substituting eqs. (17), (18), and (20) in eq. (10), we obtain

$$
\begin{aligned}
\mathcal{J}_\infty(1,2) = \iint\int_{h=h'}^{\infty} \Bigg\{ & [f_2^*(\mathbf{p}_1; -\varDelta\mathbf{p}) - f_2^*(\mathbf{p}_1; \varDelta\mathbf{p})]f_1(\mathbf{p}_1) \\
& - \left[f_1(\mathbf{p}_1)\,\varDelta\mathbf{p} \cdot \frac{\partial f_2^*(\mathbf{p}_1; -\varDelta\mathbf{p})}{\partial \mathbf{p}_1} \right. \\
& + f_2^*(\mathbf{p}_1; -\varDelta\mathbf{p})\,\varDelta\mathbf{p} \cdot \frac{\partial f_1}{\partial \mathbf{p}_1} \Bigg] \\
& + \frac{1}{2!} \left[f_1(\mathbf{p}_1)\,\varDelta\mathbf{p}\,\varDelta\mathbf{p} : \frac{\partial^2 f_2^*(\mathbf{p}_1; -\varDelta\mathbf{p})}{\partial \mathbf{p}_1 \partial \mathbf{p}_1} \right. \\
& + 2\,\varDelta\mathbf{p}\,\varDelta\mathbf{p} : \frac{\partial f_1}{\partial \mathbf{p}_1}\,\frac{\partial f_2^*(\mathbf{p}_1; -\varDelta\mathbf{p})}{\partial \mathbf{p}_1} \\
& + f_2^*(\mathbf{p}_1; -\varDelta\mathbf{p})\,\varDelta\mathbf{p}\,\varDelta\mathbf{p} : \frac{\partial^2 f_1(\mathbf{p}_1)}{\partial \mathbf{p}_1 \partial \mathbf{p}_1)} \Bigg] \\
& - \frac{1}{3!}\,[\ldots] + \ldots \Bigg\} B\,d\varphi h\,dh\,d^3\varDelta p.
\end{aligned}
\tag{8.2-21}
$$

Consideration of

$$
\int_{-\infty}^{+\infty} f_2^*(\mathbf{p}_1; -\varDelta\mathbf{p})\,d^3\varDelta\mathbf{p} = \int_{+\infty}^{-\infty} -f_2^*(\mathbf{p}_1; \varDelta\mathbf{p})\,d^3\varDelta p
$$

$$
= \int_{-\infty}^{+\infty} f_2^*(\mathbf{p}_1; \varDelta\mathbf{p})\,d^3\varDelta p
$$

leads to

$$
\iiint [f_2^*(\mathbf{p}_1; -\varDelta\mathbf{p})f_1 - f_2^*(\mathbf{p}_1; \varDelta\mathbf{p})f_1]\,Bh\,dh\,d\varphi\,d^3\varDelta p = 0.
$$

By defining

$$
\left.
\begin{aligned}
\langle \varDelta\mathbf{p} \rangle_{12} &= \iiint \varDelta\mathbf{p} f_2^*(\mathbf{p}_1; -\varDelta\mathbf{p})\,Bh\,dh\,d\varphi\,d^3\varDelta p \\
\langle \varDelta\mathbf{p}\,\varDelta\mathbf{p} \rangle_{12} &= \iiint \varDelta\mathbf{p}\,\varDelta\mathbf{p} f_2^*(\mathbf{p}_1; -\varDelta\mathbf{p})\,Bh\,dh\,d\varphi\,d^3\varDelta p \ldots, \text{ etc.}
\end{aligned}
\right\}
\tag{8.2-22}
$$

and substituting these in eq. (21), we obtain

$$
\left.
\begin{aligned}
\mathcal{J}_\infty(1, 2) = \;& -\frac{\partial}{\partial \mathbf{p}_1} \cdot \langle \Delta \mathbf{p} \rangle_{12} f_1(\mathbf{p}_1) \\
& + \frac{1}{2!} \frac{\partial^2}{\partial \mathbf{p}_1 \partial \mathbf{p}_1} : \langle \Delta \mathbf{p} \, \Delta \mathbf{p} \rangle_{12} f_1(\mathbf{p}_1) \\
& - \frac{1}{3!} \frac{\partial^3}{\partial \mathbf{p}_1 \partial \mathbf{p}_1 \partial \mathbf{p}_1} : \langle \Delta \mathbf{p} \, \Delta \mathbf{p} \, \Delta \mathbf{p} \rangle_{12} f_1(\mathbf{p}_1) \\
& + \ldots .
\end{aligned}
\right\}
\tag{8.2-23}
$$

This is the typical Fokker–Planck interaction factor. We may obtain $\mathcal{J}_\infty(1, 1)$, $\mathcal{J}_\infty(2, 1)$, etc., simply by changing subscripts appropriately.

8.3. Divergence of the Boltzmann integral of collision due to the Coulomb force

When collisions occur among charged particles according to the Coulomb force law

$$
\boldsymbol{\mathcal{F}}_{ij} = \varkappa \frac{\mathbf{R}_{ij}}{R_{ij}^3},
\tag{8.3-1}
$$

it is shown that $\mathcal{J}_\infty$ given by eq. (8.2-23) diverges. Let us rewrite $\langle \Delta \mathbf{p} \rangle$ given by eq. (8.2-22) again in terms of $\mathbf{p}_2$ in accordance with eq. (8.2-15):

$$
\left.
\begin{aligned}
\langle \Delta \mathbf{p} \rangle &= \int_\varphi \int_{h'} \int_{\Delta \mathbf{p}}^\infty \Delta \mathbf{p} f_2^*(\mathbf{p}_1; -\Delta \mathbf{p}) \, Bh \, d\varphi \, dh \, d^3\Delta p \\
&= -\iiint (\mathbf{p}_2' - \mathbf{p}_2) f_2(\mathbf{p}_2) m_2^{-3} v_{12} h \, dh \, d\varphi \, d^3 p_2.
\end{aligned}
\right\}
\tag{8.3-2}
$$

Considering eq. (4.4-27), we have

$$
\mathbf{p}_2' - \mathbf{p}_2 = m_2 \mathbf{c}_2' - m_2 \mathbf{c}_2 = \frac{m_1 m_2}{m_1 + m_2} (\mathbf{v}_{12}' - \mathbf{v}_{12}),
\tag{8.3-3}
$$

in which

$$
\left.
\begin{aligned}
\mathbf{v}_{12} &= \mathbf{c}_2 - \mathbf{c}_1 \\
\mathbf{v}_{12}' &= \mathbf{c}_2' - \mathbf{c}_1'
\end{aligned}
\right\}
\tag{8.3-4}
$$

According to the illustration in Fig. 4.4-2 $\mathbf{v}'_{12}$ is divided into two components; one is parallel to $\mathbf{v}_{12}$ and is denoted with $(\mathbf{v}'_{12})_{\parallel}$ and the other is perpendicular to $\mathbf{v}_{12}$ and is denoted with $(\mathbf{v}'_{12})_{\perp}$. The latter is in the direction of φ

$$(v'_{12})_{\perp} = (v'_{12})_{\varphi}. \tag{8.3-5}$$

As is re-illustrated in Fig. 8.3-1, $(v'_{12})_{\varphi+\pi}$ is in the opposite direction to $(v'_{12})_{\varphi}$, hence the integral with respect to $d\varphi$ results in

$$\int_0^{2\pi} (v'_{12})_{\perp} \, d\varphi = 0. \tag{8.3-6}$$

Secondly we consider $(v'_{12})_{\parallel}$ in detail in the following: According to Fig. 8.3-1 we have

$$(v'_{12})_{\parallel} = v'_{12} \cos(\pi - 2\theta_{\infty}) = -v_{12} \cos(2\theta_{\infty})$$
$$= -v_{12}(2 \cos^2 \theta_{\infty} - 1),$$

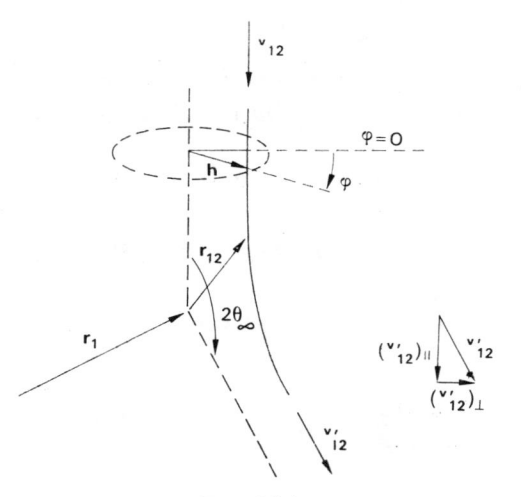

FIG. 8.3-1.

The trajectory $\mathbf{r}_{12}$ of particle 2 relative to particle 1 is illustrated. $\mathbf{v}_{12}$ is the relative velocity of particle 2 before a collision and $\mathbf{v}'_{12}$ is the relative velocity after the collision. $(v'_{12})_{\parallel}$ is the component of $\mathbf{v}'_{12}$ parallel to $\mathbf{v}_{12}$ while $(v'_{12})_{\perp}$ is the component perpendicular to $\mathbf{v}_{12}$. φ indicates the direction of the plane on which the collision takes place.

165

and hence

$$(\mathbf{p}_2' - \mathbf{p}_2)_{||} = -\frac{m_1 m_2}{m_1 + m_2} v_{12} 2 \cos^2 \theta_\infty. \tag{8.3-7}$$

From eq. (A.1-28)

$$\cos^2 \theta_\infty = \frac{K^2}{h^2 v_{12}^4 + K^2}, \quad K^2 = \frac{\varkappa^2}{M_{12}^2}$$

$$M_{12} = m_1 m_2 / (m_1 + m_2).$$

Therefore it follows that

$$\left.\begin{aligned}
\int_{h'}^\infty (\mathbf{p}_2' - \mathbf{p}_2)_{||} h\, dh &= -\int_{h'}^\infty \frac{2 M_{12} v_{12} K^2}{h^2 v_{12}^4 + K^2} h\, dh \\
&= -\frac{2 M_{12} v_{12} K^2}{2 v_{12}^4} \left| \log (h^2 v_{12}^4 + K^2) \right|_{h'}^\infty \\
&= 0 \, [\log \infty].
\end{aligned}\right\} \tag{8.3-8}$$

As regards $\langle \varDelta \mathbf{p}\, \varDelta \mathbf{p} \rangle$ (a tensor of the second rank), we simply show that $\langle (\varDelta \mathbf{p})^2 \rangle = \langle (\varDelta p_x)^2 + (\varDelta p_y)^2 + (\varDelta p_z)^2 \rangle$ diverges. Let us write

$$(\mathbf{p}_2' - \mathbf{p}_2)^2 = (\mathbf{p}_2' - \mathbf{p}_2)_{||}^2 + (\mathbf{p}_2' - \mathbf{p}_2)_\perp^2. \tag{8.3-9}$$

Since

$$(v_{12}')_\perp = v_{12} \sin (\pi - 2\theta_\infty) = 2 v_{12} \sin \theta_\infty \cos \theta_\infty$$

and

$$(v_{12})_\perp = 0,$$

we have

$$(\mathbf{p}_2' - \mathbf{p}_2)_\perp = \frac{m_1 m_2}{m_1 + m_2} [(v_{12}')_\perp - (v_{12})_\perp] = 2 M_{12} v_{12} \sin \theta_\infty \cos \theta_\infty.$$

Hence

$$(\mathbf{p}_2' - \mathbf{p}_2)_\perp^2 = 4 M_{12}^2 v_{12}^2 \left[\frac{K^2}{h^2 v_{12}^2 + K^2} - \frac{K^4}{(h^2 v_{12}^2 + K^2)^2} \right].$$

Similarly

$$(\mathbf{p}_2' - \mathbf{p}_2)^{||} = 4 M_{12}^2 v_{12}^2 \frac{K^2}{(h^2 v_{12}^2 + K^2)^2}.$$

On substitution of these in

$$(\Delta p)^2 = \int\int\int (\mathbf{p}_2' - \mathbf{p}_2)_\perp^2 f(\mathbf{p}_2) h \, dh \, d\varphi v_{12} \, d^3p_2/m_2^2$$
$$+ \int\int\int (\mathbf{p}_2' - \mathbf{p}_2)_\parallel f(\mathbf{p}_2) h \, dh \, d\varphi v_{12} \, d^3p_2/m_2^2,$$

we see that

$$\int_{h'}^{\infty} (\mathbf{p}_2' - \mathbf{p}_2)_\perp^2 h \, dh \to \infty. \tag{8.3-10}$$

8.4. The cause of the divergence of the Boltzmann collision integral

In order to avoid the divergence of the collision integral, some authors consider eq. (4.2-3) retaining the integral term involving $F^{(3)}$ in it. We note, however, that by so doing, we have to assume that the perturbation of a binary interaction by third particles occurs in time scale τ_3 which is much shorter than the time scale τ_2 of the basic binary interaction. If those particles are mutually similar, it is difficult to conceive the time scale relation. Then, for charged particles, we must abandon completely the BBGKY scheme of integration of the Liouville equation leading to eq. (3.3-8), and so forth. It should be noted that there is more than one way of treating the Liouville equation. One of them is what is given in Chapter 3 under the assumption of time scale hierarchy (3.3-13). By coarse-graining, for example, eq. (2.4-19), instead of eq. (2.4-11), we may obtain another series of which the implication is different from the implication of eq. (3.3-8), etc. In order to choose a proper method of approach, we have to understand the cause of the divergence of the binary collision integral.

Let us first suppose that the effect of multiple collisions between a test particle (particle 1) and field particles (particles 2, 3, 4, ...) is divided into three parts: (1) *the effect of the forces exerted on the test particle simultaneously by many field particles*, (2) *the effect of reactive forces exerted by the test particle on the field particles*, (3) *the effect of mutual interactions among the field particles*. Since we

167

do not know, in general, the way to synthesize the total effect from these partial effects, that is a many-body problem, the above classification seems simply fictitious, with no definite physical meaning. We note, however, that it is possible to conceive particular conditions under which effects (2) and (3) are ignored either completely or partially, and yet interactions are multiple. By studying such particular cases, we may obtain some aspects of the statistical effects of multiplicity of interactions. Then, we hope, we may find some clue for treating properly multiple interactions among charged particles. For the purpose described above, we consider the following models of collision.

Model I. We suppose that a flat and elastic plate named A is placed perpendicularly to the x-axis. We also have N similar elastic balls.

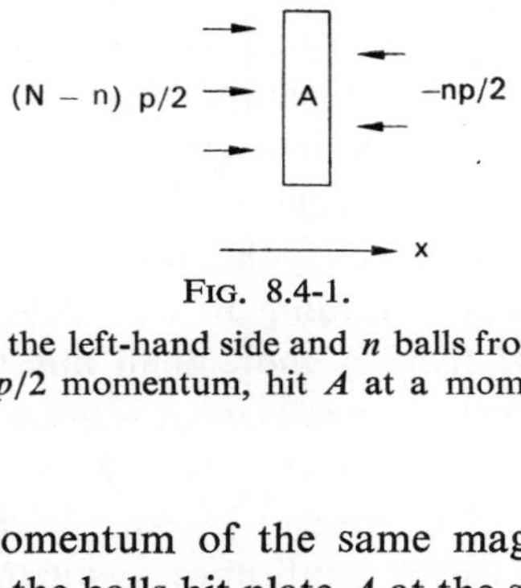

$$(N - n) \; p/2 \quad \boxed{A} \quad -np/2$$

$$\longrightarrow x$$

FIG. 8.4-1.

$N-n$ balls from the left-hand side and n balls from the right-hand side, each with $p/2$ momentum, hit A at a moment of time and are bounced.

Each ball has a momentum of the same magnitude $\mathbf{p}/2$ parallel to the x-axis and all the balls hit plate A at the same time, n of them from the right-hand side of A and $N-n$ from the opposite side as is illustrated in Fig. 8.4-1. As a result, the plate gains momentum

$$\varDelta\mathbf{p} = (N-n)\mathbf{p} - n\mathbf{p} = (N-2n)\mathbf{p}. \qquad (8.4\text{-}1)$$

If the magnitude of the gain is sufficiently small, and the mass of the plate is sufficiently large, the plate may exhibit a Brownian motion along the x-axis due to many repeated sets of multiple collisions with N balls. The statistical distribution F_A of the state

of plate A is known to be governed by the Fokker–Planck equation

$$
\left.\begin{aligned}
\left(\frac{\partial}{\partial t}+\mathbf{p}_A\cdot\frac{\partial}{\partial x}\right)F_A &= -\langle\varDelta\mathbf{p}\rangle\,\frac{\partial}{\partial\mathbf{p}_A}F_A \\
&+\frac{1}{2!}\langle\varDelta\mathbf{p}\,\varDelta\mathbf{p}\rangle\frac{\partial^2}{\partial\mathbf{p}_A\partial\mathbf{p}_A}F_A \\
&-\frac{1}{3!}\langle\varDelta\mathbf{p}\,\varDelta\mathbf{p}\,\varDelta\mathbf{p}\rangle\frac{\partial^3}{\partial\mathbf{p}_A\partial\mathbf{p}_A\partial\mathbf{p}_A}F_A \\
&+\ldots
\end{aligned}\right\} \tag{8.4-2}
$$

where $\mathbf{p}_A$ is the momentum of plate A. It is assumed that the velocity of A is sufficiently small and $\varDelta\mathbf{p}$ is independent of $\mathbf{p}_A$. We repeat for many times similar multiple bombardments with N balls. The choice of n at each time is completely random. Since these balls are indistinguishable, the probability weight of each case depends on the value of n:

If probability weight $= 1$ for $n = 0$

then probability weight $= N(N-1)\ldots(N-n+1)/n!$

for $n > 0$

$$\varDelta\mathbf{p} = (N-2n)\mathbf{p}\quad\text{(per unit time)}$$

We obtain for $\langle\varDelta\mathbf{p}\rangle$

$$
\left.\begin{aligned}
\langle\varDelta\mathbf{p}\rangle &= \frac{1}{2^N}\left[N\mathbf{p}+(N-2)N\mathbf{p}+(N-4)\frac{N(N-1)\mathbf{p}}{2!}\right. \\
&\quad+\ \ldots -N\mathbf{p}] \\
&= 0,
\end{aligned}\right\} \tag{8.4-3}
$$

where it is taken into account that

$$
1+N+\frac{N(N-1)}{2!}+\ldots+\frac{N(N-1)\ldots(N-n+1)}{n!}+\ldots+1
$$

$$
= (1+1)^N = 2^N.
$$

We also have

$$
\begin{aligned}
\langle \varDelta \mathbf{p} \, \varDelta \mathbf{p} \rangle &= \frac{1}{2^N} \left\{ (N\mathbf{p})^2 + N[(N-2)\mathbf{p}]^2 \right. \\
&\quad + \frac{N(N-1)}{2!} [(N-4)\mathbf{p}]^2 + \ldots \\
&\quad + \frac{N(N-1)\ldots(N-n+1)}{n!} [(N-2n)\mathbf{p}]^2 \\
&\quad \left. + \ldots + (N\mathbf{p})^2 \right\} \\
&= \frac{1}{2^N} [2^N N p^2] = N p^2
\end{aligned} \qquad (8.4\text{-}4)
$$

by the help of the theorem verified in Appendix D.

In view of the above results, we conclude that so far as $\langle \varDelta \mathbf{p} \rangle$ and $\langle \varDelta \mathbf{p} \varDelta \mathbf{p} \rangle$ are concerned, the present mode of multiple collisions is equivalent to binary collisions where each collision takes place separately. (At this moment, it is not known if the equivalence does exist regarding $\langle \varDelta \mathbf{p} \, \varDelta \mathbf{p} \, \varDelta \mathbf{p} \rangle$ and those of higher ranks. In view of the weakness of the effects of collisions on A, however, we may ignore those of higher ranks, in the same way as we do for collisions between charged particles at long distances.) Thus we may conclude that the divergence of Boltzmann's integral for charged particles must be due to our ignorance of effects (2) and (3), but is not due to ignorance of the simultaneity of collisions, effect (1), mentioned previously. Effect (2) is known, however, to be trivial for collisions at long distances. Then we have to consider the consequence of ignoring effect (3).

Model II. In model I, we are using an assumption similar to the Stosszahlansatz: The choice of n, from 0 to N, is completely arbitrary. Suppose, however, that there are some interactions among N balls and the choice of n cannot be so arbitrary. Suppose, by these interactions, the balls tend to spread more evenly on both

sides and $(N-n)/n$ tend to be near unity. As a result, $\langle \Delta \mathbf{p}\, \Delta \mathbf{p} \rangle$ becomes much smaller than the value given by eq. (8.4-4).

In a real gaseous system the distribution of a particle is different from the distribution which we expect according to a uniform probability distribution. According to a uniform probability distribution, for example, we may expect that all the particles come together in a small domain of the space, no matter how small the probability might be. But it is not feasible to expect so. The reason for saying so, may be summarized as follows: The speed and acceleration of a particle is always finite. Therefore, the change rate of the state of a particle is also finite. The displacement of the position and the acceleration of the velocity of any particle occurs gradually with some time scale. On the other hand, the purely probabilitistic consideration is assuming that the changes are instantaneous or, in other words, that the state of a particle may change with an indefinitely large change rate. If we consider this point, we realize that the accumulation of the particles in a system into one spot must be preceded by preliminary arrangements of particles which would result in such an accumulation. These procedures preceding the accumulation are dynamical and should be in accordance with dynamical laws. In other words, the problem is not simply a matter of probability. We realize, therefore, that Stosszahlansatz is only conditionally valid.

It should also be noted that, in a real system, the correlation between two specific particles cannot continue to exist for an indefinitely long period of time at long distances, because the interactions of each of these two specific particles with other particles can be much stronger than the interactions between these two specific particles separated at long distances. Of course, such an unrealistic situation of binary interaction does not result in any serious difficulty, if the range of interaction force is short. For charged particles, however, the situation is serious. In order to demonstrate the gist of the problem, we consider an electron at rest for the test particle; the field electrons are distributed at remote distances from the test electron. A field electron which passes by the test electron with rela-

tive position vector $\mathbf{r}$ at the nearest point and with velocity $\mathbf{c}$, gives the test electron the following momentum

$$\left.\begin{aligned}
\mathbf{p} &= \int_{-\infty}^{+\infty} \frac{e^2\mathbf{r}\,dt}{(r^2+c^2t^2)^{3/2}} \\
&= \frac{2e^2\mathbf{r}}{r^2c}
\end{aligned}\right\} \tag{8.4-5}$$

The amount of the contribution of that field electron to the diffusion factor $\langle \Delta\mathbf{p}\,\Delta\mathbf{p} \rangle$ in the Fokker–Planck equation of the test electron similar to eq. (2) is $4e^4/(r^2c^2)$. Let us sum up the contributions from all the field electrons passing by with $\mathbf{r}$ between $\mathbf{r}_1$ and $\mathbf{r}_2$ in unit time. Thus, we obtain

$$\left.\begin{aligned}
\langle \Delta\mathbf{p}\,\Delta\mathbf{p} \rangle &= \frac{8}{3}\,\pi e^4 \iiint \frac{f}{c}\,d^3c \int_{r_1}^{r_2} \frac{dr}{r}\,\mathbf{U} \\
&\quad \mathbf{U}:\text{ unit tensor,}
\end{aligned}\right\} \tag{8.4-6}$$

where f is the distribution function of electrons with respect to $\mathbf{c}$ and is assumed to be independent of $\mathbf{r}$ according to the Stosszahlansatz. Obviously the results diverge as $\mathbf{r}_2$ increases to ∞. As $\mathbf{r}_2$ increases, however, the result given by eq. (5) is not realistic, since a field particle does not move such a long distance without being disturbed by other field particles near it.[†]

To sum up consideration of the effects of interactions among field particles is essential in treating multiple (more than binary) interactions. Due to interactions among field particles, the application of the Stosszahlansatz must be restricted, as is suggested by model II. The spatial and temporal scales of the molecular-ordered motion of a field particle are also restricted by interactions among field particles, as is demonstrated in the above. These restrictions to be imposed on the Stosszahlansatz and on molecular-ordered collisions are not prescribed by Boltzmann's collision integral.

[†] Functions (8.3-10) and (8.4-6) also diverge respectively at $h = 0$ and at $r_1 = 0$. This sort of divergence is due to our ignoring precise trajectories at short distances, and is easily avoided.

8.5. The difficulty in the BBGKY hierarchy

The difficulty of the divergence of the Boltzmann collision integral shows that the assumption on which the collision integral is based is not feasible in the case of charged particles which interact with long range forces. In the last section, it was shown that the difficulty arises from ignorance of the effect of interactions among field particles. In order to take into account the effect neglected in the Boltzmann collision model, we first consider the BBGKY hierarchy as given in Section 3.3. But we find a difficulty in the hierarchy considered as the basis of treating charged particles in an ionized gas as follows:[†] Suppose that particle 1 is interacting with two particles, particle 2 and particle 3, at the same time in a system. The time scale of the interaction between particle 1 and particle 2 is denoted by $\tau(1, 2)$ and the time scale of the interaction between particle 1 and particle 3 is denoted by $\tau(1, 3)$, etc. If they are similar particles with the same mass and the same charge, it is most likely that

$$\tau(1, 2) \simeq \tau(1, 3) \simeq \tau(2, 3). \qquad (8.5\text{-}1)$$

But this is not the case for which BBGKY hierarchy is applicable; because the hierarchy is derived under the assumption that

$$\left.\begin{aligned}
\tau(1, 2) &\gg \tau(1, 3) \simeq \tau(2, 3) \\
\tau(2, 3) &\gg \tau(1, 2) \simeq \tau(1, 3) \\
\tau(1, 3) &\gg \tau(2, 3) \simeq \tau(1, 2).
\end{aligned}\right\} \qquad (8.5\text{-}2)$$

or

or

If particle 1 and particle 2 are ions and particle 3 is an electron, the situation is favorable for the BBGKY hierarchy: Ions have heavy masses, each at least about 2000 times larger than the electron mass. It is to be expected that the velocities of the ions are smaller than the velocity of the electron. Hence

$$\tau(1, 2) \gg \tau(1, 3) \simeq \tau(2, 3).$$

[†] The relation between ensemble averages and time averages is discussed in Section 3.5.

The slow interaction between ion 1 and ion 2 is disturbed by electron 3 which passes through the vicinity of the ions quickly. The feasible application of the BBGKY hierarchy is limited to such special cases. The situation will be discussed later in detail.

8.6. The Vlasov equation

In view of the complete independence of each field particle from the other field particles, the binary collision assumption accompanied with the "Stosszahlansatz" is an extreme assumption. There is another assumption which is also extreme in a different sense.

In eq. (2.4-10) we assume that

$$F_{ij}^{(2)} = F_i^{(1)} F_j^{(1)} \tag{8.6-1}$$

in the integrand. This assumption is feasible if the interaction between i and j is extremely weak. Relation (1) reduces eq. (2.4-10) to

$$\left. \begin{aligned} \left(\frac{\partial}{\partial t} + \frac{\mathbf{p}_i}{m} \cdot \frac{\partial}{\partial \mathbf{r}_i}\right) F_i^{(1)} + \sum_{j \neq i} \mathcal{F}_{ij} F_j^{(1)} \, dX_j \cdot \frac{\partial}{\partial \mathbf{p}_i} F_i^{(1)} = 0, \\ i = 1, 2, 3, \ldots, N. \end{aligned} \right\} \tag{8.6-2}$$

There are N similar equations. But they are closed by themselves. If we consider a single system and define the $F^{(1)}$'s then the $F^{(1)}$'s are given in terms of δ-functions. Let us consider coarse-graining eq. (2) with respect to time and particles in a way similar to that considered in Section 3.3.

$$\left. \begin{aligned} \left(\frac{\partial}{\partial t} + \frac{\mathbf{p}_1}{m} \cdot \frac{\partial}{\partial \mathbf{r}_1}\right) \overline{\langle F^{(1)}(X_1) \rangle_{\tau_{12}}} \\ + (N-1) \left\langle \overline{\int \mathcal{F}_{12} F^{(1)}(X_2) \, dX_2 \cdot \frac{\partial}{\partial \mathbf{p}_1} F^{(1)}(X_1)} \right\rangle_{\tau_{12}} = 0. \end{aligned} \right\} \tag{8.6-3}$$

Here we have only one equation which involves functions $\langle F^{(1)} \rangle$ and $F^{(1)}$. If we assume that individual particles are almost in free flight, then it is easily shown that the effect of interaction between 1 and 2 in eq. (3) diverges. Specifically $\langle \Delta \mathbf{p} \rangle = 0$ and $\langle \Delta \mathbf{p} \, \Delta \mathbf{p} \rangle = \infty$.

Vlasov (1950) ignored such long lasting self-correlation in $F^{(1}$ along the time axis, and rewrote eq. (3) as follows:

$$\left.\begin{array}{l} \left(\dfrac{\partial}{\partial t}+\dfrac{\mathbf{p}_1}{m}\cdot\dfrac{\partial}{\partial \mathbf{r}_1}\right)\langle\overline{F^{(1)}(X_1)}\rangle \\[3mm] \quad +(N-1)\displaystyle\int \mathscr{F}_{12}\langle\overline{F^{(1)}(X_2)}\rangle\,dX_2\cdot\dfrac{\partial}{\partial \mathbf{p}_1}\langle\overline{F^{(1)}(X_1)}\rangle = 0. \end{array}\right\} \tag{8.6-4}$$

When represented by $\langle\overline{F^{(1)}(X_2)}\rangle$, particle 2 appears as if spread over a large domain of the space, even when $D^{(N)}$, from which $F^{(1)}$ is derived, is defined with respect to a single system. Hence there is no more microscopic interaction taken into account in eq. (4), and the result converges. Such behavior of particle 2 is not due to mutual reactions of the field particles. It is caused simply by our particular way of coarse-graining. But eventually the coarse-graining has resulted in the same desirable effect as that caused by the interactions among field particles which tend to make the time period of self-correlation in $F^{(1)}$ extremely short.

Vlasov's theory concurs neither with Boltzmann's collision nor with Gibbs's ensembles.[†] In order to justify his theory, he considered the following postulates in his book referred to above:

1. Abandoning a strictly localized description of microparticles. The concept of a particle being a point, conserving this property independently of any connection with the medium and other particles is only an approximate approach to reality. At the present time, both the experimental facts and the internal difficulties of existing

[†] In Vlasov's theory, the distribution of particles (not of the probability of a particle) is continuous and may be non-uniform only in the macroscopic sense. This condition may be realized by increasing the number density of particles infinitely or by abandoning the localized description of particles, as Vlasov did. There is no interaction between a pair of such particles with a finite correlation period; the period of a discrete correlation is infinitely short. In this sense, Vlasov's interaction is different from Boltzmann's collision. There is no thermal fluctuation in Vlasov's distribution. Hence Vlasov's theory is different from Gibbs's theory. (Vlasov introduced eq. (4) as a postulate.)

By abandoning discrete description of particles, Vlasov achieved an effect which may be obtained by a coarse-graining operation under certain conditions. See eq. (9.4-47). In his theory we see some influence of quantum mechanics.

theories make it essential to create a theory based on a new treatment of the concept of a particle. In particular, the theory should express the independence of the extension of the particle from the physical conditions it encounters.

2. A new approach to the concept of the closure of a physical system. It seems to us that in essence there is a departure from the concept of closure in the sense of classical mechanics (the apparatus of statistical and quantum mechanics) even in existing theories. The particle dynamics developed in this book is characterized by a special method of calculating the connection of the particle with the surrounding medium. Thanks to this, the concept of closure acquires a new sense. The transition to classical theories here is linked with the introduction of certain limitations to this connection.

3. The attempt to construct a theory in which motion is an inseparable property of the object, and is not the result of the action of any "sources" (forces in classical mechanics, the heat reservoir in statistics, charges and currents in electrodynamics). The effect of sources of this nature is essentially that motion is introduced into the physical system from outside. The idea in question is realized in the present theory by having each particle described by an extended function of the space distribution of coordinates and velocities.

The above reasoning by Vlasov is excessively intuitive, tending to assimilate phenomena of different origins by analogy. As will be discussed later (pp. 181, 200), Vlasov's equation is to be explained in terms of time scales of correlation. It is noted, however, that Vlasov was obviously aware of the difficulty of accepting Gibbs' ensembles for representing those systems under consideration.

8.6-1. SUPPLEMENTARY NOTE ON MICROSCOPIC SYMMETRY AND MOLAR DISORDER

If we assume that $D^{(N)}$, as defined in Chapter 3, is microscopically symmetric, it follows that

$$F_{12}^{(2)}(X_1, X_2; t) = F_{13}^{(2)}(X_1, X_3; t)$$

provided that

$$X_2 = X_3 = X.$$

It is noted that if X_2 can be X at t, then X_3 can be X at the same time, according to the microscopic symmetry. This situation is apparently contradictory to our physical thought unless we assume that the interactions among the particles are extremely weak. Under the present condition, eq. (4) is obtained immediately from eq. (2.4-10). There, one may eliminate symbols $\langle \quad \rangle$ from eq. (4). In effect, no collision in the Maxwell–Boltzmann sense exists. The result is exactly the same as that obtained by Vlasov by abandoning the concept of discrete particles.

In the last century, the concept of molar disorder was introduced by Maxwell, Boltzmann and others. The concept implies the symmetry of $D^{(N)}$, due to coarse-graining, in the sense of probability. Obviously Boltzmann's Stosszahlansatz is a tool by which the molecular order of particles colliding in a microscopic time scale is connected asymptotically to the molar disorder on a larger time scale. At that time, S. H. Burbury[†] was of the opinion that the distribution of particles of a gas is always molecular-ordered. He seems to be right, if we consider matter in the microscopic sense. (Obviously, he is against the microscopic-symmetry assumption of $D^{(N)}$.) By considering various time scales of phenomena, the question raised by Burbury is answered as discussed in detail in Chapter 3.

It is noted that there is a great difference between a microscopically uniform distribution[‡] and a uniform probability distribution. By a microscopically uniform distribution it is implied that the particles are distributed in space uniformly as if they constituted a continuum in the microscopic sense. There is no fluctuation in the distribution. Vlasov's distribution belongs to this category. On the other hand, by a uniform probability distribution, it is implied that each particle is distributed with a uniform probability. As a result, the real distri-

---

[†] See Boltzmann's quotation (1896).

[‡] The distribution may not be uniform in the macroscopic sense.

bution at a microscopic moment of time is not uniform. A molar-disordered distribution belongs to this category.

A feasible assumption on which the theory of charged particles is based must be found between the two extreme assumptions, the molar-disorder assumption and the microscopically uniform distribution (Vlasov's) assumption.

Exercises

1. In the experiment illustrated in Fig. 8.4-1, it holds that

$$\langle \Delta \mathbf{p} \rangle = 0$$
$$\langle \Delta \mathbf{p} \, \Delta \mathbf{p} \rangle = Np^2.$$

Show that

$$\langle \Delta \mathbf{p} \, \Delta \mathbf{p} \, \Delta \mathbf{p} \rangle = 0$$
$$\langle \Delta \mathbf{p} \, \Delta \mathbf{p} \, \Delta \mathbf{p} \, \Delta \mathbf{p} \rangle \neq Np^4.$$

2. In problem 1, we assume a restrictive condition

$$N - 2n \geq 1.$$

Calculate $\langle \Delta \mathbf{p} \rangle$ and $\langle \Delta \mathbf{p} \, \Delta \mathbf{p} \rangle$. If you have a difficulty in solving the problem in general, assume $N = 3, 4, 5$, etc.

3. Nowadays, one can visit anywhere in the world. Suppose you met a noticeable stranger at 9:00 a.m., 17 March 1967 on a street in New York. Later, one of your friends reported that he met the same stranger at 11:00 a.m. of the same day on a street in Washington D.C. You may trust the report. Another friend reported that he met the same stranger at 12:00 a.m. of the same day (New York local time) on a street in London. Do you believe it? If not, give the reason.

CHAPTER 9

Kinetic Equations for Ionized Gases

9.1. General scheme

As discussed in Sections 8.3 and 8.4 the divergence of the Boltzmann collision integral due to the Coulomb force implies that the assumptions of binary collision and molar disorder are unfeasible. The divergence will be avoided by taking into account the effect of mutual interactions among field particles. The application of the BBGKY hierarchy is one way of considering the effect. But the time scale assumption necessary for the derivation of the hierarchy imposes a particular condition on the mode of interaction and is not plausible except for the special case given in Section 3.9.[†] Therefore we have to find another way of taking into account the effect; the way must be feasible considered in view of the general characteristics of those interactions. Before doing so, we should realize that our ability to treat precise dynamics of interaction is limited to the two-body problem. We cannot treat more than two-body problems precisely. Our effort must be directed toward converting many-body problems to superimposed two-body problems.

[†] There are several theories, which do not directly utilize the BBGKY hierarchy, proposed by Thompson and Hubbard (1960), Hubbard (1961), Kihara *et al.* (1963), and others. They begin with master equations in which close interactions and remote interactions are treated separately. In view of the separation of the two sorts of interaction, they appear somewhat similar to the theory developed in the following. A significant difference is that the shielding effect which is justified by the original BBGKY theory is one of the underlying concepts in those theories.

Suppose that particle 1 is the test particle whose time evolution is our main concern.

One of the field particles is named 2. What is the effect of particle 2 on the test particle? If particle 2 happens to come close to the test particle within a certain distance, they will interact with each other, as if the pair were isolated from the other field particles; their mutual interaction is much stronger than their interactions with the other field particles. But such a strong and distinctive interaction continues to exist only for a short period of time. Particle 2 will soon be remote from the test particle, and particle 2 will be in a

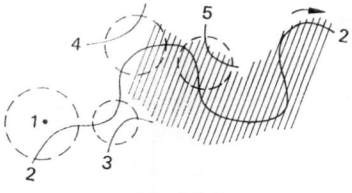

FIG. 9.1-1.

A field particle 2 interacts with the test particle 1 at close distances with time scale τ; after the interaction, particle 2 interacts with particle 3, particle 4, and so forth. The time scale of those close interactions is the same as τ. The space domain in which particle 2 is localized over a longer period of time is indicated with shadow. The force exerted on particle 1 by particle 2 is classified as follows: (1) The force during the close interaction of particle 2 with particle 1; (2) the force during the close interactions of particle 2 with particle 3, 4, etc.; (3) the averaged force during the existence of particle 2 in the shadowed domain.

strong interaction with its new nearest neighbor, particle 3. Of course, particle 2 does still continue to exert a force on the test particle. But the behavior of particle 2 is almost independent of the behavior of particle 1 and hence the force exerted by particle 2 on particle 1, as a function of time, changes due to the mode of interaction between particle 2 and particle 3; the behavior of particle 2 appears as if at random from the view point of particle 1. In spite of such fluctuations appearing in the behavior of particle 2, the state of particle 2 is steadily localized on a larger scale, because

it has finite velocity. Therefore, the average of the fluctuating force caused by particle 2 over a proper time period does not vanish; particle 2 exerts a weak but almost stationary force on particle 1. Such weak forces due to many field particles of similarly localized states result in the Vlasov-type force exerted on particle 1. (Fig. 9.1-1).

According to the above investigation, there are at least three different time scales of the force exerted on particle 1 by particle 2: (1) the time scale of the close interaction between the test particle and particle 2; (2) the time scale of the close interaction between a field particle and particle 2; (3) the time scale of the average flight of particle 2. If all the particles are of the same single species, time scale 1 and time scale 2 are of the same order. On the other hand, if the system under consideration is composed of particles of more than two species, the time scale of the interaction between the test particle and particle 2 may be different from the time scale of the interaction between particle 2 and a third particle; the latter may also vary depending on the species of the third particle. Finally the time scale of the third category is almost macroscopic.

A conclusion derived from the above consideration is that, in the simplest case where the system consists of particles of a single species, it is necessary to take for ν in eq. (2.4-21) at least 2, so that the close interaction between two neighboring field particles is taken into consideration with the same time scale as that of the close interaction between the test particle and a field particle. This precaution is essential for coarse-graining eq. (2.4-8) with respect to time.

Since it has been realized that consideration of the time scales of close interactions between two nearest neighboring particles is essential, we investigate the orders of magnitude of such time scales with respect to typical particles in the following:

By assuming that the gas under consideration is fully ionized, the constituent particles are ions and electrons. It is also assumed that those ions are of a single species. The charge of an electron is denoted by $-e$, the mass by m_e, and the total number of the electrons in the system by N_e. The charge of an ion is denoted by ε, the mass

181

by m_I and the total number of ions by N_I. In general we may assume that

$$-N_e e + N_I \varepsilon = 0 \qquad (9.1\text{-}1)$$

$$m_I/m_e \geqslant 2000. \qquad (9.1\text{-}2)$$

We also assume that

$$\frac{\varepsilon}{e} \ll \frac{m_I}{m_e}. \qquad (9.1\text{-}3)$$

From relation (2), the velocity of an electron is usually much larger than the velocity of an ion, not only when the gas is in thermal equilibrium, but also when the state is non-uniform: In thermal equilibrium, it may easily be shown that

$$\frac{\text{(the average magnitude of the velocity of electron)}}{\text{(the average magnitude of the velocity of an ion)}} \geqslant 50. \qquad (9.1\text{-}4)$$

If the gas is not in thermal equilibrium, the situation is not so simple. However, if the acceleration of an electron and the acceleration of an ion are caused by the same external electromagnetic field, relation (4) may be a reasonable expectation, because the acceleration of an ion is $(\varepsilon/e)(m_e/m_I)$ times larger than the acceleration of an electron.

The time scale of the interaction between two nearest neighboring electrons is of the order of

$$\tau_{ee} = n_e^{-1/3}/\langle c_e \rangle, \qquad (9.1\text{-}5)$$

where n_e is the number density of electrons and $\langle c_e \rangle$ is the average speed of an electron. Compared with the average speed of an electron, the average speed of an ion is much smaller; an ion appears as if it were at rest, while an electron appears to move swiftly. The time scale of the interaction between an electron and its nearest neighbor ion is of the order of

$$\tau_{eI} = n_I^{-1/3}/\langle c_e \rangle, \qquad (9.1\text{-}6)$$

where $\langle c_e \rangle$ is the average speed of an electron and n_I is the number density of ions. Since n_I and n_e are assumed to be of the same order,

we have

$$\tau_{el} \simeq \tau_{ee}.$$

On the other hand, the time scale of the interaction between two nearest neighbor ions is of the order of

$$\tau_{II} = n_I^{-1/3}/\langle c_I \rangle \qquad (9.1\text{-}7)$$

and is much longer than τ_{el} and/or τ_{ee} due to $\langle c_I \rangle \ll \langle c_e \rangle$. To sum up, we have

$$\tau_{II} \gg \tau_{el} \simeq \tau_{ee}. \qquad (9.1\text{-}8)$$

9.2. The probability of two
particles being their mutual nearest neighbors

As considered in Section 9.1, we assume that two particles which are their mutual nearest neighbors interact according to the scheme of the Boltzmann binary collision. Therefore, it is necessary to introduce the probability that two specified particles i and j are their mutual nearest neighbors (Fig. 9.2-1).

If the N particles constituting a system are distributed in a container of volume V with uniform probability, the probability of no particle appearing in a domain of volume v is given by

$$w(v) = \exp(-nv)$$
$$n = N/V. \qquad (9.2\text{-}1)$$

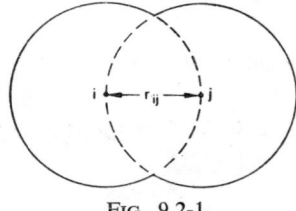

FIG. 9.2-1.

If two particles i and j are the mutual nearest neighbors, there is no other particle in the space enclosed with two spheres of radius r_{ij}, one with its center at i and the other at j. The volume of the enclosed space is $9\pi r_{ij}^3/4$.

This will be proved as follows. The probability of a particle appearing in an elementary volume δv is $\delta v/V$. Hence the probable number of particles appearing in δv is given by

$$\sum \frac{\delta v}{V} = \frac{N\,\delta v}{V} = n\,\delta v,$$

$$(\textstyle\sum: \text{with respect to all the particles}).$$

The probability of any v particles appearing at the same time in δv is denoted by $w_v(\delta v)$. Then, we have

$$\sum_{v=1}^{N} v w_v\,(\delta v) = n\,\delta v. \tag{9.2-2}$$

The probability of any number (not zero) of particles appearing in δv is given by

$$\sum_{v=1}^{N} w_v\,(\delta v),$$

while the probability of no particle appearing in δv is denoted by $w_0\,(\delta v)$

$$w_0(\delta v) + \sum_{v=1}^{N} w_v\,(\delta v) = 1. \tag{9.2-3}$$

Since $w_v(\delta v)$ is proportional to $(\delta v)^v$ when δv approaches zero,[†] relation (2) results in

$$\lim_{\delta v \to 0} w_1 = n\,\delta v$$

$$\lim_{\delta v \to 0} w_v \propto (\delta v)^v$$

† Let the probability of particle i being in δv be denoted by P_i. Then for example, w_3 is given by

$$w_3 = \sum_{i}^{N} \sum_{<j<} \sum_{k} P_i P_j P_k \prod_l (l - P_l)$$

$$l \neq i, j, k$$

$$P_i = P_j = P_k = \ldots = \delta v/V,$$

Hence

$$w_3 \propto (\delta v/V)^3$$

if $\delta v/V \to 0$. In general $w_v \propto (\delta v/V)^v$.

184

Hence, according to eq. (3) we have

$$w_0(\delta v) + n \, \delta v = 1 \qquad (9.2\text{-}3)'$$

$$(\delta v \to 0).$$

The probability $w_0(v + \delta v)$ of no particle appearing in $v + \delta v$ is obviously equal to the product of $w_0(v)$ and $w_0(\delta v)$:

$$w_0(v + \delta v) = w_0(v)w_0(\delta v). \qquad (9.2\text{-}4)$$

By expanding $w_0(v + \delta v)$ in a Taylor series and taking into account eq. (3), eq. (4) yields

$$w_0(v) + \frac{dw_0(v)}{dv} \, \delta v = w_0(v)(1 - n \, \delta v)$$

or

$$\frac{dw_0(v)}{dv} = -n \, w_0(v).$$

On integration of the above and consideration of $w_0(0) = 1$, one obtains

$$w_0(v) = \exp(-nv). \qquad (9.2\text{-}5)$$

The probability w_{ij} of a particular particle j being the nearest neighbor of particle i is equal to the probability that no other particle is inside the sphere with its center at i and with radius $R_{ij} = |\mathbf{r}_i - \mathbf{r}_j|$. The volume of the sphere is $(4/3)\pi R_{ij}^3$. Hence

$$w_{ij} = \exp(-4\pi R_{ij}^3 n/3).$$

The probability W_{ij} of two particles i and j being their mutual nearest neighbors is the probability of no other particle appearing in the part of the space which, as illustrated in Fig. 9.2-1, is cut out by two spheres of radius R_{ij}, one with its center at i and the other with the center at j. The volume of the domain is $(9/4)\pi R_{ij}^3$. Hence

$$W_{ij} = \exp\left(-\frac{9}{4} \pi R_{ij}^3 n\right). \qquad (9.2\text{-}6)$$

In the above investigation, the interactions among particles and the finiteness of the velocity of a particle are completely ignored.

185

The event that particle j comes close to particle i is assumed to be a matter of probability, instead of dynamics. Therefore, the result is physically valid only in the approximation that particles are in complete disorder as if observed over an indefinitely long time scale. (The hypothesis of equal *a priori* probabilities is applied as if valid unconditionally.) As will become clear in due course, however, the present result is utilized only as a means of qualitative classification of interparticle interactions; the classification is useful for classifying approximate methods necessary for dealing with many-body problems. W_{ij} introduced in the above enables us to convert a more-than-two-body problem to a superposition of two-body problems, and furthermore W_{ij} specifies a feasible approximate method for each of the two-body problems.

9.3. Separation of particles
in pairs of mutual nearest neighbors

First we consider three particles i, j, and k. The distribution function $F_{ijk}^{(3)}(X_i, X_j, X_k; t)$ as defined by eq. (2.4-4) is divided into parts in the following manner:

$$F^{(3)}(ijk) \equiv F_{ijk}^{(3)}(X_i, X_j, X_k; t), \qquad (9.3\text{-}1)$$

$$\left.\begin{aligned}
F(i/j/k) &= (1 - W_{ij})(1 - W_{ik})(1 - W_{jk})F^{(3)}(ijk), \\
F(ij/k) &= W_{ij}(1 - W_{ik})(1 - W_{jk})F^{(3)}(ijk), \\
F(ik/j) &= (1 - W_{ij})W_{ik}(1 - W_{jk})F^{(3)}(ijk), \\
F(i/jk) &= (1 - W_{ij})(1 - W_{ik})W_{jk}F^{(3)}(ijk), \\
F(ij/ik) &= W_{ij}W_{ik}(1 - W_{jk})F^{(3)}(ijk), \\
F(ik/jk) &= (1 - W_{ij})W_{ik}W_{jk}F^{(3)}(ijk), \\
F(ij/jk) &= W_{ij}(1 - W_{ik})W_{jk}F^{(3)}(ijk), \\
F(ij/ik/jk) &= W_{ij}W_{ik}W_{jk}\,F^{(3)}(ijk).
\end{aligned}\right\} \qquad (9.3\text{-}2)$$

The sum of the members on the right-hand side is shown to be $F^{(3)}(ijk)$ itself. We notice the following: If $W_{ij} = 1$, then the other W_i's and/or W_j's vanish. If any of the other W_i's and W_j's is unity,

then W_{ij} vanishes. Hence it is assumed that

$$\left.\begin{aligned} W_{ij}W_{ik} &\ll 1 \quad \text{if } k \neq j, \\ W_{ij}W_{jk} &\ll 1 \quad \text{if } k \neq i. \end{aligned}\right\} \qquad (9.3\text{-}3)$$

It is possible that $W_{ij}W_{kl}$ is of the order of unity. Consideration[†] of eq. (3) reduces eq. (2) to

$$\left.\begin{aligned} F(i/j/k) &= (1 - W_{ij} - W_{ik} - W_{jk})F^{(3)}(ijk), \\ F(ij/k) &= W_{ij}F^{(3)}(ijk), \\ F(ik/j) &= W_{ik}F^{(3)}(ijk), \\ F(i/jk) &= W_{jk}F^{(3)}(ijk). \end{aligned}\right\} \qquad (9.3\text{-}4)$$

Obviously it follows that

$$F(i/j/k) + F(ij/k) + F(ik/j) + F(i/jk) = F^{(3)}(ijk). \qquad (9.3\text{-}5)$$

The relations between i, j, k, which are represented by those F's are illustrated in Fig. 9.3-1 schematically. If we consider five particles

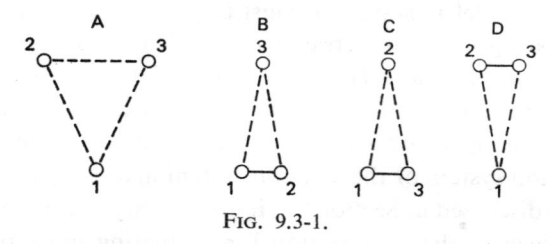

Fig. 9.3-1.

Particle 1 is the test particle; particle 2 and particle 3 represent the field particles. There are four typical relations among them: (a) the three particles are mutually remote; (b) particle 1 and particle 2 are their mutual nearest neighbors; (c) particle 1 and particle 3 are their mutual nearest neighbors; (d) particle 2 and particle 3 are their mutual nearest neighbors.

† Eventually we are thinking of a set.

i, j, k, l, m, then we obtain:

$$
\begin{aligned}
F(i/j/k/l/m) &= (1 - W_{ij} - W_{ik} - W_{il} - W_{im} - W_{jk} - W_{jl} \\
&\quad - W_{jm} - W_{kl} - W_{km} - W_{lm} + W_{ij}W_{kl} + W_{ij}W_{km} + \dots \\
&\quad + W_{jk}W_{lm})F^{(5)}(ijklm), \\
F(ij/k/l/m) &= W_{ij}(1 - W_{kl} - W_{km} - W_{lm})F^{(5)}(ijklm) \\
&\quad \text{(ten similar functions in total)}, \\
F(ij/kl/m) &= W_{ij}W_{kl}F^{(5)}(ijklm) \\
&\quad \text{(fifteen similar functions in total)},
\end{aligned}
\right\} \quad (9.3\text{-}6)
$$

and it holds that

$$
F(i/j/k/l/m) + F(ij/k/l/m) + \dots = F^{(5)}(ijklm). \quad (9.3\text{-}7)
$$

Relations among those particles represented by the F's are illustrated in Fig. 9.3-2.

9.4. Model (scheme of approximation) I

9.4-1. GENERAL SCHEME

The first model is a system consisting of similar particles and a uniform background of eletric charge which compensates the total charge of the particles. The present model is simply a model by which the procedure of manipulations typical in our schemes is demonstrated. It is too hasty to assume that the model simulates either the ion system or the electron system in a real plasma (ionized gas). As is discussed in Section 9.1, it is necessary to investigate model II as is given in the next section for evaluating more precisely all the effects of possible interactions on the evolution of the ion distribution as well as of the electron distribution. A test particle (a particular particle to be observed continuously) may experience three main sorts of interaction with field particles (particles other than the test particle). (1) Strong interaction with its nearest neighbor. (2) Interaction with particles which are not its nearest neighbors but are

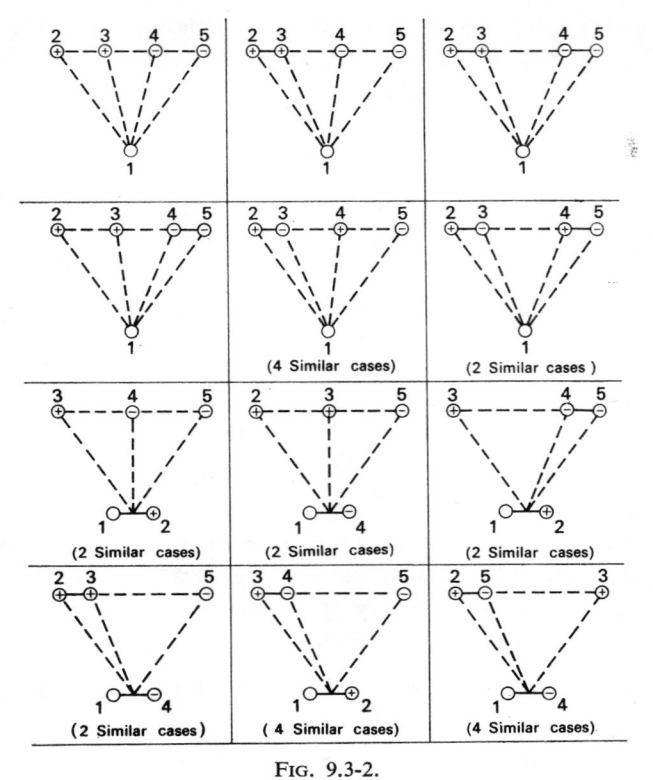

FIG. 9.3-2.

Particle 1 is the test particle; particles 2, 3, 4, 5 represent the field particles. Among them particles 2 and 3 are ions, and particles 4 and 5 are electrons. There are 26 relations among them. Solid and short lines indicate nearest neighborhood and long and dotted lines indicate remote relation.

fairly close to it; each of these field particles has its own nearest neighbor and exerts a fluctuating force on the test particle. (3) The force exerted by remote field particles; the force due to each field particle is trivial, but forces by many field particles result in a Vlasov-type force in the macroscopic sense. In order to present these effects in a kinetic equation, it is necessary to consider at least

189

three-particle subsystems in which three particles evolve in the same time scale. Instead of eq. (2.4-10), we begin with eq. (2.4-19) and the equation of evolution of $F_{ijk}^{(3)}(X_i, X_j, X_k; t)$.

$$\left.\begin{array}{l} \left(\dfrac{\partial}{\partial t} + \dfrac{\mathbf{p}_i}{m} \cdot \dfrac{\partial}{\partial \mathbf{r}_i}\right) F_i^{(1)}(X_i; t) \\[3mm] + \displaystyle\sum_{j \neq k} \int \left((\mathcal{F}_{ij} + \mathcal{F}_{ik}) \cdot \dfrac{\partial}{\partial \mathbf{p}_i} F_{ijk}^{(3)}(X_i, X_j, X_k; t)\right) dX_j \, dX_k = 0. \end{array}\right\} \quad (9.4\text{-}1)$$

$$\left.\begin{array}{l} \left[\dfrac{\partial}{\partial t} + \dfrac{\mathbf{p}_i}{m} \cdot \dfrac{\partial}{\partial \mathbf{r}_i} + \dfrac{\mathbf{p}_j}{m} \cdot \dfrac{\partial}{\partial \mathbf{r}_j} + \dfrac{\mathbf{p}_k}{m} \cdot \dfrac{\partial}{\partial \mathbf{r}_k} + (\mathcal{F}_{ij} + \mathcal{F}_{ik}) \cdot \dfrac{\partial}{\partial \mathbf{p}_i}\right. \\[3mm] + (\mathcal{F}_{ji} + \mathcal{F}_{jk}) \cdot \dfrac{\partial}{\partial \mathbf{p}_j} \\[3mm] \left. + (\mathcal{F}_{ki} + \mathcal{F}_{kj}) \cdot \dfrac{\partial}{\partial \mathbf{p}_k}\right] F_{ijk}^{(3)}(X_i, X_j, X_k; t) = 0. \end{array}\right\} \quad (9.4\text{-}2)$$

Equation (1) is a partial differential equation with X_i and t for the independent variables. It is possible, in general, to determine $F_i^{(1)}$ (X_i, t) along a certain trajectory of X_i during the time period from t to $t+s$. If the trajectory is given by

$$\left.\begin{array}{l} X_i' = X_i(s) = X_i + \Delta X_i(s) \\[2mm] \Delta X_i(0) = 0, \end{array}\right\} \quad (9.4\text{-}3)$$

$F_i^{(1)}$ along the trajectory is

$$F_i^{(1)}(X_i'; t+s). \quad (9.4\text{-}4)$$

It is noted that the trajectory in the above does not necessarily mean the real trajectory of particle i. We may take for X_i' an arbitrary function of s as long as $\Delta X_i(0) = 0$ is satisfied. Considering the above, we coarse-grain eq. (1) with respect to s from 0 to τ along trajectories determined by

$$\left.\begin{array}{l} X_i' = \mathbf{p}_i', \mathbf{r}_i' \\[2mm] \mathbf{p}_i' = \mathbf{p}_i \quad \text{(independent of s)} \\[2mm] \dfrac{d\mathbf{r}_i'}{ds} = \dfrac{\mathbf{p}_i}{m}, \end{array}\right\} \quad (9.4\text{-}5)$$

$$\text{(trajectory 0).}$$

From now on, trajectories determined by eq. (5) will be referred to as class 0, and we assume that τ is much shorter than the macroscopic time scale and much longer than the time scale of interaction between two neighboring particles. The coarse-graining of the first two terms of eq. (1) leads to

$$
\left.\begin{aligned}
\frac{1}{\tau} \int_0^\tau & \left[\left(\frac{\partial}{\partial s} + \frac{\mathbf{p}_i'}{m} \cdot \frac{\partial}{\partial \mathbf{r}_i'} \right) F_i^{(1)}(X_i'; t+s) \right] ds \quad \text{(along 0)} \\
&= \frac{1}{\tau} \int_0^\tau \frac{d}{ds} F_i^{(1)}(X_i'; t+s) \, ds \\
&= \left(\frac{\partial}{\partial t} + \frac{\mathbf{p}_i}{m} \cdot \frac{\partial}{\partial \mathbf{r}_i} \right) \langle F_i^{(0)} \rangle_0,
\end{aligned} \right\} \quad (9.4\text{-}6)
$$

where

$$
\langle F_i^{(1)} \rangle_0 = \frac{1}{\tau} \int_0^\tau F_i^{(1)}(X_i'; t+s) \, ds \qquad \text{(along 0)}. \quad (9.4\text{-}7)
$$

The integral term in eq. (1), by the same coarse-graining, yields

$$
\langle J_i \rangle_0 = \frac{1}{\tau} \int_0^\tau \sum_{jk} \left[\int (\mathcal{F}_{ij}' + \mathcal{F}_{ik}') \cdot \frac{\partial}{\partial \mathbf{p}_i} F_{ijk}^{(3)}(X_i', X_j', X_k'; t+s) \, dX_j \, dX_k \right] ds.
$$
$$
(9.4\text{-}8)
$$

Through the same reasoning for applying the hypothesis of equal *a priori* probabilities, as given in Section 4.3, to derive the Boltzmann equation, $\sum_{jk}$ means that similar factors are to be summed up with respect to $(N-1)/2$ pairs of particles as considered in Section 2.4. It is noted that the factor of a pair cannot be decomposed into two factors, each made with respect to one single-field particle, when the factor is coarse-grained with respect to time. The reason for this is that the interaction among three particles, i, j, and k, is a non-linear phenomenon in a single time scale. The equation of evolution of $\langle F_i^{(1)} \rangle_0$ is given by

$$
\left(\frac{\partial}{\partial t} + \frac{\mathbf{p}_i}{m} \cdot \frac{\partial}{\partial \mathbf{r}_i} \right) \langle F^{(1)} \rangle_0 + \langle J_i \rangle_0 = 0. \quad (9.4\text{-}9)
$$

191

To obtain $F_{ijk}^{(3)}$ to be inserted in $\langle J_i \rangle_0$, it is necessary to consider eq. (2), a three-body problem. The solution must be given along trajectories 0 determined by eq. (5). In the following, however, we obtain particular solutions of eq. (2) integrated along several different classes of trajectories of particles i, j, and k by means of successive approximation methods. Later, the differences between the results, caused by differences among the classes of trajectories, are eliminated by considering the proper presentations of distribution functions in generic space. For the purpose of providing $F_{ijk}^{(3)}$ during the time between t and $t+s$, we rewrite eq. (2) as follows:

$$
\left.
\begin{aligned}
&\left[\frac{\partial}{\partial s} + \frac{\mathbf{p}_i'}{m} \cdot \frac{\partial}{\partial \mathbf{r}_i'} + \frac{\mathbf{p}_j'}{m} \cdot \frac{\partial}{\partial \mathbf{r}_j'} + \frac{\mathbf{p}_k'}{m} \cdot \frac{\partial}{\partial \mathbf{r}_k'} + (\mathcal{F}_{ij}' + \mathcal{F}_{ik}') \cdot \frac{\partial}{\partial \mathbf{p}_i} \right. \\[2ex]
&\qquad + (\mathcal{F}_{ji}' + \mathcal{F}_{jk}') \cdot \frac{\partial}{\partial \mathbf{p}_j'} \\[2ex]
&\qquad \left. + (\mathcal{F}_{ki}' + \mathcal{F}_{kj}') \cdot \frac{\partial}{\partial \mathbf{p}_k'} \right] F_{ijk}^{(3)}(X_i', X_j', X_k'; t+s) = 0.
\end{aligned}
\right\} \quad \text{(9.4-10)}
$$

As is obvious, $F_{ijk}^{(3)}$ is invariant, if eq. (10) is integrated along a trajectory determined by the characteristic equations of eq. (10):

$$
\left.
\begin{aligned}
\frac{d\mathbf{p}_i'}{ds} &= \mathcal{F}_{ij}' + \mathcal{F}_{ik}', & \frac{d\mathbf{r}_i'}{ds} &= \frac{\mathbf{p}_i'}{m} \\[2ex]
\frac{d\mathbf{p}_j'}{ds} &= \mathcal{F}_{ji}' + \mathcal{F}_{jk}', & \frac{d\mathbf{r}_j'}{ds} &= \frac{\mathbf{p}_j'}{m} \\[2ex]
\frac{d\mathbf{p}_k'}{ds} &= \mathcal{F}_{ki}' + \mathcal{F}_{kj}', & \frac{d\mathbf{r}_k'}{ds} &= \frac{\mathbf{p}_k'}{m}.
\end{aligned}
\right\} \quad \text{(9.4-11)}
$$

Since solution of eqs. (11) is a three-body problem, we decompose it to two-body problems which approximate to the three-body problem under various circumstances. For each case of approximation, we take a different set of differential equations in place of eqs. (11). For each case, the initial conditions are

$$
\left.
\begin{aligned}
X_i' = X_i, \quad X_j' = X_j, \quad X_k' = X_k, \\[2ex]
s = 0.
\end{aligned}
\right\} \quad \text{(9.4-12)}
$$

when

Each different set of differential equations to replace eqs. (11) determines a different set of trajectories. Along those trajectories, $F_{ijk}^{(3)}$ is no longer invariant; it is a function of s. In each case, $F_{ijk}^{(3)}$ is obtained by solving eq. (10) by a different successive approximation method. To introduce proper sets of differential equations in place of eqs. (11), we consider the expression of $F_{ijk}^{(3)}$ given by eq. (9.3-5) where W_{ij} is the probability that particle i and particle j are their mutual nearest neighbors. For example, $F(i/j/k)$ is the joint distribution function of particles i, j and k among which none is probably the nearest neighbor of the others. In solving eq. (10) for obtaining $F^{(3)}(ijk)$, that is $F_{ijk}^{(3)}(X_i, X_j, X_k; t)$, appearing in eqs. (9.3-4) and (9.3-5), we have four different methods of approximation. For example, for calculating $F^{(3)}(ijk)$ involved in $F(i/j/k)$, we may assume that the interactions among the three particles are always weak, and hence, in the zeroth approximation, these three particles are regarded as being in free flight. On the other hand, for $F^{(3)}(ijk)$ in $F(ij/k)$, it is essential to assume that the interaction between particle i and particle j is strong, although these two particles interact with particle k only weakly. On obtaining $F^{(3)}(ijk)$ in four different cases respectively by four different methods, the results are presented as follows:

$$
\left.
\begin{array}{ll}
\text{I.} & F^{(3)}(ijk) = F(i/j/k)^{(0)} + F(i/j/k)^{(1)} + \ldots \\
\text{II.} & F^{(3)}(ijk) = F(ij/k)^{(0)} + F(ij/k)^{(1)} + \ldots \\
\text{II}'. & F^{(3)}(ijk) = F(ik/j)^{(0)} + F(ik/j)^{(1)} + \ldots \\
\text{III.} & F^{(3)}(ijk) = F(i/jk)^{(0)} + F(i/jk)^{(1)} + \ldots
\end{array}
\right\}
\quad (9.4\text{-}13)
$$

After obtaining $F^{(3)}(ijk)$ in four different cases, we substitute each of the solutions in its proper place in eq. (9.3-4). Thus for $F^{(3)}(ijk)$ as represented by eq. (9.3-5), we obtain

$$
F^{(3)}(ijk) = F^{(3)}(ijk)^{(0)} + F^{(3)}(ijk)^{(1)} + \ldots, \quad (9.4\text{-}14)
$$

where

$$
\left.
\begin{array}{l}
F^{(3)}(ijk)^{(0)} = (1 - W_{ij} - W_{ik} - W_{jk})F(i/j/k)^{(0)} \\
\qquad + W_{ij}F(ij/k)^{(0)} + W_{ik}F(ik/j)^{(0)} \\
\qquad + W_{jk}F(i/jk)^{(0)}
\end{array}
\right\}
\quad (9.4\text{-}15)
$$

$$\left.\begin{aligned}
F^{(3)}(ijk)^{(1)} &= (1 - W_{ij} - W_{ik} - W_{jk})F(i/j/k)^{(1)} \\
&\quad + W_{ij}F(ij/k)^{(1)} + W_{ik}F(ik/j)^{(1)} \\
&\quad + W_{jk}F(i/jk)^{(1)}, \quad \text{etc.}
\end{aligned}\right\} \quad (9.4\text{-}16)$$

In the next step of our treatment, we substitute $F^{(3)}(ijk)$ represented by eq. (14) in the integral member in eq. (1):

$$\left.\begin{aligned}
J_i &= \sum_{jk} \iint (\mathscr{F}_{ij} + \mathscr{F}_{ik}) \cdot \frac{\partial}{\partial \mathbf{p}_i} F^{(3)}(ijk) \, dX_j \, dX_k \\
&= J^{(0)} + J^{(1)} + J^{(2)} + \dots,
\end{aligned}\right\} \quad (9.4\text{-}17)$$

where $J^{(0)}$, for example, is due to $F^{(3)}(ijk)^{(0)}$ given by eq. (15):

$$\left.\begin{aligned}
J^{(0)} &= \sum_{jk} \iint (\mathscr{F}_{ij} + \mathscr{F}_{ik}) \cdot \frac{\partial}{\partial \mathbf{p}_i} F^{(3)}(ijk)^{(0)} \, dX_j \, dX_k \\
&= J_1^{(0)} + J_2^{(0)} + J_{2'}^{(0)} + J_3^{(0)},
\end{aligned}\right\} \quad (9.4\text{-}18)$$

and

$$J_1^{(0)} = \sum_{jk} \iint (\mathscr{F}_{ij} + \mathscr{F}_{ik}) \cdot \frac{\partial}{\partial \mathbf{p}_i} (1 - W_{ij} - W_{ik} - W_{jk})F(i/j/k)^{(0)} \, dX_j dX_k \quad (9.4\text{-}19)$$

$$J_2^{(0)} = \sum_{jk} \iint (\mathscr{F}_{ij} + \mathscr{F}_{ik}) \cdot \frac{\partial}{\partial \mathbf{p}_i} W_{ij}F(ij/k)^{(0)} \, dX_j \, dX_k \quad (9.4\text{-}20)$$

$$J_{2'}^{(0)} = \sum_{jk} \iint (\mathscr{F}_{ij} + \mathscr{F}_{ik}) \cdot \frac{\partial}{\partial \mathbf{p}_i} W_{ik}F(ik/j)^{(0)} \, dX_j \, dX_k \quad (9.4\text{-}21)$$

$$J_3^{(0)} = \sum_{jk} \iint (\mathscr{F}_{ij} + \mathscr{F}_{ik}) \cdot \frac{\partial}{\partial \mathbf{p}_i} W_{jk}F(i/jk)^{(0)} \, dX_j \, dX_k. \quad (9.4\text{-}22)$$

Similarly we have

$$J^{(1)} = J_1^{(1)} + J_2^{(1)} + J_{2'}^{(1)} + J_3^{(1)}, \quad (9.4\text{-}23)$$

in which

$$\left.\begin{aligned}
J_1^{(1)} &= \sum_{jk} \iint (\mathscr{F}_{ij} + \mathscr{F}_{ik}) \cdot \frac{\partial}{\partial \mathbf{p}_i} (1 - W_{ij} - W_{ik} \\
&\quad - W_{jk})F(i/j/k)^{(1)} \, dX_j \, dX_k
\end{aligned}\right\} \quad (9.4\text{-}24)$$

$$J_2^{(1)} = \sum_{ik} \iint (\mathscr{F}_{ij} + \mathscr{F}_{ik}) \cdot \frac{\partial}{\partial \mathbf{p}_i} W_{ij}F(ij/k)^{(1)} \, dX_j \, dX_k \quad (9.4\text{-}25)$$

$$J_{2'}^{(1)} = \sum_{jk} \int\int ((\mathcal{F}_{ij} + \mathcal{F}_{ik}) \cdot \frac{\partial}{\partial \mathbf{p}_i} W_{ik} F(ik/j)^{(1)} \, dX_j \, dX_k \qquad (9.4\text{-}26)$$

$$J_{3}^{(1)} = \sum_{jk} \int ((\mathcal{F}_{ij} + \mathcal{F}_{ik}) \cdot \frac{\partial}{\partial \mathbf{p}_i} W_{jk} F(i/jk)^{(1)} \, dX_j \, dX_k, \quad \text{etc.} \quad (9.4\text{-}27)$$

For coarse-graining J with respect to time from t to $t+\tau$, we may have more than one method. In eq. (8), X_i' changes as a function of s according to eqs. (5), while X_j' and X_k' are invariant during the time of coarse-graining. If we choose for X_i', X_j' and X_k' a different class of functions of s, we obtain a different result of coarse-graining. In the following, we consider four different functions for $F_{ijk}^{(3)}(X_i', X_j', X_k'; t+s)$ by integrating eq. (10) along four classes of trajectory. These classes of trajectory are also different from the one determined by eqs. (5). The result of coarse-graining J, and/or a part of J, along a class of trajectories is different from the result made along another class of trajectories. Later, however, it will be shown that, by proper coarse-graining operations with respect to similar particles (formation of distribution functions in generic spaces), the differences among the results caused by the differences among classes of trajectory along which the coarse-graining with respect to time is made are eliminated. In the following, we obtain for $F^{(3)}$ four different functions of s, corresponding respectively to four different series of expansions given by eq. (13).

9.4-2. Equations for subsystems

We treat $F^{(3)}(ijk)$ in $F(i/j/k)$, $F(ij/k)$, $F(ik/j)$ and $F(i/jk)$ defined by (9.3-4) respectively in different ways.

$F^{(3)}(ijk)$ in $F(i/j/k)$. According to eq. (13), we define $F(i'/j'/k'; t+s)^{(\mu)}$ for $F(i/j/k)^{(\mu)}$, where X_i, X_j, X_k, and t are replaced respectively by X_i', X_j', X_k', and $t+s$. Here X_i', X_j', and X_k' are functions of s, as will be specified soon. We assume that $F(i'/j'/k'; t+s)^{(0)}$ satisfies

$$\left(\frac{\partial}{\partial s} + \frac{p_i'}{m} \cdot \frac{\partial}{\partial \mathbf{r}_i'} + \frac{\mathbf{p}_j'}{m} \cdot \frac{\partial}{\partial \mathbf{r}_j'} + \frac{\mathbf{p}_k'}{m} \cdot \frac{\partial}{\partial \mathbf{r}_k'} \right) F(i'/j'/k'; t+s)^{(0)} = 0 \quad (9.4\text{-}28)$$

and $F(i'/j'/k'; t+s)^{(\mu)}$ for $\mu = 1, 2, \ldots$ satisfies

$$
\left.\begin{aligned}
&\left(\frac{\partial}{\partial s} + \frac{\mathbf{p}_i'}{m}\cdot\frac{\partial}{\partial \mathbf{r}_i'} + \frac{\mathbf{p}_j'}{m}\cdot\frac{\partial}{\partial \mathbf{r}_j'} + \frac{\mathbf{p}_k'}{m}\cdot\frac{\partial}{\partial \mathbf{r}_k'}\right)F(i'/j'/k'; t+s)^{(\mu)} \\
&= -\left[(\mathcal{F}_{ij}' + \mathcal{F}_{ik}')\cdot\frac{\partial}{\partial \mathbf{p}_i'} + (\mathcal{F}_{ji}' + \mathcal{F}_{jk}')\cdot\frac{\partial}{\partial \mathbf{p}_j'}\right. \\
&\qquad \left.+ (\mathcal{F}_{ki}' + \mathcal{F}_{kj}')\cdot\frac{\partial}{\partial \mathbf{p}_k'}\right]F(i'/j'/k'; t+s)^{(\mu-1)} \\
&\qquad\qquad \mu = 1, 2, 3, \ldots
\end{aligned}\right\} \quad (9.4\text{-}29)
$$

where $\mathcal{F}_{ij}'$ is a function of $\mathbf{r}_i' - \mathbf{r}_j'$ instead of $\mathbf{r}_i - \mathbf{r}_j$ and so forth. By taking

$$F(i'/j'/k'; t+s)^{(0)} = F(i'; t+s)^{(0)}F(j'; t+s)^{(0)}F(k'; t+s)^{(0)} \quad (9.4\text{-}30)$$

eq. (28) leads to

$$
\left.\begin{aligned}
&\left(\frac{\partial}{\partial s} + \frac{\mathbf{p}_i'}{m}\cdot\frac{\partial}{\partial \mathbf{r}_i'}\right)F(i'; t+s)^{(0)} = 0, \\
&\left(\frac{\partial}{\partial s} + \frac{\mathbf{p}_i'}{m}\cdot\frac{\partial}{\partial \mathbf{r}_j'}\right)F(j'; t+s)^{(0)} = 0, \\
&\left(\frac{\partial}{\partial s} + \frac{\mathbf{p}_k'}{m}\cdot\frac{\partial}{\partial \mathbf{r}_k'}\right)F(k'; t+s)^{(0)} = 0.
\end{aligned}\right\} \quad (9.4\text{-}31)
$$

On integration of eqs. (31) along trajectories determined by

$$
\left.\begin{aligned}
&\frac{d\mathbf{r}_i'}{ds} = \frac{\mathbf{p}_i'}{m}, \quad \frac{d\mathbf{r}_j'}{ds} = \frac{\mathbf{p}_k'}{m} \\
&\frac{d\mathbf{r}_k'}{ds} = \frac{\mathbf{p}_k'}{m}.
\end{aligned}\right\} \quad (9.4\text{-}32)
$$

$$
\left.\begin{aligned}
&\mathbf{p}_i' = \mathbf{p}_i, \qquad \mathbf{p}_j' = \mathbf{p}_j, \qquad \mathbf{p}_k' = \mathbf{p}_k \\
&\mathbf{r}_i'(0) = \mathbf{r}_i, \quad \mathbf{r}_j'(0) = \mathbf{r}_j, \quad \mathbf{r}_k'(0) = \mathbf{r}_k \\
&\qquad\qquad \text{[trajectory I]},
\end{aligned}\right\} \quad (9.4\text{-}33)
$$

we have

$$
\left.\begin{array}{l}
F(i'; t+s)^{(0)} = F(i, t)^{(0)}, \\
F(j'; t+s)^{(0)} = F(j; t)^{(0)}, \\
F(k'; t+s)^{(0)} = F(k; t)^{(0)}.
\end{array}\right\} \tag{9.4-34}
$$

The next procedure is to obtain $F(i'/j'/k'; t+s)^{(1)}$ by solving eq. (29) for $\mu = 1$. On substituting eq. (34) in the right-hand side of eq. (29), we have

$$
\left.\begin{array}{l}
\left(\dfrac{\partial}{\partial s} + \dfrac{\mathbf{p}_i'}{m}\cdot\dfrac{\partial}{\partial \mathbf{r}_i'} + \dfrac{\mathbf{p}_j'}{m}\cdot\dfrac{\partial}{\partial \mathbf{r}_j} + \dfrac{\mathbf{p}_k}{\partial \mathbf{r}_k'}\right) F(i'/j'/k'; t+s)^{(1)} \\[2mm]
= -\left[(\mathcal{F}_{ij}' + \mathcal{F}_{ik}')\cdot\dfrac{\partial}{\partial \mathbf{p}_i'} + (\mathcal{F}_{ji}' + \mathcal{F}_{jk}')\cdot\dfrac{\partial}{\partial \mathbf{p}_j'}\right. \\[2mm]
\left. + (\mathcal{F}_{ki}' + \mathcal{F}_{kj}')\cdot\dfrac{\partial}{\partial \mathbf{p}_k'}\right] F(i'/j'/k'; t+s)^{(0)}.
\end{array}\right\} \tag{9.4-35}
$$

Since the right-hand side member is already given, we may obtain $F(i'/j'/k'; t+s)^{(1)}$ along trajectories I determined by eqs. (32) and (33). We may repeat the same procedure to obtain $F(i'/j'/k'; t+s)^{(\mu)}$ for $\mu > 1$. It is obvious that

$$
\left.\begin{array}{l}
F(i'/j'/k'; t+s)^{(\mu)} = 0, \\
\text{if} \quad \mu \neq 0, \quad s = 0,
\end{array}\right\} \tag{9.4-36}
$$

since we assume that

$$
F(i/j/k; t)^{(0)} = F^{(1)}(X_i; t)F^{(1)}(X_j; t)F^{(1)}(X_k; t) \tag{9.4-37}
$$

$F^{(3)}(ijk)$ in $F(ij/k) \equiv W_{ij}F^{(3)}(ijk)$. In this case, particle i and particle j are in a close interaction. By taking the second expansion of $F^{(3)}(ijk)$ given by eq. (13) and defining $F(i'\,j'/k'; t+s)^{(0)}$, etc., in the same way as of $F(i'/j'/k'; t+s)^{(0)}$, etc., we have

$$
\left.\begin{array}{l}
\left(\dfrac{\partial}{\partial s} + \dfrac{\mathbf{p}_i'}{m}\cdot\dfrac{\partial}{\partial \mathbf{r}_i'} + \dfrac{\mathbf{p}_j'}{m}\cdot\dfrac{\partial}{\partial \mathbf{r}_j'} + \dfrac{\mathbf{p}_k'}{m}\cdot\dfrac{\partial}{\partial \mathbf{r}_k'}\right. \\[2mm]
\left. + \mathcal{F}_{ij}'\cdot\dfrac{\partial}{\partial \mathbf{p}_i'} + \mathcal{F}_{ji}'\cdot\dfrac{\partial}{\partial \mathbf{p}_j'}\right) F(i'j'/k'; t+s)^{(0)} = 0
\end{array}\right\} \tag{9.4-38}
$$

197

and

$$
\left.\begin{aligned}
&\left[\frac{\partial}{\partial s}+\frac{\mathbf{p}_i'}{m}\cdot\frac{\partial}{\partial\mathbf{r}_i'}+\frac{\mathbf{p}_j'}{m}\cdot\frac{\partial}{\partial\mathbf{r}_j'}+\frac{\mathbf{p}_k'}{m}\cdot\frac{\partial}{\partial\mathbf{r}_k'},\right.\\
&\quad+\mathscr{F}_{ij}'\cdot\frac{\partial}{\partial\mathbf{p}_i'}+\mathscr{F}_{ji}'\cdot\frac{\partial}{\partial\mathbf{p}_j'}\bigg]F(i'j'/k';\,t+s)^{(\mu)}\\
&=-\left[\mathscr{F}_{ik}'\cdot\frac{\partial}{\partial\mathbf{p}_i'}+\mathscr{F}_{jk}'\cdot\frac{\partial}{\partial\mathbf{p}_j'}\right.\\
&\quad+(\mathscr{F}_{ki}'+\mathscr{F}_{kj}')\cdot\frac{\partial}{\partial\mathbf{p}_k'}\bigg]F(i'j'/k';\,t+s)^{(\mu-1)}\\
&\qquad\mu=1,\,2,\,3,\,\ldots.
\end{aligned}\right\}
\tag{9.4-39}
$$

These equations are integrated successively along trajectories II determined by

$$
\left.\begin{aligned}
\frac{d\mathbf{r}_i'}{ds}&=\frac{\mathbf{p}_i'}{m},\quad \frac{d\mathbf{p}_i'}{ds}=\mathscr{F}_{ij}'\\
\frac{d\mathbf{r}_j'}{ds}&=\frac{\mathbf{p}_j'}{m},\quad \frac{d\mathbf{p}_j'}{ds}=\mathscr{F}_{ji}'\\
\frac{d\mathbf{r}_k'}{ds}&=\frac{\mathbf{p}_k'}{m},\quad \mathbf{p}_k'=\mathbf{p}_k
\end{aligned}\right\}
\tag{9.4-40}
$$

(trajectories II)

with initial conditions at $s=0$

$$
\left.\begin{aligned}
\mathbf{r}_i'&=\mathbf{r}_i,\quad \mathbf{p}_i'=\mathbf{p}_i\\
\mathbf{r}_j'&=\mathbf{r}_j,\quad \mathbf{p}_j'=\mathbf{p}_j\\
\mathbf{r}_k'&=\mathbf{r}_k
\end{aligned}\right\}
\tag{9.4-41}
$$

We may assume that

$$
F(i'j'/k';\,t+s)^{(0)}=F(i'j';\,t+s)^{(0)}F(k',\,t+s)^{(0)},
\tag{9.4-42}
$$

where $F(i'j';\,t+s)^{(0)}$ and $F(k';\,t+s)^{(0)}$ are solutions of

$$
\left.\begin{aligned}
&\left(\frac{\partial}{\partial s}+\frac{\mathbf{p}_i'}{m}\cdot\frac{\partial}{\partial\mathbf{r}_i}+\frac{\mathbf{p}_j'}{m}\cdot\frac{\partial}{\partial\mathbf{r}_j'}\right.\\
&\quad+\mathscr{F}_{ij}'\cdot\frac{\partial}{\partial\mathbf{p}_i'}+\mathscr{F}_{ji}'\cdot\frac{\partial}{\partial\mathbf{p}_j'}\bigg)F(i'j';\,t+s)^{(0)}=0
\end{aligned}\right\}
\tag{9.4-43}
$$

and

$$\left(\frac{\partial}{\partial s} + \frac{\mathbf{p}'_k}{m} \cdot \frac{\partial}{\partial \mathbf{r}'_k}\right) F(k'; t+s)^{(0)} = 0 \qquad (9.4\text{-}44)$$

when integrated along trajectories II determined by eqs. (40) and (41). Since we assume that

$$F(i'j'/k'; t+s)^{(\mu)} = 0 \qquad (9.4\text{-}45)$$

$$\mu > 0$$

when

$$s = 0,$$

it is easily seen that

$$\left.\begin{array}{l} F(i'j'; t+s)^{(0)} = F^{(2)}(ij) \\ F(k'; T+s)^{(0)} = F^{(1)}(k) \end{array}\right\} \qquad (9.4\text{-}46)$$

when

$$s = 0.$$

Solution of eq. (43) is a two-body problem; we may imitate the method of Boltzmann setting Stosszahlansatz for the initial condition of a binary collision. Of course, it is to be expected that the solution will become meaningless as the distance between two particles i and j increases. However, at the same time W_{ij} tends to vanish, and hence such meaningless solutions do not affect the final result, $F(ij/k)$.

$F^{(3)}(ijk)$ in $F(ik/j) \equiv W_{ik}F^{(3)}(ijk)$. We may repeat the same treatment in this case as in the case of $F(ij/k)$, simply by changing subscripts. The trajectories which correspond to trajectories II are denoted by trajectories II' in this case.

$F^{(3)}(ijk)$ in $F(i/jk) \equiv W_{jk}F^{(3)}(ijk)$. Trajectories along which coarsegraining operations are done are named trajectories III. The treatment is similar to those in the two preceding cases subject to the condition that the interaction between j and k is strong.

Considering $F^{(3)}(X'_iX'_jX'_k; t+s)$ obtained in four cases in the above, we may coarse-grain $J_1^{(0)}$, $J_2^{(0)}$, $J_{2'}^{(0)}$ and $J_3^{(0)}$, with respect to time, respectively along trajectories I, II, II', and III.

199

9.4-3. COARSE-GRAINING

Consideration of eqs. (19), (30), and (37) leads to

$$
\langle J_1^{(0)}\rangle_{\mathrm{I}} = \frac{1}{\tau}\int_0^\tau \left[\sum_{jk}\int (\mathcal{F}_{ij}' + \mathcal{F}_{ik}')\cdot\frac{\partial}{\partial\mathbf{p}_i'}(1 - W_{ij}' - W_{ik}' - W_{jk}')\right.
$$

$$
\left. F(i'\,;\,t+s)^{(0)}F(j'\,;\,t+s)^{(0)}F(k'\,;\,t+s)^{(0)}\,dX_j'\,dX_k'\right]\,ds
$$

$$
= \frac{N-1}{2}\left\langle\int (1 - W_{ij} - W_{ik} - W_{jk})(\mathcal{F}_{ij} + \mathcal{F}_{ik})F^{(1)}(j)F^{(1)}(k)\right.
$$

$$
\left.\cdot\frac{\partial}{\partial\mathbf{p}_i}F^{(1)}(i)\,dX_j\,dX_k\right\rangle_{\mathrm{I}}
$$

$$
= (N-1)\left\langle\int (1 - W_{ij})\mathcal{F}_{ij}F^{(1)}(j)\,dX_j\cdot\frac{\partial}{\partial\mathbf{p}_i}F^{(1)}(i)\right\rangle_{\mathrm{I}}. \quad (9.4\text{-}47)
$$

In the above, $\sum_{jk}$ means the sum with respect to a possible set of pairs made up of all the particles except for particle i; hence the number of the pairs is $(N-1)/2$. After time averaging, the symmetry (the hypothesis of equal *a priori* probabilities) is introduced in the distribution function. It is also assumed that

$$
\sum_{jk}\iint W_{jk}F^{(1)}(j)F^{(1)}(k)\,dX_j\,dX_k
$$

is negligible compared with the other members. $\langle J_1^{(0)}\rangle_{\mathrm{I}}$ gives the Vlasov effects. With necessary precautions similar to those for eq. (47), we obtain

$$
\langle J_2^{(0)}\rangle_{\mathrm{II}} = \frac{N-1}{2}\left\langle\int \mathcal{F}_{ij}W_{ij}\cdot\frac{\partial}{\partial\mathbf{p}_i}F^{(2)}(ij)\,dX_j\right\rangle_{\mathrm{II}}
$$

$$
+ \frac{N-1}{2}\left\langle\int \mathcal{F}_{ik}F^{(1)}(k)\,dX_k\cdot\frac{\partial}{\partial\mathbf{p}_i}\int F^{(2)}(ij)W_{ij}dX_j\right\rangle_{\mathrm{II}} \quad\Big\}\quad (9.4\text{-}48)
$$

$$
\langle J_2^{(0)}\rangle_{\mathrm{II'}} = \frac{N-1}{2}\left\langle\int \mathcal{F}_{ik}W_{ik}\cdot\frac{\partial}{\partial\mathbf{p}_i}F^{(2)}(ik)\,dX_k\right\rangle_{\mathrm{II'}}
$$

$$
+ \frac{N-1}{2}\left\langle\int \mathcal{F}_{ij}F^{(1)}(j)\,dX_j\cdot\frac{\partial}{\partial\mathbf{p}_i}\int F^{(2)}(ik)W_{ik}\,dX_k\right\rangle_{\mathrm{II'}} \quad\Big\}\quad (9.4\text{-}49)
$$

It is noted that $\int F^{(1)}(X)\,dX = 1$, and $|\mathcal{F}_{ij}| \gg |\mathcal{F}_{ik}|$ in eq. (48) and $|\mathcal{F}_{ij}| \ll |\mathcal{F}_{ik}|$ in eq. (49). Therefore, the second member in each is ignored, and the sum of them leads to

$$\langle J_2^{(0)} \rangle_{\text{II}} + \langle J_2^{(0)} \rangle_{\text{II}'} = (N-1) \left\langle \int \mathcal{F}_{ij} W_{ij} \cdot \frac{\partial}{\partial \mathbf{p}_i} F^{(2)}(ij)\,dX_j \right\rangle_{\text{II}}. \quad (9.4\text{-}50)$$

This will be converted to the Boltzmann collision integral by proper treatment. Here the convergency of the result is assured by the existence of W_{ij}. Finally we have

$$\left.\begin{aligned}\langle J_3^{(0)} \rangle_{\text{III}} = \frac{(N-1)}{2} &\left\langle \int\int (\mathcal{F}_{ij} + \mathcal{F}_{ik}) W_{jk} F^{(2)}(jk)\,dX_j\,dX_k \right\rangle_{\text{III}} \\ &\cdot \frac{\partial}{\partial \mathbf{p}_i} \langle F^{(1)}(i) \rangle_{\text{III}}.\end{aligned}\right\} \quad (9.4\text{-}51)$$

It appears that the effect is similar to $\langle J_1^{(0)} \rangle$. The difference is that $\langle J_3^{(0)} \rangle_{\text{III}}$ involves W_{jk}. Therefore

$$\langle J_3^{(0)} \rangle_{\text{III}} \ll \langle J_1^{(0)} \rangle_{\text{I}}. \quad (9.4\text{-}52)$$

Hence we may ignore the effect given by eq. (51).

The $J^{(1)}$'s given by eqs. (24), (25), (26), and (27) are coarse-grained in the same way as the $J^{(0)}$'s. The trajectories along which those functions are coarse-grained are the same as those along which the $J^{(0)}$'s are coarse-grained respectively.

$\langle J_1^{(1)} \rangle_{\text{I}}$. There are correlations among three particles i, j, and k in this approximation. It is easily seen, however, that those particles are mutually remote. According to eq. (35), we obtain

$$\left.\begin{aligned} &F(i/j'/k'\,;\,t+s)^{(1)} \\ = -\int_0^s &\left[(\mathcal{F}'_{ij} + \mathcal{F}'_{ik}) \cdot \frac{\partial}{\partial \mathbf{p}'_i} + (\mathcal{F}'_{ji} + \mathcal{F}'_{jk}) \cdot \frac{\partial}{\partial \mathbf{p}'_j} \right. \\ &\left. + (\mathcal{F}'_{ki} + \mathcal{F}'_{kj}) \cdot \frac{\partial}{\partial \mathbf{p}'_k} \right] F(i'/j'/k'\,;\,t+s)^{(0)}\,ds. \end{aligned}\right\} \quad (9.4\text{-}53)$$

Since

$$F(i'/j'/k'\,;\,t+s)^{(0)} = F^{(1)}(i\,;\,t) F^{(1)}(j\,;\,t) F^{(1)}(k\,;\,t)$$

and those trajectories, along which the coarse-graining is done, are free mutually, the summation $\sum_{jk}$ results in cancellation among the effects of these particles. Hence we ignore the present effect.

$\langle J_2^{(1)} \rangle_{\mathrm{II}} + \langle J_{2'}^{(1)} \rangle_{\mathrm{II'}}$. It is easily shown that integration of eq. (39) and of the similar equation for $F(i'k'/j'; t+s)^{(\mu)}$ along trajectories II and II' leads to

$$
\left.
\begin{aligned}
\langle J_2^{(1)} \rangle_{\mathrm{II}} + \langle J_{2'}^{(1)} \rangle_{\mathrm{II'}} &= -\frac{N-1}{\tau} \int_0^\tau \left[\iint \mathcal{F}_{ik}' \cdot \frac{\partial}{\partial \mathbf{p}_i'} \right. \\
&\times W_{ij}' \int_0^s \mathcal{F}_{ik}' \cdot \frac{\partial}{\partial \mathbf{p}_i'} F^{(2)}(i'j'; t+s) F^{(1)}(k'; t+s)\, ds\, dX_j'\, dX_k' \Big]\, ds \\
&\quad -\frac{N-1}{\tau} \int_0^\tau \left[\iint \mathcal{F}_{ik}' \cdot \frac{\partial}{\partial \mathbf{p}_i'} W_{ij}' \int_0^s \mathcal{F}_{ki} \frac{\partial}{\partial \mathbf{p}_k'} F^{(2)}(i'j'; t+s) \right. \\
&\quad \left. \times F^{(1)}(k'; t+s)\, ds\, dX_j'\, dX_k' \right]\, ds.
\end{aligned}
\right\} \quad (9.4\text{-}54)
$$

In the above, the first member in the right-hand side gives the diffusion effect in the momentum space of particles i, and the second member the friction. The significant feature of these terms is that the correlation period is regulated by W_{ij}, the probability of strong interaction between i and j.

$\langle J_3^{(1)} \rangle_{\mathrm{III}}$. By means of a similar method to before, we obtain

$$
\left.
\begin{aligned}
\langle J_3^{(1)} \rangle_{\mathrm{III}} &= -\frac{N-1}{2} \frac{1}{\tau} \int_0^\tau \left[\iint \mathcal{F}_{ij}' \cdot \frac{\partial}{\partial \mathbf{p}_i'} W_{jk}' \right. \\
&\times \int_0^s \mathcal{F}_{ij}' \cdot \frac{\partial}{\partial \mathbf{p}_i'} F^{(2)}(j'k'; t+s) F^{(1)}(i'; t+s)\, ds\, dX_j'\, dX_k' \Big]\, ds \\
&\quad -\frac{N-1}{2} \frac{1}{\tau} \int_0^\tau \left[\iint \mathcal{F}_{ij}' \cdot \frac{\partial}{\partial \mathbf{p}_i'} W_{jk}' \right. \\
&\quad \left. \times \int_0^s \mathcal{F}_{ji}' \cdot \frac{\partial}{\partial \mathbf{p}_j'} F^{(2)}(j'k'; t+s) F^{(1)}(i'; t+s)\, dX_j'\, dX_k' \right]\, ds.
\end{aligned}
\right\} \quad (9.4\text{-}55)
$$

In effect, there is no difference between $\langle J_2^{(1)} \rangle_{\mathrm{II}}$, $\langle J_2^{(1)} \rangle_{\mathrm{II'}}$ and $\langle J_3^{(1)} \rangle_{\mathrm{III}}$.

Summing all these effects, we may write

$$
\begin{aligned}
\langle J^{(1)} \rangle = & -\frac{3}{2}(N-1)\frac{1}{\tau}\int_0^\tau \left[\int\int \mathcal{F}'_{ik}\cdot\frac{\partial}{\partial \mathbf{p}'_i}\, W'_{ij} \right. \\
& \times \int_0^s \mathcal{F}'_{ik}\cdot\frac{\partial}{\partial \mathbf{p}'_i}\, F^{(2)}(i'j';t+s)F^{(1)}(k';t+s)\,ds\,dX'_j\,dX'_k \bigg]\,ds \\
& -\frac{3}{2}(N-1)\frac{1}{\tau}\int_0^\tau \left[\int\int \mathcal{F}'_{ik}\cdot\frac{\partial}{\partial \mathbf{p}'_i}\, W'_{ij}\int_0^s \mathcal{F}'_{ki}\cdot\frac{\partial}{\partial \mathbf{p}'_k} \right. \\
& \times F^{(2)}(i'j';t+s)F^{(1)}(k';t+s)\,ds\,dX'_j\,dX'_k \bigg]\,ds,
\end{aligned}
\qquad (9.4\text{-}56)
$$

where it is noted that we have ignored the differences among trajectories over which these coarse-graining operations are considered. As is shown below, however, the difference is not essential in the result. The effect given by eq. (56) is of the Fokker–Planck type.

So far, various functions constituting J have been coarse-grained along different classes of trajectory. For completing eq. (9), however, J is to be coarse-grained with respect to the particular class of trajectories named 0 given by eq. (5). It is necessary to show that the differences between these classes of trajectory along which J and/or parts of J have been coarse-grained do not result in any inconsistency in the final result. For this purpose, we compare, for example, the results of coarse-graining $F^{(1)}(X_i;t)$ along different classes of trajectories in the following: according to eq. (2.3-10)

$$
\begin{aligned}
F^{(1)}(X_i;t) &= \int D^{(N)}\prod_{j\neq i}^N dX_j \\
&= \delta(X_i - X_i^*(t)).
\end{aligned}
\qquad (9.4\text{-}57)
$$

Here $X_i^*(t)$ is a complicated function of time because of the interaction of particle i with the other $N-1$ particles.

First, let us coarse-grain $F^{(1)}$ along trajectories determined by eq. (5) over a time period from t to $t+\tau$:

$$
\langle F_i^{(1)}(X_i;t)\rangle_0 = \frac{1}{\tau}\int_0^\tau F^{(1)}(X_i';t+s)\,ds
\qquad (9.4\text{-}58)
$$

203

where

$$X_i' = X_i + x_i'(s).$$

These trajectories, according to eq. (5), are independent of the other particles. None of these trajectories is similar to $X_i^*(t+s)$ in view of time scale τ. Hence $\langle F_i^{(1)}(X_i; t)\rangle_0$ is spread over a comparatively broad domain of X_i. The situation is similar to the one illustrated in Fig. 4.3-2 as regards J_i. There, in A, the curved solid line is the precise trajectory $X^*(t+s)$ on which $F^{(1)}(X; t)$ exists; straight dotted lines are trajectories 0 along which $\langle \ \rangle_0$ is made. For illustrating the present situtation by B in the same figure,

$$J_i, \quad \langle J_i\rangle_0, \quad \langle J_i\rangle_{\text{I}}$$

are to be replaced respectively by

$$F^{(1)}, \quad \langle F^{(1)}\rangle_0, \quad \langle F^{(1)}\rangle_{\text{along precise trajectory}}$$

There may be a group of ν_i particles, $i_1, i_2, \ldots$, of which

$$\langle F_{i1}^{(1)}(X; t)\rangle_0 = \langle F_{i2}^{(1)}(X; t)\rangle_0 = \ldots.$$

These are localized in a narrow domain of X. We define $\langle F^{(1)}(X; t)\rangle_0$ by

$$\left.\begin{aligned}
N\langle F^{(1)}(X; t)\rangle_0 &= \sum_{i=1}^{N} \langle F_i^{(1)}(X; t)\rangle_0 \\
&= \nu_{i'}\langle F_{i'}^{(1)}(X; t)\rangle_0 \\
&\quad + \nu_{i''}\langle F_{i''}^{(1)}(X; t)\rangle_0 + \ldots
\end{aligned}\right\} \tag{9.4-59}$$

$$\nu_{i'} + \nu_{i''} + \ldots = N. \tag{9.4-60}$$

Unlike $\langle F_i^{(1)}(X; t)\rangle_0$, $\langle F^{(1)}(X; t)\rangle_0$ is spread more uniformly over the entire domain of X.

We may also coarse-grain $F_i^{(1)}(X_i; t)$ along another set of trajectories

$$X_i'' = X_i + x_i''(s)$$

which, for example, is determined by eq. (40).

$$\langle F_i^{(1)}(X_i; t)\rangle_{II} = \frac{1}{\tau} \int_0^\tau F_i^{(1)}(X_i''; t+s) \, ds. \qquad (9.4\text{-}61)$$

These trajectories, according to eq. (40), are determined by taking into account the nearest neighbor interactions. Therefore, a trajectory coincides with $X_i^*(t+s)$ in the time scale τ. Hence $\langle F_i^{(1)}(X_i; t)\rangle_{II}$ is much more localized than $\langle F_i^{(1)}(X_i; t)\rangle_0$ as is illustrated in Fig. 4.3-2.[†]

$$\langle F_i^{(1)}(X_i; t)\rangle_0 \neq \langle F_i^{(1)}(X_i; t)\rangle_{II}. \qquad (9.4\text{-}62)$$

Nevertheless, it is obvious that

$$\int \langle F_i^{(1)}(X_i; t)\rangle_0 \, dX_i = \int \langle F_i^{(1)}(X_i; t)\rangle_{II} \, dX_i. \qquad (9.4\text{-}63)$$

We may define $\langle \overline{F^{(1)}(X; t)}\rangle_{II}$ by

$$\langle \overline{F^{(1)}(X; t)}\rangle_{II} = \frac{1}{N} \sum_i \langle F_i^{(1)}(X; t)\rangle_{II}. \qquad (9.4\text{-}64)$$

If N is sufficiently large, the coarse-graining in the sense of eqs. (59) and (64) may result in

$$\langle \overline{F^{(1)}(X; t)}\rangle_0 = \langle \overline{F^{(1)}(X; t)}\rangle_{II}. \qquad (9.4\text{-}65)$$

In the above, we have seen that coarse-graining operations in the sense of eqs. (59) and (64) are essential to reconcile two classes of time averages. In other words, time averages are not sufficient for deriving proper kinetic equations; it is necessary to take averages over many particles.

Applying the same consideration as above, we make the average of eq. (9) with respect to particles so that $\langle J\rangle$'s made with respect to different classes of trajectory are equivalent to those made with respect to trajectories 0. By this procedure of coarse-graining over particles, we obtain in effect the same function as f defined by eq. (2.5-1). (The Boltzmann equation is the very equation which governs the evolution of f of a gas where the collisions are assumed to be

[†] J_i is to be replaced by $F_i^{(1)}$ and $\langle \ \rangle_I$ by $\langle \ \rangle_{II}$ in the figure.

binary.) After the present coarse-graining operation with respect to similar particles, the effect given by eq. (50) may amount to the Boltzmann collision integral; because of W_{ij} in the integrand, the effective interaction terminates quickly as the distance between particle i and particle j increases.

9.4-4. EVALUATION OF INTERACTION EFFECTS

Because of the W's involved in those interaction integrals, the integrals converge always. As is given by eq. (9.2-6), we take for W

$$W = \exp\left(-9\pi n r^3/4\right),$$

where n is the local number density and r is the distance between the test particle and a field particle under consideration. The range of space of a close correlation (almost binary) is of the order of

$$R_n = \left(\frac{9\pi n}{4}\right)^{-1/3}$$

and the time scale is

$$\tau = R_n/(\langle p\rangle/m).$$

Here $\langle p\rangle$ is the average magnitude of momentum of a particle

$$\frac{\langle p\rangle}{m} = 0\left[\frac{3kT}{m}\right]^{1/2}$$

If $r > R_n$, then $W \ll 1$. The Boltzmann type interaction effect $\langle J_2^{(0)}\rangle + \langle J_{2'}^{(0)}\rangle$ is of the order of

$$0[\langle J_2^{(0)}\rangle + \langle J_{2'}^{(0)}\rangle] = \pi(R_n)^2\,\frac{\langle p\rangle}{m}\,nF^{(1)}(i) = \pi n R_n^2\left(\frac{3kT}{m}\right)^{1/2}F^{(1)}(i).$$

The order of the interaction effect $\langle J_2^{(1)}\rangle + \langle J_{2'}^{(1)}\rangle$ is shown to be

$$0[\langle J_2^{(1)}\rangle + \langle J_{2'}\rangle^{(1)}] = \frac{Rn}{(3kT/m)^{1/2}}\,n\int_{R_n}^{\infty}\frac{4\pi e^4 r^2}{r^4}\,dr\,\frac{1}{p^2}\,F^{(1)}(i)$$

$$= \frac{4\pi}{3}\,\frac{ne^4}{m^2(3kT/m)^{3/2}}\,F^{(1)}(i).$$

Hence we obtain

$$\frac{O[\langle J_2^{(1)}\rangle + \langle J_{2'}^{(1)}\rangle]}{O[\langle J_2^{(0)}\rangle + \langle J_{2'}^{(0)}\rangle]} = O\left[\left(\frac{e^2 n^{1/3}}{kT}\right)^2\right]. \qquad (9.4\text{-}66)$$

If we take $T = 10^4$, $n = 10^{19}$, we obtain[†]

$$\left(\frac{e^2 n^{1/3}}{kT}\right)^2 \doteq 10^{-1}.$$

$\left(\dfrac{e^2 n^{1/3}}{kT}\right)^2$ decreases further as T increases and n decreases. $\langle J_3^{(0)}\rangle$ is of the same order as $\langle J_2^{(1)}\rangle + \langle J_{2'}^{(1)}\rangle$. The ratio given above suggests that the effect of remote interactions may be ignored in ordinary cases where $T > 10^4$ and $n < 10^{19}$. This conclusion appears to be different from those obtained by other authors, based on the original interpretation of the BBGKY series. It is noted that the present definition of close interaction according to the nearest neighbor concept, is different from the usual definition of close interaction according to the polarization effect of the Debye–Hückel type.

One who has been familiar with theories based on the BBGKY hierarchy, might ask: Why is the effect of field particles which are not nearest neighbors of the test particle so small in the present theory? The answer is as follows: by a theory based on the BBGKY hierarchy, the test particle and a field particle may interact with an indefinitely long correlation time, in spite of the presence of perturbations by third particles. On the other hand, the behavior of a particle, by the present theory, appears in microscopic order only for a short period of time during its interaction with its nearest neighbor particles. In other words, the time scales of microscopic orders are always finite. (Note that the above statement is feasible only because laws of interaction forces are not linear with respect to interparticle distances.)

[†] See exercise problem 4 of this chapter.

9.4-5. Validity of the model

As is investigated in Section 3, the time scale of a close interaction between two ions is much longer than the the time scale of a close interaction where an electron participates. Therefore the present model appears to be suitable for simulating, in an approximation, evolution of the ion distribution in a real system, if the number of the ions is the same as the number of the electrons (the charge of an ion being the same as that of a proton.) This is because the electrons appear to make an almost uniform background compared with the motion of an ion. But at the same time, we find no definite reason for saying that the effect of electron–ion (close) interactions on the evolution of the ion distribution is negligible: although the average magnitude of the momentum of an electron is much smaller than the average magnitude of the momentum of an ion (the ratio being about 1/50 with respect to the lightest ion), the frequency of electron–ion collisions (close) is about 50 times higher than the frequency of close ion–ion interactions. If we wish to consider the situation more precisely and reasonably, both ions and electrons must be considered as discrete particles. In view of the above, model II will be investigated in the next section.

9.5. Model (scheme of approximation) II

As stated in Subsection 9.4-5, the validity of model I as simulating a real system is fairly dubious. It may be plausible to think that the model has a meaning only in providing an example of reducing the Liouville equation to coarse-grained kinetic equations governing the evolutions of subsystems. In this section, we consider a model which may be more realistic than the previous one. The plasma which the present model is intended to simulate is the same as considered in the last section; the gas is fully ionized and the number of ions is the same as the number of electrons.

We consider four particles, two ions and two electrons, representing the field particles. In this way, it is necessary to treat the evolution

of a five-particle distribution function $F^{(5)}(X_i, X_j, X_k, X_l, X_m; t)$ where one of the five particles is the test particle. However as a simpler approach we shall consider

$$\left. \begin{array}{c} F^{(3)}(o, i, j) \\ F^{(3)}(o, k, \xi) \\ F^{(3)}(o, \eta, \zeta), \end{array} \right\} \tag{9.5-1}$$

where particle o is the test particle, either an ion or an electron, particles i, j, k are electrons which represent the $N/3$ groups of the field electrons, and particles ξ, η, ζ are ions representing the $N/3$ groups of the field ions; $2N$ is the total number of the field particles, N electrons and N ions. The evolution of $F^{(1)}(o)$ of the test particle is obtained by partly integrating the Liouville equation of the $N+1$ particle system as follows:

$$\left. \begin{array}{l} \left(\dfrac{\partial}{\partial t} + \dfrac{\mathbf{p}_o}{m_o} \cdot \dfrac{\partial}{\partial \mathbf{r}_o}\right) F^{(1)}(o) \\[2mm] + \displaystyle\sum_{ijk} \sum_{\xi\eta\zeta} \left[\iint (\mathcal{F}_{oi} + \mathcal{F}_{oj}) \cdot \dfrac{\partial}{\partial \mathbf{p}_o} F^{(3)}(o, i, j,) \, dX_i \, dX_j \right. \\[4mm] \left. + \iint (\mathcal{F}_{ok} + \mathcal{F}_{o\xi}) \cdot \dfrac{\partial}{\partial \mathbf{p}_o} F^{(3)}(o, k, \xi) \, dX_k \, dX_\xi \right. \\[4mm] \left. + \iint (\mathcal{F}_{o\eta} + \mathcal{F}_{o\zeta}) \cdot \dfrac{\partial}{\partial \mathbf{p}_o} F^{(3)}(o, \eta, \zeta) \, dX_\eta \, dX_\zeta \right] = 0. \end{array} \right\} \tag{9.5-2}$$

After coarse-graining, $\displaystyle\sum_{ijk} \sum_{\xi\eta\zeta}$ will be replaced by multiplier $2N/6$. Equation (2) corresponds to eq. (9.4-1) for model I. Corresponding to eq. (9.4-2) we have the following three equations:

$$\left. \begin{array}{c} \left[\dfrac{\partial}{\partial t} + \dfrac{\mathbf{p}_o}{m_o} \cdot \dfrac{\partial}{\partial \mathbf{r}_o} + \dfrac{\mathbf{p}_\alpha}{m_\alpha} \cdot \dfrac{\partial}{\partial \mathbf{r}_\alpha} + \dfrac{\mathbf{p}_\beta}{m_\beta} \cdot \dfrac{\partial}{\partial \mathbf{r}_\beta} \right. \\[4mm] + (\mathcal{F}_{o\alpha} + \mathcal{F}_{o\beta}) \cdot \dfrac{\partial}{\partial \mathbf{p}_o} + (\mathcal{F}_{\alpha o} + \mathcal{F}_{\alpha\beta}) \cdot \dfrac{\partial}{\partial \mathbf{p}_\alpha} \\[4mm] \left. + (\mathcal{F}_{\beta o} + \mathcal{F}_{\beta\alpha}) \cdot \dfrac{\partial}{\partial \mathbf{p}_\beta} \right] F^{(3)}(o, \alpha, \beta,) = 0 \\[4mm] (\alpha, \beta) = (i, j), \quad (k, \xi), \quad (\eta, \zeta), \end{array} \right\} \tag{9.5-3}$$

where $m_i = m_j = m_k =$ electronic mass, $m_\xi = m_\eta = m_\zeta =$ ionic mass.

The interaction, to the zeroth approximation, is given by

$$
\begin{aligned}
J^{(0)} = -& \sum_{ijk} \sum_{\xi\eta\zeta} \left[\iint (\mathscr{F}_{oi} + \mathscr{F}_{oj}) \cdot \frac{\partial}{\partial \mathbf{p}_o} F^{(3)}(o, i, j)^{(0)} \, dX_i \, dX_j \right. \\
& + \iint (\mathscr{F}_{ok} + \mathscr{F}_{o\xi}) \cdot \frac{\partial}{\partial \mathbf{p}_o} F^{(3)}(o, k, \xi)^{(0)} \, dX_k \, dX_\xi \\
& \left. + \iint (\mathscr{F}_{o\eta} + \mathscr{F}_{o\zeta}) \cdot \frac{\partial}{\partial \mathbf{p}_o} F^{(3)}(o, \eta, \zeta)^{(0)} \, dX_\eta \, dX_\zeta \right] \\
= \ & J^{(0)}(oee)_1 + J^{(0)}(oee)_2 + J^{(0)}(oee)_{2'} + J^{(0)}(oee)_3 \\
& + J^{(0)}(oeI)_1 + J^{(0)}(oeI)_2 + J^{(0)}(oeI)_{2'} + J^{(0)}(oeI)_3 \\
& + J^{(0)}(oII)_1 + J^{(0)}(oII)_2 + J^{(0)}(oII)_{2'} + J^{(0)}(oII)_3,
\end{aligned}
\tag{9.5-4}
$$

where $J^{(0)}(oeI)_1$, for example, is an effect due to field particles k and ξ, k representing field electrons and ξ representing field ions. These members in the above may be obtained in a similar way to these $J^{(0)}$'s obtained in the last section. In coarse-graining these terms it is necessary to pay attention to the difference between the time scale of ion–ion interaction and the time scale of those in which electrons are involved. The time scale of ion–ion interaction is denoted by τ_{II} while the time scale of those involving electrons is denoted by τ_e. Then, according to the investigation given in Section 9.1, it holds that

$$\tau_{II} \gg \tau_e.$$

If the macroscopic time scale τ_m is larger than τ_{II}, we may choose τ so that

$$\tau_m \gg \tau \gg \tau_{II} \gg \tau_e. \tag{9.5-5}$$

τ is the very time scale with which we may coarse-grain those terms in eq. (4). All the procedures of coarse-graining are the same as demonstrated in Section 9.4.

Taking an ion for test particle o.

$$\langle J^{(0)}(Iee)_1 \rangle + \langle J^{(0)}(IeI)_1 \rangle + \langle J^{(0)}(III)_1 \rangle \tag{9.5-6}$$

gives the effect of the Vlasov-type interaction. The effect of the Boltzmann-type interaction among nearest neighbor particles is represented by

$$
\left.
\begin{aligned}
& \langle J^{(0)}(Iee)_2\rangle + \langle J^{(0)}(Iee)_{2'}\rangle \\
& + \langle J^{(0)}(IeI)_2\rangle + \langle J^{(0)}(IeI)_{2'}\rangle \\
& + \langle J^{(0)}(III_2)\rangle + \langle J^{(0)}(III)_{2'}\rangle.
\end{aligned}
\right\}
\tag{9.5-7}
$$

We may also obtain

$$
\left.
\begin{aligned}
& \langle J^{(1)}(Iee)_2\rangle + \langle J^{(1)}(Iee)_{2'}\rangle \\
& + \langle J^{(1)}(IeI)_2\rangle + \langle J^{(1)}(IeI)_{2'}\rangle \\
& + \langle J^{(1)}(III)_2\rangle + \langle J^{(1)}(III)_{2'}\rangle
\end{aligned}
\right\}
\tag{9.5-8}
$$

for the significant effect in the approximation of the next order. By comparing the effect given by eq. (8) with the effect given by eq. (7) in the same way as we did by eq. (9.4-66), we may see that effect (8) is negligible in ordinary cases. The situation is explained as follows: (1) First, let us take an ion for the test particle o. Then, take an electron for the particle which is nearest neighbor to the test particle o. The effect of the interaction (a part of the zeroth approximation effect) is larger than the effect of the force exerted by two mutually neighboring field particles of which one is an electron. Note that the time scales of the two events are the same. Take an ion for the nearest neighbor particle of the test particle o. Then the effect of the interaction is larger than the effect of the force exerted by two mutually neighboring field particles of which both are ions. (2) The situation is similar for the test particle which is an electron.

9.6. Model (scheme of approximation) III

Let us suppose that an ionized gas is composed of N electrons and $N' = N/\nu$ ions of single species; the charge of one ion Q is given by

$$
\left.
\begin{aligned}
Q &= \nu e \\
e &= \text{the electronic charge.}
\end{aligned}
\right\}
\tag{9.6-1}
$$

If v is much larger than unity and we wish to investigate the evolution of the distribution of ions, the models given in the previous sections are not feasible. Model I is not feasible because the density of electrons is not necessarily uniform due to large and localized ion charges in the present gas; model II is not feasible because $N \gg N'$. Due to the large mass and the large charge of an ion, two nearest-neighbor ions, separated by a distance much larger than the average distance between two nearest neighbor electrons, may have a strong correlation whose time scale is much longer than the time scale of interactions involving electrons. This condition is quite favorable for the valid application of the first two equations of the BBGKY hierarchy, eq. (3.3-8) and eq. (3.3-10). Here particle 1 is to be the test ion whose evolution is our main concern; particle 2 represents the field ions, and particle 3 represents the electrons. The solution of this case has been given by Bogoliubov (1946), Tchen (1959), Rostoker and Rosenbluth (1960), and others[†]. Two ions interact through shielding electrons surrounding the ions. As a result, the interaction force of the ions appear as in accordance with the Debye–Hückel law instead of the Coulomb law. The situation is explained as follows.[‡]

Because the time scale of ion–ion interaction is much longer than the time scale of electron behavior and also because the distance between two neighboring ions is much longer than the average distance between two neighboring electrons, the electric field induced by ions appears not only almost stationary in time but also almost uniform spatially referred to the effect on an electron (Fig. 9.6-1). An electron has many chances of interaction with other electrons while moving from the vicinity of one ion to the vicinity of another ion. Therefore it appears that electrons are locally in thermal equilibrium in the field induced by ions from the viewpoint of an ob-

---

[†] Also see Appendix C.

[‡] Of course, this explanation is simply heuristic. Since these particles are in motion, the explanation must be given based on dynamical equations of the particles. That is what has been done by the authors mentioned in the above; because of the velocities of ions, the Debye–Hückel law is modified.

server with the time scale of ion–ion interaction. (If $\nu \simeq 1$, an electron must experience abrupt changes in the field induced by ions so that there is no chance of thermalization in accordance with such abrupt fluctuations in the field).[†] The density of electrons

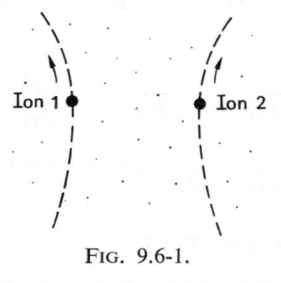

FIG. 9.6-1.

Ion 1, with a large charge and a large mass, interacts with a similar ion 2. Many electrons, depicted with small dots, interfere with the ion–ion interaction.

in thermal equilibrium in potential field ψ is given by

$$\left.\begin{array}{l} n = n_o \exp\left[-(-e)\psi/(kT)\right] \\ \quad = n_o + n_o e\psi/(kT). \end{array}\right\} \quad (9.6\text{-}2)$$

Since n_o is spatially uniform, n_o does not contribute to potential ψ, which is assumed to be originated by the ions.

$$\Delta\psi = 4\pi e(n - n_o)$$
$$= \varkappa^2\psi \qquad \text{(Poisson's eq.)} \quad (9.6\text{-}3)$$
$$\varkappa^2 = \frac{4\pi e^2 n_o}{kT}. \quad (9.6\text{-}4)$$

The position of each ion is a singular point of ψ. The solution is

$$\psi = \sum_\alpha Q_\alpha \frac{\exp\left(-\varkappa r'_\alpha\right)}{r'_\alpha} \quad (9.6\text{-}5)$$

[†] Furthermore there is a paradox involved in this consideration: If an electron interferes in an interaction between two ions, another ion, with the same probability of the electron interference, should interfere in the interaction between the two ions. Thus there is no interaction between two ions which is interfered with by electrons only.

213

where r'_α is the distance between a point where ψ is measured and the position of ion α. Equation (3.3-10) is now replaced by

$$\left(\frac{\partial}{\partial t}+\frac{\mathbf{p}_1}{m_1}\cdot\frac{\partial}{\partial \mathbf{r}_1}+\frac{\mathbf{p}_2}{m_2}\cdot\frac{\partial}{\partial \mathbf{r}_2}+\mathscr{F}'_{12}\cdot\frac{\partial}{\partial \mathbf{p}_1}+\mathscr{F}'_{21}\cdot\frac{\partial}{\partial \mathbf{p}_2}\right)F^{(2)}_{12} = 0, \quad (9.6\text{-}6)$$

in which

$$\left. \begin{aligned} \mathscr{F}'_{12} &= -\mathscr{F}'_{21} = -\frac{\partial\psi'_{12}}{\partial \mathbf{r}_1} \\[2mm] \psi'_{12} &= Q_1 Q_2\frac{\exp\left(-\varkappa r_{12}\right)}{r_{12}} \\[2mm] r_{12} &= |\mathbf{r}_2-\mathbf{r}_1|. \end{aligned} \right\} \qquad (9.6\text{-}7)$$

Eventually $\mathscr{F}'_{12}$ is the sum of $\mathscr{F}_{12}$ and the force exerted by field electrons represented by particle 3 in eq. (3.3-10). $1/\varkappa$ is the Debye shielding length as is well known. The above explanation is simply heuristic. Precise investigations by the authors mentioned above show that the shielding effect is more dynamical, deviating considerably from the above static shielding effect, due to the velocities of ions and electrons. In any case, however, the shielding effect, either static or dynamical, results from time scales

$$\tau_1 \gg \tau_2 \gg \tau_3,$$

by which the first two equations of the BBGKY hierarchy are justified as valid.

For investigating the evolution of the distribution of electrons, we have to change our approach. Again the BBGKY hierarchy is not feasible as a basis. A conceivable approach is to use the technique used for model I, modified by consideration of the force field which is induced by ions, and is almost secular in comparison with the time scale of the electron evolution. These two necessary treatments, the first for electrons and the second for ions, must be considered simultaneously; as a matter of practice, these may constitute an iteration method. In this method, the consideration of the time scales governing the behavior of the particles is essential.

9.7. Remarks on the difficulties in real systems

In view of the discussions presented thus far, it is difficult to cover dynamics of ionized gases with axiomatic formalism. The approach of each case tends to be *ad hoc*; the situation is similar to that of the dynamics of rarefied gases.

So far, the time scale of an electromagnetic field induced from the outside, if ever present, is assumed to be much larger than the time scales of particle interactions. If the time scale of an external field is comparable and/or shorter than the time scale of particle interaction, it is necessary to modify the previous approaches. If the time scale of the external field is the very time scale of our observation, our previous methods of coarse-graining must be changed. The difference between microscopic and macroscopic phenomena is not discrete. The situation is quite similar to the situation of rarefied gas dynamics. Even when we admit that the time scale of our observation is much longer than the time scale of an external force, the difficulty does not decrease if the external force is regularly controlled by us. The essential statistical mechanical weapon, the hypothesis of equal *a priori* probabilities, cannot be used in such cases, as has been discussed by Oberman *et al.* (1962).[†]

The function of a wall in contact with an ionized gas is quite different from that of a wall in contact with a neutral gas. The wall in contact with an ionized gas may be an electrode, may have an electric charge and exert a long-range Coulomb force field, may absorb and emit electrons and/or neutralize ions which collide with it. These effects cannot be solved simply by considering the dynamics of particles whose states at the walls are assumed to be stable.

If the charged particles move with speeds comparable with the speed of light, their mutual interactions are governed not only by

---

[†] Their interpretation of the time scale of the third particle interaction is not always feasible, but the nature of the problem of high frequency external force is well considered and demonstrated.

electro-static forces but also by magnetic forces. Inevitably, electro-magnetic waves may be emitted and/or absorbed by those charged particles, if they are accelerated and/or decelerated by their mutual interactions. The situation may introduce complexities in our treatments as has been shown by Simon and Harris (1960).

Exercises

1. Show that the sum of the right-hand side members of eq. (9.3-2) is equal to $F^{(3)}(ijk)$.

2. Show that

$$\sum_{j \neq k} \int (\mathcal{F}_{ij} + \mathcal{F}_{ik}) \cdot \frac{\partial}{\partial \mathbf{p}_i} F_{ijk}^{(3)}(X_i, X_j, X_k; t) \, dX_j \, dX_k$$

$$= \sum_j \int \mathcal{F}_{ij} \cdot \frac{\partial}{\partial \mathbf{p}_i} F_{ij}^{(2)}(X_i, X_j; t) \, dX_j.$$

3. We may write for $e^2 n^{1/3}/(kT)$ given by eq. (9.4-66) $\frac{1}{4\pi} \varkappa^2 n^{-2/3}$ where

$$\varkappa^2 = \frac{4\pi e^2 n}{kT}.$$

Show that $\varkappa^{-1}$ has the dimensions of length. $\varkappa^{-1}$ is called the Debye–Hückel length.

4. In Subsection 9.4-4, we evaluated the effect of the Boltzmann type interaction by assuming that two particles collide as if they were solid elastic particles of radius R_n. This is a crude overestimation. If we replace R_n with R_e defined by

$$R_e^2 = e^2/kT$$

the result will be an underestimation. How will ratio (9.4-66) change? Notice the following: e^2/R_e^2 is the potential energy when the distance between two electrons is R_e; kT is the average heat energy; hence R_e is of the order of the distance between two particles in a possible collision.

Concluding remarks

THE main theme of investigation has been the feasible application of the hypothesis of equal *a priori* probabilities. As has been shown repeatedly in various cases, the application of the hypothesis varies from one case to another according to the time scales of various phenomena appearing in each case. Such evaluations of phenomena with respect to time scale demand that we have some extensive knowledge about the phenomena under consideration; a knowledge consisting of repeated trial and error, attempted either instantaneously or successively. In this sense, we may need time to pass judgement on the validity of some of the proposed investigations presented here.

Another theme which may be important and yet has not been studied sufficiently in this book, and elsewhere, is the kinetic-theoretical consideration of the interaction between a wall and a gas. So far as this matter is concerned, approaches adopted in this book are mostly statistical-mechanical and often *ad hoc*. It has been felt that, particularly regarding phenomena in rarefied gases and in ionized gases, a genuinely kinetic-theoretical approach of treating the wall effect is essential.

The author strongly feels that we human beings are, through rarefied gas dynamics and plasma dynamics, developing abilities close and similar to those of Maxwell's sorting demon (Appendix G), although we humbly and repeatedly deny this.

Appendices

Appendices

APPENDIX A

The Boltzmann collision integral[†]

A.1. Dynamics of two-particle interaction (the solution of eq. (4.4-14))

We write for eq. (4.4-14)

$$\ddot{\mathbf{r}} = K \frac{\mathbf{r}}{r^{s+1}}, \tag{A.1-1}$$

where

$$\mathbf{r} = \mathbf{R}_{12}, \quad K = -\frac{\varkappa}{M_{12}} \tag{A.1-2}$$

$$\varkappa < 0 \text{ for repulsive forces,}$$

$$\varkappa > 0 \text{ for attractive forces.}$$

As is shown in Section 4.4, $\mathbf{r}$ remains in the same plane during a collision. Hence we consider a polar coordinate system as illustrated in Fig. 4.4-2, and write for eq. (1)

$$\ddot{r} - r\dot{\theta}^2 = \frac{K}{r^s} \tag{A.1-3}$$

$$\frac{d}{dt}(\mathbf{r}^2\dot{\theta}) = 0. \tag{A.1-4}$$

[†] Grad (1949) has studied the matter with great mathematical skill and sophistication.

On integration of eq. (4), we obtain

$$r^2\theta = \eta \qquad \text{(invariant).} \tag{A.1-5}$$

At $t = -\infty$, we have

$$\lim_{\substack{r \to \infty \\ \theta \to 0}} r\theta = h \qquad \text{(impact parameter)}$$

as is obvious in Fig. 4.4-2. Hence, at the same limit,

$$\dot{r}\theta + r\dot{\theta} = 0,$$

or

$$\dot{r} = -v_{12} = \frac{-r\dot{\theta}}{\theta} \qquad (t \to -\infty). \tag{A.1-6}$$

Consequently we may have

$$\left. \begin{aligned} \eta = r^2\dot{\theta} &= r\theta v_{12} \\ &= hv_{12} \qquad (t \to -\infty). \end{aligned} \right\} \tag{A.1-7}$$

On substitution of θ from eq. (5), eq. (3) yields

$$\ddot{r} - \frac{\eta^2}{r^3} = \frac{K}{r^s}, \tag{A.1-3$'$}$$

which is integrated to result in

$$\frac{\dot{r}^2}{2} + \frac{\eta^2}{2r^2} + \frac{K}{(s-1)r^{s-1}} = \alpha. \tag{A.1-8}$$

At the limit $r \to \infty$, we may obtain, considering eq. (6),

$$\alpha = \frac{v_{12}^2}{2}. \tag{A.1-9}$$

Since it holds that

$$\left. \begin{aligned} \dot{r} &= \frac{dr}{d\theta}\,\dot{\theta} = \frac{dr}{d\theta}\,\frac{\eta}{r^2} \\ \ddot{r} &= \frac{d\dot{r}}{d\theta}\,\dot{\theta} = \frac{\eta}{r^2}\frac{d}{d\theta}\left(\frac{\eta}{r^2}\frac{dr}{d\theta}\right) \\ &= \frac{\eta^2}{r^2}\frac{d^2}{d\theta^2}\left(-\frac{1}{r}\right), \end{aligned} \right\} \tag{A.1-10}$$

hence eq. (8) yields

$$\left(\frac{dr}{d\theta}\right)^2 = \frac{2r^4}{\eta^2}\left[\alpha - \frac{\eta^2}{2r^2} - \frac{K}{(s-1)r^{s-1}}\right]. \tag{A.1-11}$$

On definition of ξ by

$$\xi = \frac{h}{r}, \tag{A.1-12}$$

eq. (11) yields

$$d\theta = \frac{d\xi}{\left[1 - \xi^2 - 2\dfrac{K}{(s-1)v_{12}^2}\left(\dfrac{\xi}{h}\right)^{s-1}\right]^{1/2}} \tag{A.1-13}$$

or

$$\theta = \int_0^\xi \frac{d\xi}{\left[1 - \xi^2 - \dfrac{2}{s-1}\left(\dfrac{\xi}{\zeta}\right)^{s-1}\right]^{1/2}}, \tag{A.1-14}$$

where

$$\zeta = h\left(\frac{v_{12}^2}{K}\right)^{1/(s-1)}, \tag{A.1-15}$$

and it is noted that the condition $\xi = 0$ is equivalent to the condition $r = \infty$. The direction of the apse-line is the direction along which r is minimal:

$$\frac{dr}{d\theta} = 0. \qquad (\theta = \theta_\infty)$$

This condition is, according to eq. (11), equivalent to

$$1 - \xi^2 - \frac{2}{s-1}\left(\frac{\xi}{\zeta}\right)^{s-1} = 0. \tag{A.1-16}$$

By solving eq. (16), we may obtain ξ_0 for solution, by which

$$\theta_\infty = \int_0^{\xi_0} \frac{d\xi}{\left[1 - \xi^2 - \dfrac{2}{s-1}\left(\dfrac{\xi}{\zeta}\right)^{s-1}\right]^{1/2}}. \tag{A.1-17}$$

223

It is noted that, when $r \to \infty$, there are two values of $\dot{r}$ obtained from eq. (8):

$$\dot{r} = \mp v_{12}. \qquad \text{(A.1-18)}$$

The upper sign is for the relative velocity before the collision and the lower sign for the relative velocity after the collision. After the collision, we have, by comparison with eq. (7),

$$\lim r\theta = h' = -\frac{\eta}{v_{12}} = -h \quad (t \to +\infty) \qquad \text{(A.1-19)}$$

for the distance between the asymptotic trajectory of particle 2 and the line which passes particle 1 and is parallel to the asymptotic trajectory of particle 2. The negative sign for h' means that the trajectory of particle 2 is on the opposite side of the line passing particle 1 compared with the geometrical relation before the collision. See Fig. 4.4-2.

Since the Newtonian equations of these two particles remain unchanged when we change the sign of time, the motions are time-reversible. In other words, if we make the directions of the two velocities c_1' and c_2' of the two particles opposite, suddenly at a moment after the collision, the two particles will go back along their previous trajectories with velocities of opposite direction compared with their previous motion. The situation is illustrated in Fig. A-1. Secondly we consider a collision where the initial velocities are respectively c_1' and c_2', and the impact parameter is h. Such a collision is realized by turning through 180 degrees the diagram b in Fig. A-1, and is illustrated by diagram c. Thereby, we obtain a rule: If the initial condition of a collision is (c_1, c_2, h) and the resultant condition of the collision is $(c_1', c_2', -h)$, then the initial condition (c_1', c_2', h) results in $(c_1, c_2, -h)$ after the collision.

Special case 1. $\mathcal{F}_{12} = -M_{12}K\dfrac{\mathbf{R}_{12}}{R_{12}^{s+1}}$, $s = 2$. By considering eq. (10) and $s = 2$, we obtain from eq. (3)′

$$\frac{d^2}{d\theta^2}\left(\xi + \frac{hK}{\eta^2}\right) + \left(\xi + \frac{hK}{\eta^2}\right) = 0, \qquad \text{(A.1-20)}$$

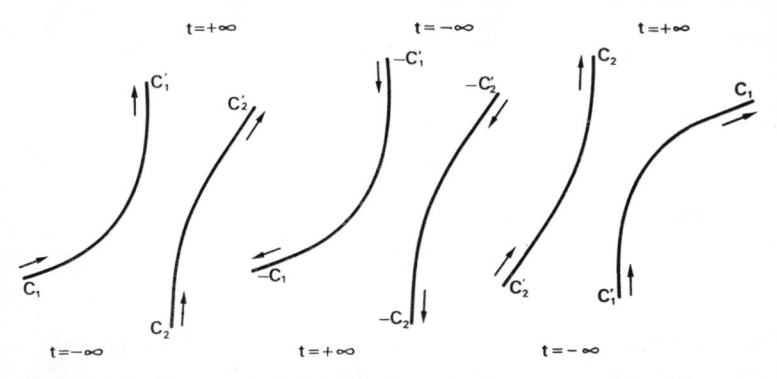

a. Original collision   b. Time-reversed collision   c. Inverse collision

FIG. A-1.

Three akin sets of binary collisions: (a) Original collision; (b) time-reversed collision; (c) inverse collision. The impact parameters of these collisions are the same.

where ξ is defined by eq. (12). On integration of eq. (20) with respect to θ, we obtain

$$\frac{1}{r} + \frac{K}{\eta^2} = \beta \cos (\theta - \theta_\infty) \qquad \text{(A.1-21)}$$

$$\beta = \text{invariant.}$$

Then, consideration of eq. (10) leads to

$$\dot{r} = \eta \beta \sin (\theta - \theta_\infty). \qquad \text{(A.1-22)}$$

In the above, θ_∞ is the magnitude of θ at which

$$\dot{r} = 0, \, r = r_0, \, \theta = \theta_\infty. \qquad \text{(A.1-23)}$$

According to eq. (17), we have

$$\theta_\infty = \int_0^{\xi_0} \frac{d\xi}{\left[1 - \xi^2 - 2 \left(\dfrac{\xi}{\zeta} \right) \right]^{1/2}}, \qquad \text{(A.1-24)}$$

where

$$\xi_0 = h/r_0$$

and ξ_0 is the solution of eq. (16)

$$1 - \xi^2 - 2\xi/\zeta = 0.$$

The solution yields

$$r_0 = \frac{K \pm [K^2 + h^2 v_{12}^4]^{1/2}}{v_{12}^2}. \qquad \text{(A.1-25)}$$

On consideration of $\mathbf{r}_0 > 0$, we take the solution with the positive sign. From eqs. (21) and (22), it follows that

$$\left. \begin{array}{l} \beta^2 = \left(\dfrac{\dot{r}}{\eta}\right)^2 + \left(\dfrac{1}{r} + \dfrac{K}{\eta^2}\right)^2 \\[2ex] = \dfrac{1}{h^2} + \dfrac{K^2}{h^4 v_{12}^4}, \quad r = \infty. \end{array} \right\} \qquad \text{(A.1-26)}$$

β may be obtained also from eq. (21) by considering that

$$\beta = \frac{1}{r_0} + \frac{K}{\eta^2} \quad (\theta = \theta_\infty), \qquad \text{(A.1-27)}$$

where r_0 is given by eq. (25). By considering that $r = \infty$ when $\theta = 0$, we obtain from eq. (21)

$$\cos \theta_\infty = \frac{K}{\beta \eta^2} = K \left[\frac{1}{K^2 + h^2 v_{12}^4} \right]^{1/2} \qquad \text{(A.1-28)}$$

and from eq. (22)

$$\sin \theta_\infty = h v_{12}^2 \left[\frac{1}{K^2 + h^2 v_{12}^4} \right]^{1/2}. \qquad \text{(A.1-29)}$$

Of course, eq. (24) is equivalent to eq. (28) and/or eq. (29). From eq. (24), we obtain

$$\theta_\infty = \sin^{-1} \frac{\xi_0 + 1/\zeta}{[1/\zeta^2 + 1]^{1/2}} - \sin^{-1} \frac{1/\zeta}{[1/\zeta^2 + 1]^{1/2}}$$

by consulting a handy table of integrals. On substitution of

$$\xi_0 = h/r_0, \quad \zeta = hv_{12}^2/K$$

it is shown that

$$\frac{\xi_0 + 1/\zeta}{[1/\zeta^2 + 1]^{1/2}} = 1$$

$$\frac{1/\zeta}{[1/\zeta^2 + 1]^{1/2}} = \frac{K}{[K^2 + h^2 v_{12}^4]^{1/2}}.$$

Hence

$$\theta_\infty = \frac{\pi}{2} - \sin^{-1} \frac{K}{[K^2 + h^2 v_{12}^4]^{1/2}}.$$

This equation is easily reduced to eq. (28).

Special case 2. The Maxwell model: $\mathcal{F}_{12} = -M_{12}K\dfrac{\mathbf{R}_{12}}{R_{12}^{s+1}}$, $s = 5$. In this case, eq. (17) yields

$$\theta_\infty = \int_0^{\xi_0} \frac{d\xi}{\left[1 - \xi^2 - \dfrac{1}{2}\left(\dfrac{\xi}{\zeta}\right)^4\right]^{1/2}}, \tag{A.1-30}$$

where ξ_0 is the solution of

$$1 - \xi^2 - \frac{1}{2}\left(\frac{\xi}{\zeta}\right)^4 = 0$$

or

$$\xi_0^2 = -\zeta^4 + (\zeta^8 + 2\zeta^4)^{1/2}. \tag{A.1-31}$$

From eq. (15) it follows that

$$h\, dh = \frac{K^{1/2}}{v_{12}} \zeta\, d\zeta. \tag{A.1-32}$$

Hence we have

$$v_{12}h\, dh = K^{1/2}\zeta\, d\zeta. \tag{A.1-33}$$

Special case 3. Rigid elastic sphere model:

$$\mathcal{F}_{12} = -M_{12}K \frac{\mathbf{R}_{12}}{R_{12}^{s+1}}, \, s = \infty. \text{ We take for } K$$

$$K = K'\sigma^{s-1}, \, K' > 0 \, \text{(repulsive)}. \tag{A.1-34}$$

Then ζ given by eq. (15) is

$$\zeta = h \left(\frac{v_{12}^2}{K'\sigma^{s-1}} \right)^{1/(s-1)}$$

$$= \frac{h}{\sigma} \left(\frac{v_{12}^2}{K'} \right)^{1/(s-1)}.$$

Hence

$$\lim_{s \to \infty} \zeta = \frac{h}{\sigma}. \tag{A.1-35}$$

We have for eq. (16)

$$1 - \left(\frac{h}{r} \right)^2 - \frac{2}{s-1} \left(\frac{\sigma}{r} \right)^{s-1} \frac{K'}{v_{12}^2} = 0. \tag{A.1-36}$$

If $r > \sigma$, the left-hand side of eq. (36) yields, at the limit $s \to \infty$,

$$1 - (h/r)^2.$$

In case of a repulsive force ($K > 0$), h/r is smaller than unity so that $d\theta$ given by eq. (13) is real. On the other hand, if $r < \sigma$, the left-hand side of eq. (36) yields, at $s \to \infty$,

$$1 - (h/r)^2 - \infty,$$

which is always negative. Hence eq. (35) is satisfied by

$$\sigma/r_0 = 1 + \varepsilon, \tag{A.1-37}$$

where ε is positive and infinitesimal. Hence

$$\xi_0 = h/r_0 = (1 + \varepsilon)h/\sigma.$$

In the domain of ξ from 0 to $\xi_0 - h\varepsilon/\sigma$, it holds that

$$\frac{\xi}{\zeta} \frac{\xi_0 - h\varepsilon/\sigma}{\zeta} = 1,$$

and hence

$$\lim_{s \to \infty} \frac{1}{s-1} \left(\frac{\xi}{\zeta}\right)^{s-1} = 0.$$

Thereby eq. (17) yields

$$\theta_\infty = \int_0^{\xi_0 - h\varepsilon/\sigma} \frac{d\xi}{(1-\xi^2)^{1/2}}$$

or

$$\sin \theta_\infty = h(1-\varepsilon)/\sigma. \tag{A.1-38}$$

In practice, we may take $\varepsilon = 0$. Then it follows that

$$d\theta_\infty \cos \theta_\infty = dh/\sigma$$

and hence

$$h \, dh = \sigma^2 \sin \theta_\infty \cos \theta_\infty \, d\theta_\infty. \tag{A.1-39}$$

Special case 4. Soft elastic sphere model:

$$\mathcal{F}_{12} = -M_{12}K \frac{\mathbf{R}_{12}}{R_{12}^{s+1}}, \quad s = \infty. \text{ We take for } K$$

$$K = K'\sigma^{s-1} \left(\frac{v_{12}^*}{v_{12}}\right)^{(s-1)/2}, \quad K' > 0, \tag{A.1-40}$$

where v_{12}^* is invariant. As in case III, we obtain

$$\lim_{s \to \infty} \zeta = \frac{h}{\sigma} \left(\frac{v_{12}}{v_{12}^*}\right)^{1/2}. \tag{A.1-41}$$

After repeating the same argument as in case III, we obtain

$$\sin \theta_\infty = \frac{h}{\sigma} \left(\frac{v_{12}}{v_{12}^*}\right)^{1/2} \tag{A.1-42}$$

229

and hence

$$v_{12}h\,dh = \sigma^2 v_{12}^* \sin\theta_\infty \cos\theta_\infty\,d\theta_\infty. \qquad \text{(A.1-43)}$$

Since v_{12} vanishes in the collision integrand, the treatment is very much simplified. Furthermore each collision appears like a collision between two solid spherical bodies, although the diameters (cross sections) change as v_{12} changes. If v_{12} becomes larger, the cross section of a molecule becomes smaller.

The viscosity coefficient μ and the heat conductivity λ of each model calculated by the Chapman–Enskog theory (to the first approximation) are as follows:

		μ	λ	c_v
II	Maxwellian ($\varkappa < 0$)	$\dfrac{-2mkT}{0.436 \times 3\pi\varkappa}$	$\dfrac{5}{2}\,\mu c_v$	$\dfrac{3}{2}\dfrac{k}{m}$
III	Rigid sphere	$\dfrac{5(mkT)^{1/2}}{16\sigma^2\pi^{1/2}}$	$\dfrac{5}{2}\,\mu c_v$	$\dfrac{3}{2}\dfrac{k}{m}$
IV	Soft sphere	$\dfrac{2kT}{\sigma^2 v_{12}^*}$	$\dfrac{5}{2}\,\mu c_v$	$\dfrac{3}{2}\dfrac{k}{m}$

We note that the Maxwellian model and the soft sphere model have similar characteristics as far as those coefficients are concerned.

A.2. Moments of the collision integral

Let us consider a collision between particle 1 with mass m_1 and particle 2 with mass m_2. The velocity of particle 1 before the collision is denoted by $\mathbf{c}_1$ and the velocity after the collision by $\mathbf{c}_1'$; the velocity of particle 2 is $\mathbf{c}_2$ before the collision and $\mathbf{c}_2'$ after the collision. According to the Liouville theorem, it holds that

$$d^3r_1\,d^3r_2 m_1^3\,d^3c_1 m_2^3\,d^3c_2 = d^3r_1'\,d^3r_2' m_1^3\,d^3c_1' m_2^3\,d^3c_2', \qquad \text{(A.2-1)}$$

where d^3r_1 is the variation of the space domain which particle 1 occupies before the collision and d^3r_2 is the same for particle 2. Corresponding to these, d^3r_1' and d^3r_2' are the variations of the space domains occupied respectively by particle 1 and particle 2. The correspondence between d^3c_1 and d^3c_1' and/or between d^3c_2 and d^3c_2' is similar. Since it is known that the center of gravity

$$\mathbf{R}_g = (m_1\mathbf{r}_1 + m_2\mathbf{r}_2)/(m_1 + m_2)$$

moves uniformly, we have

$$d^3\mathbf{R}_g = d^3\mathbf{R}_g'. \tag{A.2-2}$$

According to the consideration in Section 4.4, we have

$$\mathbf{r} = \mathbf{r}_2 - \mathbf{r}_1$$
$$d^3r = h\,dh\,d\varphi v_{12}\,d\tau$$

before the collision, and

$$\mathbf{r}' = \mathbf{r}_2' - \mathbf{r}_1'$$
$$d^3r' = h'\,dh'\,d\varphi' v_{12}'\,d\tau'$$

after the collision.

According to results of the investigation in Section A.1, we have

$$|h| = |h'|$$
$$v_{12} = v_{12}'$$
$$\varphi = \varphi'.$$

Hence, it is a easy matter to explain that

$$d\tau = d\tau'.$$

A delay $d\tau$ of the beginning of a collision results in the same delay of the end of the collision. Hence, we obtain

$$d^3\mathbf{R}_g\,d^3r = d^3\mathbf{R}_g'\,d^3r'.$$

Since $\mathbf{R}_g$ and $\mathbf{r}$ are linear functions of $\mathbf{r}_1$ and $\mathbf{r}_2$, we may conclude that

$$d^3r_1 \, d^3r_2 = d^3r_1' \, d^3r_2'. \tag{A.2-3}$$

On substitution of the above in eq. (1), we obtain

$$d^3c_1 \, d^3c_2 = d^3c_1' \, d^3c_2'. \tag{A.2-4}$$

Let us suppose that

$$G(\mathbf{c}_1, \mathbf{c}_2), \quad H(\mathbf{c}_1, \mathbf{c}_2)$$

are two arbitrary functions of $\mathbf{c}_1$ and $\mathbf{c}_2$. Then, under the condition that the impact parameter h and the collision plane φ are specified, it holds that

$$\left. \begin{aligned} \iint G(\mathbf{c}_1', \mathbf{c}_2')H(\mathbf{c}_1, \mathbf{c}_2) \, d^3c_1' \, d^3c_2' \\ = \iint G(\mathbf{c}_1, \mathbf{c}_2)H(\mathbf{c}_1', \mathbf{c}_2') \, d^3c_1 \, d^3c_2. \end{aligned} \right\} \tag{A.2-5}$$

The proof is as follows: as illustrated in Fig. A-1, diagram c, if $\mathbf{c}_1$ and $\mathbf{c}_2$ are the initial conditions of a collision which result in the final conditions $\mathbf{c}_1'$ and $\mathbf{c}_2'$, then there is a collision in which the initial and final conditions are inverted. The integral with respect to $d^3c_1' \, d^3c_2'$ over all the domain is equivalent to the integral with respect to $d^3c_1 \, d^3c_2$.

On substitution of eq. (4) in eq. (5), we have another relation:

$$\left. \begin{aligned} \iint G(\mathbf{c}_1', \mathbf{c}_2')H(\mathbf{c}_1, \mathbf{c}_2) \, d^3c_1 \, d^3c_2 \\ = \iint G(\mathbf{c}_1, \mathbf{c}_2)H(\mathbf{c}_1', \mathbf{c}_2') \, d^3c_1 \, d^3c_2. \end{aligned} \right\} \tag{A.2-6}$$

We are now ready to discuss moments of the Boltzmann collision integral

$$-J_{12} = \iiint [(f_1(\mathbf{c}_1')f_2(\mathbf{c}_2') - f_1(\mathbf{c}_1)f_2(\mathbf{c}_2)]h \, dh \, d\varphi \mathbf{v}_{12} \, d^3c_2. \tag{A.2-7}$$

Let us take $\phi(\mathbf{c}_1)$, a function of $\mathbf{c}_1$, and consider

$$\left. \begin{aligned} -\int \phi(\mathbf{c}_1)J_{12} \, d^3c_1 \\ = \iiiint \phi(\mathbf{c}_1) \, [f_1(\mathbf{c}_1')f_2(\mathbf{c}_2') - f_1(\mathbf{c}_1)f_2(\mathbf{c}_2)]h \, dh \, d\varphi \mathbf{v}_{12} d^3c_2 \, d^3c_1. \end{aligned} \right\} \tag{A.2-8}$$

According to eq. (6), the right-hand side yields

$$= \iiint [\phi(\mathbf{c}_1') - \phi(\mathbf{c}_1)] f_1(\mathbf{c}_1) f_2(\mathbf{c}_2) h \, dh \, d\varphi v_{12} \, d^3 c_2 \, d^3 c_1. \quad \text{(A.2-9)}$$

If particle 1 and particle 2 are of the same species, we obtain

$$-\int \phi'(\mathbf{c}_1) J_{12} \, d^3 c_1 = 0 \quad \text{(A.2-10)}$$

for

$$\phi'(\mathbf{c}_1) = 1, \quad m_1 \mathbf{c}_1, \quad m_1 c_1^2; \quad m_1 = m_2$$

in accordance with the mass, momentum, and energy conservation laws of an isolated system. In general, it holds that

$$\int \phi'(\mathbf{c}_1) J_{12} \, d^3 c_1 + \int \phi'(\mathbf{c}_2) J_{21} \, d^3 c_2 = 0. \quad \text{(A.2-11)}$$

In (9), $\mathbf{c}_1'$ depends not only on $\mathbf{c}_1$, $\mathbf{c}_2$, h, but also on the force law which governs the collision. Therefore, the resultant value given by eq. (9) varies as the force law (collision model) varies. In rarefied-gas dynamics, consideration of moments of orders higher than those of

$$\int f(\mathbf{c}) \, d^3 c, \quad \int m\mathbf{c} f(\mathbf{c}) \, d^3 c, \quad \int mc^2 f(\mathbf{c}) \, d^3 c$$

are essential, and hence the choice of a feasible collision model is important even when the gas under consideration consists of a single species of particles.

A.3. The Bhatnagar–Gross–Krook model[†]

Instead of considering the collision mechanism based on a certain force law, we assume that

$$-J = \Theta (\bar{f} - f), \quad \text{(A.3-1)}$$

where Θ is a constant with dimension of time^{-1}, and $\bar{f}$ is given by

$$\bar{f} = n \left(\frac{m}{2\pi kT} \right)^{3/2} \exp \left[-\frac{m}{2kT} (\mathbf{c} - \mathbf{u})^2 \right], \quad \text{(A.3-2)}$$

[†] The model was proposed by Bhatnagar, Gross, and Krook (1954), Gross and Krook (1956), and Krook (1959).

in which

$$n = \int f \, d^3c$$
$$n\mathbf{u} = \int m\mathbf{c} \, f \, d^3c$$
$$\frac{3}{2} nkT = \int \frac{1}{2} m(\mathbf{c}-\mathbf{u})^2 f \, d^3c. \tag{A.3-3}$$

The collision factor $-J$ given by the above possesses some of the properties of the Boltzmann collision integral:

1. The H-theorem holds[†]

2. $\quad \int J \, d^3c = 0, \quad \int m\mathbf{c}J \, d^3c = 0, \quad \int mc^2 J \, d^3c = 0.$ (A.3-4)

Let us take an arbitrary function $\phi(c)$ of $\mathbf{c}$, and consider

$$-\int \phi(c)J \, d^3c = \Theta \int (c) \bar{f} \, d^3c - \Theta \int \phi(c) f \, d^3c \tag{A.3-5}$$

[†] Boltzmann defined H by

$$H = \int f \log f \, d^3c. \tag{i}$$

Hence

$$\frac{\partial H}{\partial t} = \int (1 + \log f) \frac{\partial f}{\partial t} \, d^3c. \tag{ii}$$

If the distribution is spatially uniform, we have

$$\frac{\partial f}{\partial t} = \Theta (\bar{f} - f) \tag{iii}$$

according to the present model. On substitution of (iii), eq. (ii) yields

$$\frac{\partial H}{\partial t} = \Theta \int (1 + \log f)(\bar{f} - f) \, d^3c = \Theta \int (\log f)(\bar{f} - f) \, d^3c.$$

According to eq. (2), $\log \bar{f}$ is a linear function of $(\mathbf{c}-\mathbf{u})^2$, and hence

$$\int (\log \bar{f})(\bar{f} - f) \, d^3c = 0.$$

Thereby, it follows that

$$\frac{\partial H}{\partial t} = \Theta \int \log \left(\frac{f}{\bar{f}} \right)(\bar{f} - f) \, d^3c. \tag{iv}$$

According to eq. (iv), if $\bar{f} > f$, then $\partial H/\partial t$ is negative; if $\bar{f} < f$, then $\partial H/\partial t$ is also negative. If $\bar{f} = f$, then

$$\partial H/\partial t = 0.$$

by comparison with what may be derived from eq. (A.2-9):

$$-\int \phi(c)J\,d^3c = \int \left[\int\int\int \phi(c')f(c_1)h\,dhv_{12}\,d\varphi\,d^3c_1\right]f(c)\,d^3c \atop -\int \phi(c)\left[\int\int\int f(c_1)h\,dhv_{12}\,d\varphi\,d^3c_1\right]f(c)\,d^3c. \right\} \quad \text{(A.3-6)}$$

The significance of eq. (5) is that if we take for $\phi(c)$ a function which is odd with respect to $(\mathbf{c}-\mathbf{u})$, the first member of the right-hand side vanishes:

$$\int \phi(c)\,\bar{f}\,d^3c = 0.$$

For example,

$$\int (\mathbf{c}-\mathbf{u})^2(\mathbf{c}-\mathbf{u})\,\bar{f}\,d^3c = 0.$$

On the other hand, the first member of the right-hand side of eq. (6) does not do so, in general. In view of the above, the application of the present collision model is to be made with caution especially when the state of a gas under consideration deviates considerably from thermal equilibrium, and moments of f derived with respect to odd functions of $(\mathbf{c}-\mathbf{u})$ have significant meanings.

There will be confusion arising from the model if one applies the Chapman–Enskog method of solution to it. The confusion seems to manifest characteristics of the model. Some details are investigated below.

By the present collision model, the Boltzmann equation is given by

$$\frac{df}{dt} = \Theta\,(\bar{f}-f), \qquad\qquad \text{(A.3-7)}$$

where

$$\frac{d}{dt} = \frac{\partial}{\partial t} + \mathbf{c}\cdot\frac{\partial}{\partial \mathbf{r}}.$$

We take for the first approximation of f

$$f^{(1)} = \bar{f}+\varphi^{(1)}. \qquad\qquad \text{(A.3-8)}$$

According to the Chapman–Enskog method, as given in Section

5.2, let us determine $\varphi^{\langle 1 \rangle}$ by the following

$$\frac{d\bar{f}}{dt} = \Theta \left[\bar{f} - (\bar{f} + \varphi^{\langle 1 \rangle}) \right] = -\varphi^{\langle 1 \rangle} \Theta. \qquad (A.3-9)$$

We now realize that eq. (9) is the same as eq. (5.3-18) from which $\varphi^{\langle 1 \rangle}$ is obtained there. Therefore, regarding $f^{\langle 1 \rangle}$ determined by eq. (9), we have to repeat all the arguments which are given regarding $\varphi^{\langle 1 \rangle}$ in Section 5.3. For example, see eq. (5.3-34).

For the next approximation, we may write for f

$$f^{\langle 2 \rangle} = \bar{f} + \varphi^{\langle 2 \rangle} \qquad (A.3-10)$$

and obtain, according to the Chapman–Enskog method,

$$\frac{df^{\langle 1 \rangle}}{dt} = \Theta [\bar{f} - f^{\langle 2 \rangle}]. \qquad (A.3-11)$$

In accordance with eq. (5.3-4), however, it is obvious that the corresponding equation by the Boltzmann collision integral is quite different from eq. (11). First, in Section 5.3, we cannot put

$$[f_s^{\langle 1 \rangle} \Theta_s^{\langle 1 \rangle}]' \rightarrow f_s^{\langle 1 \rangle}(\mathbf{c}) \Theta_s^{\langle 1 \rangle}.$$

We may assume as an approximation, that

$$[f_s^{\langle 1 \rangle} \Theta_s^{\langle 1 \rangle}]' \rightarrow f_s^{\langle 1 \rangle}(\mathbf{c}') \Theta_s^{\langle 1 \rangle},$$

where $\mathbf{c}'$ is the velocity of a particle after a collision while $\mathbf{c}$ is its velocity before the collision (see Fig. A-1). Then we obtain, in place of eq. (5.3-17),

$$f^{\langle 2 \rangle}(\mathbf{c}) = f^{\langle 1 \rangle}(\mathbf{c}') \left[1 - \frac{1}{\Theta^{\langle 1 \rangle}} \frac{d \log f^{\langle 1 \rangle}(\mathbf{c}')}{dt} \right],$$

or

$$\frac{df^{\langle 1 \rangle}(\mathbf{c}')}{dt} = \Theta^{\langle 1 \rangle} (f^{\langle 1 \rangle}(\mathbf{c}') - f^{\langle 2 \rangle}(\mathbf{c})) \qquad (A.3-12)$$

corresponding to eq. (11).

236

Finally it is noted that the development of the BGK collision model appears to have been motivated by the same intuition as that of Clausius and Meyer which motivated the development of their transport theory in the last century. The present model contains the same inaccuracy as Clausius–Meyer's theory. See footnote of p. 103. Therefore great caution is necessary in using the BGK equation as a substitute for the Boltzmann equation. Particularly the inaccuracy is enhanced when one treats the equation by a method similar to the Chapman–Enskog method under the conditions that the Knudsen number of a gas field under investigation is not small and the state of the gas deviates significantly from thermal equilibrium. Of course, as is discussed in detail in Part II, the Chapman–Enskog method itself becomes less plausible as the above condition prevails, even when the method is applied to the original Boltzmann equation. Within the limiting condition where the Chapman–Enskog method as applied to the Boltzmann equation is valid, however, the deficiency embedded in the BGK equation is enhanced in the solution obtained by the Chapman–Enskog method. If we consider some other method of solving the Boltzmann equation, noticing that the main characteristics of a rarefied gas flow are determined predominantly by boundary and initial conditions instead of the thermalization effect due to collisions, as exemplified in Section 7.4, and apply the method to the BGK equation, the situation is rather different. The inaccuracy of the collision factor of the BGK equation may not affect the result seriously, because the collision effect is, after all, a minor perturbation factor in the solution. An interesting application was made by Chu (1965) investigating the formation of a shock wave. The author (1965) notices that it is difficult to generalize the model without destroying the simplicity.

APPENDIX B

Difficulties in usual derivations of the Boltzmann equation

THERE have been different derivations proposed by several authors. As typical examples, the derivations by Kirkwood and Ross, by Bogoliubov, and by Grad are investigated in the following. Because of the assumption of symmetry of $D^{(N)}$ considered in the microscopic sense, these derivations involve common difficulties.

DERIVATION BY KIRKWOOD AND ROSS (1958)

We may point out the following four difficulties in this derivation based on the BBGKY hierarchy.

1. By coarse-graining eq. (3.2-3) with respect to time, we obtain

$$\left.\begin{aligned}\left(\frac{\partial}{\partial t}+\frac{\mathbf{p}_i}{m}\cdot\frac{\partial}{\partial \mathbf{r}_i}\right)\langle F_i^{(1)}(X_i;\,t)\rangle_\tau \\ +\frac{(N-1)}{\tau}\int_0^\tau\left(\mathcal{F}_{ij}\cdot\frac{\partial}{\partial \mathbf{p}_i}\right)F_{ij}^{(2)}(X_i,X_j;\,t+s)\,dX_j\,ds,\end{aligned}\right\} \quad \text{(B-1)}$$

where

$$\langle F_i^{(1)}(X_i;\,t)\rangle_\tau = \frac{1}{\tau}\int_0^\tau F_i^{(1)}(X_i;\,t+s)\,ds \quad \text{(B-2)}$$

and $\mathcal{F}_{io}$ has been ignored. According to the assumption of symmetry, we may replace

$$\left.\begin{aligned}F_i^{(1)}(X_i;\,t) \quad \text{with} \quad F^{(1)}(X_1;\,t) \\ F_{ij}^{(2)}(X_i,X_j;\,t) \quad \text{with} \quad F^{(2)}(X_1,X_2;\,t).\end{aligned}\right\} \quad \text{(B-3)}$$

The next procedure is to define $K^{(2)}$ by

$$F^{(2)}(X_1, X_2; t+s) = \int K^{(2)}(X_1, X_2/X_1', X_2'; s) \, F^{(2)}(X_1', X_2'; t) \, dX_1' \, dX_2'.$$
(B-4)

Since $K^{(2)}$ is given explicitly by

$$K^{(2)}(X_1, X_2/X_1', X_2'; s) = \delta(X_1 - X_1' - \Delta X_1(s)) \, \delta(X_2 - X_2' - \Delta X_2(s)),$$
(B-5)

it is easily shown that

$$F^{(2)}(X_1, X_2; t+s) = F^{(2)}(X_1 - \Delta X_1(s), X_2 - \Delta X_2(s); t). \quad \text{(B-6)}$$

According to Kirkwood and Ross, $\Delta X_1(s)$, standing for $\Delta \mathbf{p}_1(s)$ and $\Delta \mathbf{r}_1(s)$, and $\Delta X_2(s)$, standing for $\Delta \mathbf{p}_2(s)$ and $\Delta \mathbf{r}_2(s)$, are the changes in momenta and space coordinates of particle 1 and particle 2 determined by solving the equations of motion of the two particles in accordance with the assumption of binary collision:

$$\left. \begin{aligned} \frac{d\Delta \mathbf{r}_1(s)}{ds} &= \frac{\mathbf{p}_1 + \Delta \mathbf{p}_1(s)}{m} \\[2mm] \frac{d\Delta \mathbf{p}_1(s)}{ds} &= \mathcal{F}_{12}(s) \end{aligned} \right\}$$
(B-7)

and similar equations for particle 2. Under these circumstances, the authors claim that $F^{(2)}$ given by eq. (6) is a solution of eq. (3.2-4) where the integral term is ignored and $\partial/\partial t$ is replaced by $\partial/\partial s$:

$$\left(\frac{\partial}{\partial s} + \frac{\mathbf{p}_1}{m} \cdot \frac{\partial}{\partial \mathbf{r}_1} + \frac{\mathbf{p}_2}{m} \cdot \frac{\partial}{\partial \mathbf{r}_2} + \mathcal{F}_{12} \cdot \frac{\partial}{\partial \mathbf{p}_1} + \mathcal{F}_{21} \cdot \frac{\partial}{\partial \mathbf{p}_2} \right) F^{(2)} = 0. \quad \text{(B-8)}$$

Here the external forces are ignored, and s, $\mathbf{p}_1$, $\mathbf{p}_2$, $\mathbf{r}_1$, and $\mathbf{r}_2$ are to be independent variables. It is obvious, however, that $F^{(2)}$ given by eq. (6) under condition (7) does not satisfy eq. (8). Instead, it is obvious that $F^{(2)}$ satisfies eq. (8), if $X_1(s)$ and $X_2(s)$ are solutions of

$$\frac{d\Delta \mathbf{r}_1(s)}{ds} = \frac{\mathbf{p}_1}{m}, \quad \frac{d\Delta \mathbf{p}_1(s)}{ds} = \mathcal{F}_{12}, \quad \text{etc.} \quad \text{(B-9)}$$

in place of eq. (7). Note that $\mathbf{p}_1$, $\mathbf{p}_2$, $\mathbf{r}_1$, and $\mathbf{r}_2$ are independent of s in eq. (9), and hence the equations are not the equations of motion of the two particles. Only when $\Delta X_1(s)$ and $\Delta X_2(s)$ are extremely small, eqs. (9) coincide with eqs. (7). It is noted that the particular solution of eq. (8) integrated along trajectories determined by eqs. (7) is given in Section 4.4.

2. Although $\Delta X_1(s)$ and $\Delta X_2(s)$ satisfying eqs. (9) are not the proper trajectories of the two particles in interaction, such as expected by the authors, $F^{(2)}$ given by eq. (6) is still a correct solution of eq. (8) under condition (9). Therefore, if the succeeding treatment is proper, it may lead to a correct result. By substituting $F^{(2)}$ given by eq. (6) in the collision integral of eq. (1), however, we will meet a great difficulty in the following treatment. Since X_1 and X_2 are independent variables, the domain of the integration with respect to $d\mathbf{r}_2$ is to be the entire configuration space; $\mathcal{F}_{12}$ and/or $\mathcal{F}_{21}$ are functions of $\mathbf{r}_1$ and $\mathbf{r}_2$, and are completely independent of $\Delta \mathbf{r}_1(s)$ and $\Delta \mathbf{r}_2(s)$ determined by eq. (9). Therefore, $\Delta \mathbf{r}_1(\tau) - \Delta \mathbf{r}_2(\tau)$ is not a factor which affects the magnitude of $\mathcal{F}_{12}$. Even when $\Delta \mathbf{r}_1(\tau) - \Delta \mathbf{r}_2(\tau)$ is extremely large, $\mathcal{F}_{12}$ may not vanish if $\mathbf{r}_1 - \mathbf{r}_2$ is small, and vice versa. Hence there is no reason for limiting the domain of integration with respect to $d\mathbf{r}_2$ in the direction of $\mathbf{p}_2 - \mathbf{p}_1$ by $\tau \,|\, \mathbf{p}_2 - \mathbf{p}_1 \,|/m$ that is a function of τ.

3. The difficulty mentioned in the above seems to have stemmed from the authors' belief that the X's and t must always be independent variables. This belief is a rational consequence of their assumption that $D^{(N)}$ given in Section 2.2 is always symmetric with respect to the interchange of coordinates between two similar particles. Indeed, according to the assumption, it is pointless to say that an individual particle moves along a continuous trajectory; there is no such individual particle distinguishable from the others by its continuous trajectory. In spite of the technical difficulty mentioned, it appears that the authors' approach is at least consistent with their belief that $D^{(N)}$ is symmetric. But the situation is not necessarily so. Contrary to the author's expectation, $F^{(2)}(X_1 - \Delta X_1(s), \ X_2 - \Delta X_2(s);\ t)$ given by eq. (6) is not symmetric, as is shown below. Suppose

240

that we consider $F^{(2)}$ at $X_1 = \Delta X_1(s)$ and $X_2 = \Delta X_2(s)$. Then, according to the symmetry assumption, it must hold that

$$F^{(2)}(0, 0; t) = F^{(2)}(\Delta X_2(s) - \Delta X_1(s), \Delta X_1(s) - \Delta X_2(s); t).$$

Since $\Delta X_2(s) - \Delta X_1(s)$ may increases as s increases, the above equation implies that $F^{(2)}(X_1, X_2; t)$ is uniform along a line given by $X_1 = -X_2$. If we displace the origin of the coordinate system by keeping the axes parallel to those before the displacement, we can see that $F^{(2)}$ is uniform (invariant) over the entire phase space. This obvious paradox is caused by the attempt to represent a microscopic collision in terms of $F^{(2)}$ which is assumed to be symmetric.

4. Microscopic collisions are conceivable only when we begin a theory by taking $D^{(N)}$ of a single system as given by eq. (2.3-10) which is not symmetric. By taking $X_i = X_i^*(s)$, we are observing $D^{(N)}$ along the trajectory of particle i. It is worth while noticing that there are various solutions of the partial differential equation (8), according to our choice of functions of s to be assigned to p_1, p_2, r_1, and r_2:

$$\left. \begin{array}{ll} \mathbf{p}_1 = \mathbf{p}_1^*(s), & \mathbf{r}_1 = \mathbf{r}_1^*(s), \\ \mathbf{p}_2 = \mathbf{p}_2^*(s), & \mathbf{r}_2 = \mathbf{r}_2^*(s). \end{array} \right\} \tag{B-10}$$

In the special case where these functions given in the above satisfy the characteristic equations of eq. (8), which are the very equations of motion of the two particles, $F^{(2)}$ is invariant with respect to s. Otherwise, $F^{(2)}$ is not invariant.

In view of the above investigations, it appears that Kirkwood and Ross believed the symmetry of $D^{(N)}$ in the microscopic sense. This belief, in spite of their reasonable approach of coarse-graining with respect to time, seems to have jeopardized their derivation. In general, the same difficulty as that found in the derivation by Kirkwood and Ross is pointed out commonly in derivations beginning with the symmetry assumption of $D^{(N)}$.

DERIVATION BY BOGOLIUBOV (1946)

The derivation by Bogoliubov is similar to the derivation by Kirkwood and Ross. Bogoliubov defined a "streaming operator" which has the same implication as that of $K^{(2)}$ given by eq. (5). Therefore, the difficulty seen in Bogoliubov's derivation is of the same nature as that of Kirkwood and Ross.

DERIVATION BY GRAD (1958)

The derivation by Grad is anomalous in the sense that the derivation is consistent in spite of the symmetry of $D^{(N)}$ assumed in the microscopic sense. This paradoxical situation is explained in the following. Grad defined "truncated distribution function". For example, $F_1^{\alpha}(X_1)$ is the expectation of finding no molecule within a distance σ of molecule 1, provided that molecule 1 is in state X_1. It is also assumed that the sphere of radius σ limits the domain of influence of molecule 1. Grad derived the equation of evolution of $F_1^{\alpha}(X_1)$ from the Liouville equation, instead of the equation of evolution of $F^{(1)}(X_1)$. This is equivalent to considering the distribution function of molecules as if in states of free flight, in the same way as is intended by the Boltzmann equation. Also by assuming the existence of the sphere of influence, the further treatment appears as a treatment of collisions among elastic (solid) spherical bodies of diameter σ, instead of collisions between force fields. Therefore, the spatial domain of the collision integral with respect to a field particle is always the space outside the sphere of influence of particle 1. In this way, Grad could avoid the cause of the common difficulty, that is the consideration of trajectories of particles during their collisions. To complete the derivation by giving the equation obtained above the same implication as that of the Boltzmann equation, however, it is necessary to assume the existence of "molecular order" in the behavior of two particles within the distance σ. This assumption is not compatible with the

postulate that the symmetry of $D^{(N)}$ and hence the BBGKY hierarchy is valid in the microscopic sense. This condition is out of the scope of Grad's theory. Grad's scheme is ingenious in the sense that it has separated itself from the treatment of collision mechanism which is not compatible with the symmetry assumption of $D^{(N)}$.

In conclusion, we notice the following:

1. The Boltzmann collision integral can be derived from the Liouville equation only by considering that the distribution function $D^{(N)}$ of a system is not symmetric in the microscopic sense.

2. The microscopic symmetry of $D^{(N)}$, by which a particle is indistinguishable from the others, is not compatible with the Boltzmann collision integral where a particle is distinguishable during its collision by its continuous and ordered trajectory.

3. If we accept the Boltzmann equation as feasible, we must admit that kinetic theory must begin with a non-symmetric $D^{(N)}$.

APPENDIX C

Kinetic theories which are not based on the BBGKY hierarchy

There is a method of treating many-body systems proposed by Prigogine and Balescu. There, the distribution function $D^{(N)}$ of N particle systems is expanded in Fourier's series with respect to time and the configuration-space coordinates of the particles.

$$D^{(N)} = \varrho_0 + \sum_k \sum_j \varrho_k^j \exp [i\mathbf{k} \cdot (\mathbf{r}_j - \mathbf{p}_j t)$$

$$+ \sum_k \sum_{k'} \sum_j \sum_l \varrho_{kk'}^{jl} \exp [i\mathbf{k} \cdot (\mathbf{r}_j - \mathbf{p}_j t) + i\mathbf{k'} \cdot (\mathbf{r}_l - \mathbf{p}_l t)] + \ldots, \quad \text{(C-1)}$$

in which $\mathbf{k}$, $\mathbf{k'}$, ... are wave vectors; subscripts j, l, ... indicate individual particles, $i^2 = -1$; $\mathbf{r}$ is the position vector and $\mathbf{p}$ the momentum of a particle. If there is no interaction among the particles, the ϱ's in $D^{(N)}$ are independent of time. If there are interactions among the particles, the ϱ's must be considered as functions of time. On substitution of $D^{(N)}$ given above in the Liouville equation and integration with respect to the $\mathbf{r}$'s, we obtain a set of equations which govern the time evolutions of the ϱ's. The conservation law for the momenta of particles in mutual interaction is translated in to the conservation law for wave vectors, and each of the basic and typical modes of interaction in terms of wave vectors is represented by a diagram. So far as the above principle is concerned, the presentation is illustrative and at the same time is as precise as the Liouville equation itself.

In order to apply the formulation to a practical many-body problem, however, we have to coarse-grain the original formulae so that the many-body problem is reduced to a superposition of certain two-body problems. In the process of reduction, summations $\sum_j, \sum_l, \ldots$ are replaced with multiplication by $(N-1)$, $(N-2)$, $\ldots$. This operation is exactly the same as done in deriving eq. (3.2-3) from eq. (2.4-10), and eq. (3.2-4) from eq. (2.4-11), and so forth. The theory is based on the same symmetry assumption as the one on which the BBGKY theory is based. Therefore it is to be expected that the results obtained by the present method are similar to those obtained from the BBGKY hierarchy.

For example, Balescu (1960) applied the method to his investigation of irreversible processes in ionized gases (electron gases in the ordinary sense). If we translate his treatment to a treatment by means of the BBGKY hierarchy, the procedure is described as follows:

With respect to the first equation of the BBGKY hierarchy

$$\left(\frac{\partial}{\partial t} + \frac{\mathbf{p}_1}{m} \cdot \frac{\partial}{\partial \mathbf{r}_1}\right) F_1^{(1)} + (N-1) \int \mathcal{F}_{12} \cdot \frac{\partial}{\partial \mathbf{p}_1} F_{12}^{(2)} \, dX_2 = 0,$$

he (Balescu) expands $F_{12}^{(2)}$ in a series

$$F_{12}^{(2)} = (F_{12})_1 + (F_{12})_2 + (F_{12})_{2'} + \ldots.$$

He determines $(F_{12})_1$ by solving

$$\left(\frac{\partial}{\partial t} + \frac{\mathbf{p}_1}{m} \cdot \frac{\partial}{\partial \mathbf{r}_1} + \frac{\mathbf{p}_2}{m} \cdot \frac{\partial}{\partial \mathbf{r}_2} + \mathcal{F}_{12} \cdot \frac{\partial}{\partial \mathbf{p}_1} + \mathcal{F}_{21} \cdot \frac{\partial}{\partial \mathbf{p}_2}\right) (F_{12})_1 = 0$$

which constitutes a part of the second equation of the BBGKY hierarchy. Secondly, $(F_{12})_2$ is determined by the following two simultaneous equations

$$\left(\frac{\partial}{\partial t} + \frac{\mathbf{p}_1}{m} \cdot \frac{\partial}{\partial \mathbf{r}_1} + \frac{\mathbf{p}_2}{m} \cdot \frac{\partial}{\partial \mathbf{r}_2}\right) (F_{12})_2 + (N-2) \mathcal{F}_{23} \cdot \frac{\partial}{\partial \mathbf{p}_2} (F_{123})_1 \, dX_3 = 0$$

245

(another part of the second equation of the BBGKY) and

$$\left(\frac{\partial}{\partial t} + \frac{\mathbf{p}_1}{m}\cdot\frac{\partial}{\partial \mathbf{r}_1} + \frac{\mathbf{p}_2}{m}\cdot\frac{\partial}{\partial \mathbf{r}_2} + \frac{\mathbf{p}_3}{m}\cdot\frac{\partial}{\partial \mathbf{r}_3} + \mathscr{F}_{13}\cdot\frac{\partial}{\partial \mathbf{p}_1} + \mathscr{F}_{31}\cdot\frac{\partial}{\partial \mathbf{p}_3}\right)(F_{123})_1 = 0$$

(a part of the third equation of the BBGKY).

The treatment proceeds similarly. Of course, these procedures constitute an approximate method for reducing a many-body problem to a superposition of two-body problems.

It is also noted that Weinstock (1964) proposed another method which is similar to the above in view of the method of coarse-graining.

THE KINETIC-THEORETICAL STATUS OF MARKOV'S METHOD OF RANDOM FLIGHT

In order to explain a sort of Stark broadening of spectrum lines emitted from an ionized gas, Holtsmark (1919) calculated electric field fluctuations induced by charged particles by means of Markov's method of random flight. The same method was utilized by Chandrasekhar (1943) to calculate the gravitational force exerted on a test star by field stars. In those treatments, the probability distribution of field particles in the phase space is assumed to be

$$w(\mathbf{r}_1, \mathbf{p}_1; \mathbf{r}_2, \mathbf{p}_2; \ldots; \mathbf{r}_N, \mathbf{p}_N) = \prod_{i=1}^{N} w(\mathbf{r}_i, \mathbf{p}_i), \qquad \text{(C-2)}$$

where $\mathbf{r}_i$ is the position vector and $\mathbf{p}_i$ the momentum of particle i. In ordinary applications where condition (2) is assumed, the results obtained by the method are similar to those implied by the Boltzmann integral under the condition that inter-particle forces are extremely weak.

Assumption (2) is similar to the symmetry assumption by which eq. (2.4-10) is reduced to eq. (3.2-3), the first equation of the BBGKY hierarchy. Considering the symmetry, we may write for the equation

of the distribution function of the test particle

$$\left(\frac{\partial}{\partial t} + \frac{\mathbf{p_0}}{m_0} \cdot \frac{\partial}{\partial \mathbf{r_0}}\right) F^{(1)}(0) + N \int \mathcal{F}_{01} \cdot \frac{\partial}{\partial \mathbf{p_0}} F^{(2)}(0, 1) \, dX_1 = 0. \quad \text{(C-3)}$$

As discussed repeatedly in previous sections, however, the symmetry assumption in the microscopic sense does not lead to the Boltzmann equation. This paradox is due to our failure to understand the true implication of Markov's method. By Markov's method of random flights, the probability distribution of resultant events is given by Dirichlet's integral defined in terms of the probability distribution of causal events. But is does not specify any particular law governing the process connecting a causal event and its resultant event; the choice of a proper law is open to us. In the case of Chandrasekhar's application, condition (2) provides only the probability distribution of initial conditions of the field stars. A field star of an initial condition of which the probability is given by condition (2), may move on any trajectory according to the law chosen by us. According to Chandrasekhar, the star moves, as time passes, with an invariant velocity along a straight trajectory determined by the specific initial condition. This is a free motion of perfect auto-correlation. This motion is not prescribed by Markov's method itself. (If we apply condition (2) to those field stars during their flights, a field star may fly on a straight trajectory with only a small probability, unless $w(\mathbf{p})$ is a δ-function.) On the other hand, equations in kinetic theory must prescribe all the conditions of those processes connecting causes and resultant events.

In summary, Markov's method is a mathematical theorem of statistics; it does not specify any particular law governing physical processes following the causal events. Therefore, we have to supply the necessary physical laws in each case of application. (Of course, the merit of the method is not reduced by this statement. If we assume a proper physical law or restrictive condition, the same method may lead us even to the Vlasov mode of interaction which is quite different from the case of Chandrasekhar. The modification of Markov's method in this sense was discussed in PIBAL Report No. 954, Nov.

1965, published by Polytechnic Institute of Brooklyn, New York.) The physical implication of Chandrasekhar's treatment is the same as that of the Boltzmann collision integral considered at the limit of weak interaction. Therefore the results should be the same as those discussed in Sections 8.3 and 8.4. (Note that the gravity force law between stars and the Coulomb force law are both of the inverse square of distance, and results diverge at long distances as well as at short distances.[†])

[†] Holtsmark (1919) simply calculated the total electric force field induced by the field particles on a point in the space. Therefore, there was no danger of divergence. In Chandrasekhar approximation (1943), $\langle \varDelta \mathbf{p} \, \varDelta \mathbf{p} \rangle$ apparently converges at long distances.

APPENDIX D

A mathematical theorem

Theorem:

$$S = N^2 + N(N-2)^2 + \frac{1}{2!} N(N-1)(N-4)^2 + \ldots$$

$$+ \frac{1}{n!} N(N-1)\ldots(N-n+1)(N-2n)^2 + \ldots + N^2$$

(the last member is for $n = N$)

$$= N2^N.$$

Proof:

$$S = N^2 + N(N^2 - 4N + 4) + \frac{1}{2!} N(N-1)(N^2 - 8N + 16) + \ldots$$

$$= N^2 \left[1 + N + \frac{1}{2!} N(N-1) + \ldots \right]$$

$$- 4N^2 \left[1 + (N-1) + \frac{1}{2!} (N-1)(N-2) + \ldots \right]$$

$$+ 4N \left[1 + 2(N-1) + \frac{3}{2!} (N-1)(N-2) + \ldots \right]$$

$$= S_1 + S_2 + S_3,$$

249

where

$$S_1 = N^2(1+1)^N = N^2 2^N$$

$$S_2 = -4N^2 2^{(N-1)} = -2N^2 2^N$$

$$S_3 = 4N\left[1+(N-1)+\frac{1}{2!}(N-1)(N-2)+\ldots\right]$$

$$\quad +4N(N-1)\left[1+\frac{2}{2!}(N-2)+\frac{3}{3!}(N-2)(N-3)+\ldots\right]$$

$$\quad = 4N2^{N-1}+4N(N-1)2^{N-2}$$

$$\quad = 2N2^N+N(N-1)2^N.$$

Hence we obtain

$$S = N^2 2^N - 2N^2 2^N + 2N2^N + N(N-1)2^N$$

$$\quad = N2^N.$$

APPENDIX E

Quantum-mechanical Systems

LET US consider for a system the electrons bound in an atom. The energy eigen-function of the system is anti-symmetric according to Fermi and Dirac. On the other hand, if we consider photons enclosed in a box for a system, the energy eigen-function of the system is symmetric according to Bose and Einstein. For both systems, the density distribution is microscopically symmetric. In those systems, under the symmetry assumption, the change of the state of a particle is instantaneous, although statistical. It is also noted that those eigen states are independent either of configuration-space coordinates or of time. The situation is apparently similar to that of the statistical-mechanical state of a classical-mechanical system in thermal equilibrium. However, there is a significant difference that in a classical-mechanical system such a state is conceived as an average over an indefinitely long period of time, while those quantum-mechanical states are believed to exist in the microscopic sense. In other words, the existence of a statistical-mechanical state of a classical-mechanical system is explained in an asymptotic sense by means of ergodic theory, while the existence of a degenerate quantum-mechanical state, either symmetric or anti-symmetric, is a principle with no explanation.[†]

[†] Of course, there is the H-theorem in the quantum-mechanical sense. See ter Haar (1955). But the theorem is not for the electron distribution in an atom or molecule, but for a larger system.

The complete degeneracy of a state of those quantum-mechanical systems considered in the above sometimes tends to lead us to think that any physical system might behave in a similar manner, since particles are ultimately quantum-mechanical. Indeed, the microscopic symmetry assumption of $D^{(N)}$ of classical-mechanical particles is supported by some authors in this sense.

We have to realize, however, that those particles which are supposed to be in complete degeneracy are packed together closely as a system. Suppose that the electrons bound in an argon atom and the electrons bound in a helium atom are considered together as constituting a system. If the two atoms are sufficiently remote from each other, the density distribution of electrons cannot be symmetric with respect to the interchange of the states of two electrons, one being in the argon atom and the other in the helium atom. There is no degeneracy between the states of electrons in the argon atom and the states in the helium atom.[†] This is a rather extreme case. If we consider almost free electrons, such as in a gas at high temperature and of low density, degeneracy is also difficult to conceive, because the state of an electron which is represented by a wave packet is distinguishable from those of other electrons. The following statement by Landau and Lifshitz (1958)[‡] regarding quantum-mechanical measurement is particularly tangible to us from the above viewpoint:

> It must be remarked that there is an important exception to the statement that results of measurement cannot be reproduced: the one quantity the result of whose measurement can be exactly reproduced is the coordinate. Two measurements of the coordinates of an electron, made at a sufficiently small interval of time, must give neighboring values; if this were not so, it would mean that the electron had an infinite velocity.

(This statement would need a remark saying "with a very large probability".) If the scale of the wave packet of an electron is of the same as or smaller than the scale of a force field in which the electron moves, the change of the state of the electron cannot be instantaneous. Thus we may come to the same conclusion as we have had with respect to classical-mechanical systems, that the density distribution

† The author realizes that this is not an opinion widely accepted.
‡ The measurement of position was discussed earlier by Ruark (1928).

252

of similar systems in a phase-space is not symmetric with respect to the interchange of coordinates between two similar particles.

Consider for a system, for example, the free electrons in a metal wire, where one half is at temperature T_1 and the other half is at temperature T_2. The distribution function of the system is not symmetric with respect to the interchange of the phase-space coordinates between an electron in the part at T_1 and another electron in the other part. A similar situation may exist in a wire made by welding one end of a silver wire to one end of a copper wire, even if the temperature is uniform. According to the theory of superconductivity proposed by Bardeen *et al.* (1957), "free electrons" in a low-temperature conductor make stable pairs due to phonons produced by atoms constituting the lattice structure of the conductor. In view of the close interaction between the atoms and the "free electrons", it is possible to think that those electrons are in degeneracy in the same way as electrons are in an atom. In other words, quantum-mechanical degeneracy may appear in a macroscopic scale in a superconductor. A question is raised as follows: the conductor is of a macroscopic scale; it is possible for us to make the structure of it non-uniform. Then the degeneracy would be destroyed to some extent.

In 1932, Uehling and Uhlenbeck proposed an equation as the generalization of the Boltzmann equation for quantum-mechanical systems. Attempts have been made by Ono (1958) and others to derive rationally the Uehling–Uhlenbeck equation from the Wigner equation which is regarded as equivalent to the Schrödinger equation. The gist of the derivation is the introduction of Stosszahlansatz in the quantum-mechanical sense by preserving the assumption of binary collision which may be treated by Born's approximation. The probability of the occurrence of a binary collision decreases for Fermi particles, because the choice of the initial and final conditions of a pair is prohibited if those conditions are occupied by other particles, while the probability increases for Bose particles because the initial and final conditions of a pair in collision are superposable to those of other particles. This situation is conceivable only when the system is closely packed as electrons in an atom or in a metal so that

degeneracy is complete. But the situation seems incompatible with the assumption of binary collision.

Finally, it would be desirable to refer to quantum statistics of interacting particles in thermal equilibrium, as exemplified by a paper of Montroll and Ward (Phys. of Fluids, American Phys. Soc. 1958). Montroll and Ward consider the Bloch equation, instead of the Schrödinger equation, for the basis of treating the constituent particles of a system by means of Mayer's cluster method (1940) and Feynman's diagram method (1949). (The Bloch equation is obtained by substituting $\beta = kT$ in place of $it/\hbar$ in the Schrödinger equation; T denotes temperature and t time.) A point of our interest is that, at the limit of bringing h (Planck's constant) to zero, they obtain the Debye–Hückel mode of interaction among electrons in an electron gas. On the other hand, previously we concluded that the Debye–Hückel mode of interaction be not conceivable for an electron gas even when the system is in thermal equilibrium. See Section 9.6. The contradiction is not surprising, however, if we note that the representation of a system subjected to the Bloch equation is always and completely in statistical equilibrium from the beginning; there is no *"kinetic or temporal order"*, in any sense, to be found in the structure of a system treated by Montroll and Ward. There the distribution function of the particles is completely symmetric with respect to the interchange between any pair of position vectors of particles. If we accept the thought of Landau mentioned previously, therefore, we may say, at least, that the conclusion of Montroll and Ward should not be extended, simply by putting $h = 0$, to a system of high temperature and of low density where a particle is locally distinguishable by its state of temporal evolution in the configuration space; in order to take into account microscopic correlation energies among particles, "molecular ordered" according to Boltzmann, we have to take a kinetic-theoretical approach *even when a system is in thermal equilibrium as a whole*. (See also Appendix F, 2.) Only under a time-scale assumption which is not feasible of an electron gas, the Debye–Hückel mode interaction is the result of the BBGKY equation to the second approximation.

On the Definition of Distinguishability or of Indistinguishability of Similar Particles in Statistical Mechanics and in Kinetic Theory

THE distinguishability or indistinguishability of a particle from another similar particle is often talked about in statistical mechanics. See for example Tolman's book (1938), § 87. But it is difficult to understand what is really meant by distinguishability. Sometimes we are forced to imagine that a particle is distinguishable from another similar particle through some particular feature which is observable but does not affect the dynamical (physical) characteristics of the particle. Since a particle can be diagnosed by an external field and the interaction of the particle and the field can be described by dynamical equations (Newton's equations and/or Schrödinger's equations), it is meaningless to attach such an imaginative feature to a particle. A classical-mechanical material point is recognized by its position and momentum and its acceleration in a gravitational field.

It is well known that there are three different methods of counting the distribution of particles in a system in statistical equilibrium. The Bose–Einstein method is feasible for bosons, the Fermi–Dirac method for fermions, and the Maxwell–Boltzmann method for classical-mechanical particles. As a matter of pragmatism, similar particles, either quantal or classical, in statistical equilibrium, may be treated in any way, either indistinguishable or distinguishable. The difference in the distinguishability does not affect the conclusion seriously. The situation is explained as the answer to Gibb's paradox.

255

In principle, similar particles in statistical equilibrium are to be treated as indistinguishable in view of the indefinitely long period of time over which the state of a particle is averaged. On the other hand, if one wishes to observe the process of the evolution of a system in non-uniform states, it is necessary to treat similar particles as distinguishable. The case of statistical equilibrium is discussed in Section 1, and the case of non-uniform state in Section 2.

1. STATISTICAL EQUILIBRIUM

A system is assumed to consist of N similar particles. The number of eigen-states of energy ε_k is denoted by g_k, and the number of the particles in states of energy ε_k by n_k. The total energy of the system is invariant and is denoted by E.

$$N = \sum n_k, \tag{F-1}$$

$$E = \sum \varepsilon_k n_k. \tag{F-2}$$

If the particles are similar bosons, the number of the particles occupying an eigen-state of energy ε_k may be any number from 0 to n_k. Therefore, we obtain for the number of the different ways of distributing the particles in the eigen-states

$$G_{B.E} = \prod_k \frac{(n_k + g_k - 1)!}{n_k!(g_k - 1)!}, \tag{F-3}$$

where the particles are assumed to be indistinguishable. If they are distinguishable (simply from the statistical viewpoint), we have

$$G'_{B.E} = N! G_{B.E} \tag{F-3}'$$

in place of eq. (3).

If the particles are similar fermions, each eigen-state may be occupied by only one particle at the most. In this case, the number of different ways of distributing the particles is

$$G_{F.D} = \prod_k \frac{g_k!}{n_k!(g_k - n_k)!}, \tag{F-4}$$

where the particles are indistinguishable. If they are distinguishable, we have

$$G'_{F.D} = N!G_{F.D}. \qquad \text{(F-4)}'$$

If the particles are classical-dynamical, we may assume that

$$g_k \gg n_k \quad (h \to 0). \qquad \text{(F-5)}$$

Under this condition, both $G_{B.E}$ and $G_{F.D}$ yield the same as given by

$$G_{M.B} = \prod_k \frac{(g_k)^{n_k}}{n_k!}, \qquad \text{(F-6)}$$

and both $G'_{B.E}$ and $G'_{F.D}$ yield

$$G'_{M.B} = N!G_{M.B}. \qquad \text{(F-6)}'$$

By the usual method of variation under conditions (1) and (2), one may obtain, respectively from eqs. (3), (4), and (6), the three most probable distributions:
For bosons,

$$n_k = \frac{g_k}{-1+\exp{(\alpha+\beta\varepsilon_k)}}. \qquad \text{(F-7)}$$

For fermions,

$$n_k = \frac{g_k}{+1+\exp{(\alpha+\beta\varepsilon_k)}}. \qquad \text{(F-8)}$$

For classical-mechanical particles,

$$n_k = \frac{g_k}{\exp{(\alpha+\beta\varepsilon_k)}}. \qquad \text{(F-9)}$$

It is noted that $G'_{B.E}$, $G'_{F.D}$, and $G'_{M.B}$ also result in eqs. (7), (8), and (9) respectively. This is because $N!$ is an invariant and does not affect the results obtained by the variation method. The situation is explained physically in the following:

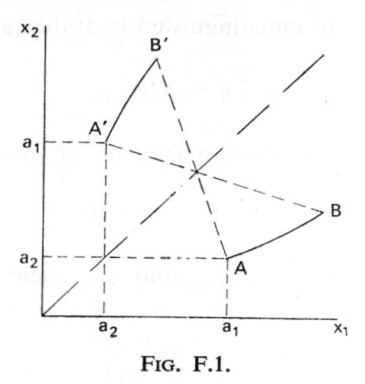

FIG. F.1.

The phase space of a two-similar-particle system. The state represented by A is equivalent to the state represented by A', and the state B is to the state B'. But the kinetic-theoretical process represented by $A-B$ and/or $A'-B'$ is distinguishable from the kinetic-theoretical process represented by $A-B'$ and/or $A'-B$.

Suppose that a system is composed of two similar particles. The coordinate of particle 1 in the phase space is given by X_1 and the coordinate of particle 2 by X_2. A representative point A is specified by

$$X_1 = a_1, \quad X_2 = a_2$$

in the phase space. See the schematic illustration in Fig. F-1. Another representative point A' is specified by

$$X_1 = a_2, \quad X_2 = a_1.$$

From the viewpoint of observation, there is no way of differentiating one state A from the other A'. One observable state is a superposition of two representative points in the phase space. If the number of similar particles in a system is N, the number of the representative points which equally represent a single observable state of the species is $N!$. It appears that the multiplicity of the representative points of a single observable state results in the increase of the probability density of the state. However, the increase of the density is the same with respect to any possible state. If we normalize the density as a

whole, the difference between the distinguishability and the indistinguishability does not affect the result, as long as the particles are similar. The situation is well known as the answer to Gibbs's paradox.

The discussion and conclusion given in the above might not satisfy the reader. "Distinguishability" and/or "indistinguishability" of similar particles in statistical equilibrium have been discussed by many authors. See ter Haar's book (1954), p. 72. The magnitude of entropy calculated according to "distinguishability" is different from the magnitude of entropy calculated according to "indistinguishability". The difference is an invariant of the system under consideration. Some authors, for example ter Haar, think that the difference is significant. Some authors, for example Fowler and Guggenheim (1960), do not. Some authors, for example Tolman (1938), think that similar classical-mechanical particles are distinguishable while similar quantum-mechanical particles are indistinguishable. The present author would like to assert that similar particles, classical as well as quantal, are indistinguishable as long as they are in statistical equilibrium. The reason for the assertion is that the state of a particle in a system considered in statistical equilibrium is the state averaged over an indefinitely long period of time. In a system not in thermal equilibrium, however, a particle must be distinguishable from the others as explained in the following.

2. NON-UNIFORM STATES

Again we take a system consisting of two similar particles. In Fig. F-1 as explained previously, A and A' are two representative points which represent a single observable state α. We now consider another pair of points B and B' which represent another observable state β. We also assume that the states are not stable, and the system evolves from α to β as time passes. The evolution may be traced along two possible sets of continuous trajectories. Of the first set, one trajectory starts at A and ends at B while the other trajectory

starts at A' and ends at B'. Both trajectories represent the same observable procedure of the change of the state of the system. Of the second set, one trajectory starts at A and ends at B' while the other starts at A' and ends at B. These two trajectories may also represent a common observable process. However, the two sets of trajectories represent respectively two different processes. Of course, only one of the two sets is to be in accordance with proper dynamical laws.[†] Choosing a correct set is a matter of dynamical investigation of the particles. An essential criterion is that any trajectory must be continuous, since the velocity and acceleration of a particle are always finite. Our conclusion is that similar particles are distinguishable because of the continuous changes of their dynamical variables.

3. ADDITIONAL REMARKS

In the case of statistical equilibrium, the interchange of states between two particles is not a dynamical (stochastic) process. On the other hand, in the second case treating non-uniform states, the change from A to B or B' and the change from A' to B' or B must occur as dynamical processes. The recognition of the difference may easily be made, if we notice that a system in statistical equilibrium is observed on an indefinitely long time scale while a system in non-uniform states is observed on finite time scales. In the former case, we do not need to know the time when a specified state occurs. We need only the relative frequency of occurence. In the latter, however, we must follow the sequence of occurence from one state to another.

With respect to quantum-mechanical systems, observing the time sequence of occurence is not always possible. This situation limits the kinetic-theoretical observation of a quantum-mechanical system.

[†] For the basis of kinetic theory, we have to choose the one in accordance with dynamical laws; the process is the very matter of concern of kinetic theory.

An Historical Sketch of Kinetic Theory

INTRODUCTION

We select the following three epochs: (1) 1856–1900. The kinetic theory of gases was initiated and developed by Krönig, Clausius, Maxwell, Boltzmann, and others. (2) 1900–1935. The main interests of physics were in quantum mechanics, statistical mechanics of general systems, classical and quantal, and others, but not in kinetic theory. The kinetic theory of gases in the classical sense had merely survived as a mathematical problem of solving the Boltzmann equation along a line set by Maxwell in 1866. (3) 1935–. We see the revival of kinetic theory. But significant influences of quantum mechanics and statistical mechanics are found in the theory. Technological interests stimulated the re-evaluation of the traditional solution of the Boltzmann equation.

1856–1900

Among the numerous papers of broad interest published by Maxwell, there are ten which deal with the kinetic theory of gases. The following two are particularly of great interest from the gas-dynamical viewpoint:

1. "On the dynamical theory of gases" (1866).
2. "On stresses in rarefied gases arising from inequalities of temperature" (1879).

In the first paper, one may find the following three notable ideas: (1) The theory was a conclusion to the preceding studies conducted by Krönig (1856), Clausius (1857), and Maxwell himself deducing gas-dynamical properties of gases from the hypothesis that "their minute parts are in rapid motion, the velocity increasing with the temperature" (Maxwell, 1860.). (2) The theory had obviously stimulated Boltzmann to propose the Boltzmann equation which is more general and more comprehensive than Maxwell's equations of transfer presented in the paper. (3) At the same time, Maxwell's theory suggested the method of deriving the Navier–Stokes equations [Navier (1822), Poisson (1829), de Saint-Venant (1845), Stokes (1845)], from the Boltzmann equation, as was completed later by Chapman (1916) and Enskog (1917) independently. (Equations of transfer proposed by Maxwell are similar to equations of moments as derived in Section 5.1, and the method of treating these equations is similar to the Chapman–Enskog method.)

In evaluating Maxwell's dynamical theory of gases from the gas-dynamical viewpoint, it must be noted that the theory is based on the assumption that the state of a gas is, at least locally, near thermal equilibrium, and hence the distribution of molecules is almost Maxwellian as proposed by Maxwell himself in 1860. He seemed to be aware of the full meaning of the assumption and supplemented the theory by the second paper mentioned above. (The elaboration and application by later authors are found in Kennard's *Kinetic Theory of Gases*, 1938).

In 1872 Boltzmann proposed the Boltzmann equation. There has been a strong tendency to regard the Boltzmann equation merely as an elaborate or abstract representation of Maxwell's equations of transfer. This appraisal of the Boltzmann equation may not be fair. Maxwell's equations of transfer may be equivalent to the Boltzmann equation, if we take an infinitely large number of these equations. Since it is impossible to do so, the number must be limited to the first few. On doing so, we have specified the orientation of solution, as similar to the Chapman–Enskog solution. In other words, the gas under consideration must be near thermal equilib-

rium. The implication of the Boltzmann equation is much broader than a limited number of equations of transfer, and the Boltzmann equation is valid with respect to rarefied gas-dynamical phenomena where, as was noted by Maxwell in the second paper cited above, the state of a gas may deviate significantly from thermal equilibrium, and Maxwell's method of considering equations of transfer fails to be valid. After the proposal of the Boltzmann equation, physics seemed to have lost interest in the kinetic theory of gases as the basis of gas dynamics. But the theory has survived as an applied mathematical problem of solving the Boltzmann equation along the line set by Maxwell in the first paper (1866). The theory was completed by Chapman (1916) and Enskog (1917). (Preceding Chapman and Enskog, there had been basic mathematical investigations by Hilbert (1911) and others. See Chapman–Cowling's book, p. 385.) The Chapman–Enskog theory is a precise mathematical one of solving the Boltzmann equation under the condition that the density of a gas and hence the molecular collision frequency is high so that the state of the gas is, at least locally, almost in thermal equilibrium; the deviation of a local state from thermal equilibrium depends on the degree of macroscopic non-uniformity of the gas. The theory is an iteration method of giving the solution in terms of an inverse power series of the gas density, whose first member is the Maxwell function. Since our limited ability for treating such complex iterations prohibits us from proceeding over the first few steps of iteration, not only convergency but also *rapid convergency* of the series is extremely important; the validity of the Chapman–Enskog solution depends on the condition that the state of the gas concerned deviates only slightly from thermal equilibrium, as was the case in Maxwell's equations of transfer.

In the mainstream of physics, the Boltzmann equation provided a useful means of clarifying the statistical meanings of thermal equilibrium, thermal fluctuations, entropy, irreversibility of thermal phenomena, and so forth, as was reviewed by the Ehrenfests (1912). Based on the Boltzmann equation, Boltzmann (1872) proposed the H-theorem which states that the distribution of the particles consti-

tuting a spatially uniform gas approaches always to the Maxwell–Boltzmann distribution, regardless of the initial distribution. Objecting to the H-theorem, Loschmidt (1876, 1877) said that the behavior of an isolated gaseous system, according to the kinetic-theoretical model, must be reversible. It is then possible that the process considered by the H-theorem is reversible. Zermelo (1896), based on a theorem of mechanics (three-body problem) by Poincaré, asserted that the behavior of a many-body system must be almost periodic. We note that these objections to the H-theorem are based on considerations of an isolated system in the microscopic sense. On the other hand, the H-theorem is to be appreciated in the statistical sense. Through those discussions, the statistical meaning of the Stosszahlansatz, on which the collision integral of Boltzmann is based, had been clarified. It may be said that modern ergodic theory given by Birkoff, Khinchin, and others is the final conclusion of these arguments given from the viewpoint of statistical mechanics dealing with thermal equilibrium. See the review by Farquhar (1964). Naturally, arguments by Loschmidt and Zermelo may be appreciated more intimately from the viewpoint of kinetic theory which deals with stochastic processes in a gaseous system.

The founders of the kinetic theory of gases, such as Krönig, Clausius, Maxwell, and Boltzmann, were enthusiastic and ambitious to *explain* thermodynamic and gas-dynamic phenomena based on the hypothesis that a gas consists of a great number of tiny particles, each behaving according to precise mechanical laws (Newton's laws). One may see Maxwell's belief in the hypothesis in his statement about a demon (in his *Theory of Heat* (1871), according to Jeans, *The Dynamical Theory of Gases*, 1925, p. 183.):

> One of the best established facts in thermodynamics is that it is impossible in a system enclosed in an envelope which permits neither change of volume nor passage of heat, and in which both the temperature and the pressure are everywhere the same, to produce any inequality of temperature or of pressure without the expenditure of work. This is the second law of thermodynamics, and it is undoubtedly true so long as we can deal with bodies only in mass and have no power of perceiving or handling the separate molecules of which they are made up. But if we conceive a being whose

faculties are so sharpened that he can follow every molecule in its course, such a being, whose attributes are still as essentially finite as our own, would be able to do what is at present impossible to us. For we have seen that the molecules in a vessel full of air at uniform temperature are moving with velocities by no means uniform though the mean velocity of any great number of them, arbitrarily selected, is almost exactly uniform. Now let us suppose that such a vessel is divided into two portions, A and B, by a division in which there is a small hole, and that a being, who can see the individual molecules, opens and closes this hole, so as to allow only the swifter molecules to pass from A to B, and only the slower ones to pass from B to A. He will thus, without expenditure of work, raise the temperature of B and lower that of A, in contradiction to the second law of thermodynamics.

Also we see an ingenious unification of the continuum model[†] and the molecular hypothesis in the Boltzmann collision integral: a pair of discrete molecules emerges out of the continuous cloud of *probability*, and they collide with each other according to Newton's law of dynamics, and then disappear again as melted in the cloud of probability.

In 1895, however, Boltzmann writes: "Gas theory has gone out of fashion in Germany." In 1898, he writes:
I am conscious of being only an individual struggling weakly against the stream of time. But it still remains in my power to contribute in such a way that, when the theory of gases is again revived, not too much will have to be rediscovered.

It is noted that O. E. Meyer designed a rather intuitive method of treating transport phenomena which is different from Maxwell's method. (Meyer's thought was closer to that of Clausius.) It seems that the apparent straightforward manner of approach attracted many authors in that era to apply the method for calculating numerical values of transport coefficients. Those authors were puzzled, however, by an inconsistency appearing in their results. The situation is well described in Jeans's *Dynamical Theory of Gases* (p. 295) and Boltzmann's *Gas Theory* (p. 107). Finally, Boltzmann declared: "This is therefore a clear proof of the inaccuracy of all these calcu-

---

† We have to note the difference between continuum and continuous cloud of probability. A coarse-graining is necessary to make the former from the latter. See Section 8.6.

lations." As is explained in Section 5.3, however, these calculations were correct; the fault was in the interpretation. (Meyer's intuition was inherited by Bhatnagar, Gross, and Krook in 1954 when they proposed a simple substitute of the Boltzmann equation. Because of the simplicity, the BGK equation is popular particularly among gas-dynamicists. It should be noted that the equation is easily misinterpreted, as is Meyer's theory. They bear a common danger of misuse.)

In summation, the kinetic theory of gases was successful in explaining various phenomena in gases. Yet there were many physicists who were against the theory. The main causes of distrust were:

1. Physical and dynamical characteristics of molecules were not well known at that time. From the classical-dynamical viewpoint, a monatomic molecule must have six degrees of freedom of motion. But experimental results of specific heat imply that the degrees of freedom are three in number. Only if a monatomic molecule were an ideal material *point*, would the three degrees of rotational freedom not exist. This is not likely. In addition, in the case of a diatomic molecule, the freedom of intrinsic vibration does not seem to exist according to experimental results of specific heat.

2. Boltzmann's derivation of the Boltzmann equation was rather intuitive. There is left a wide and obscure gap between Newton's equations of motion of the molecules constituting a gas and the Boltzmann equation. That is why Zermelo, Loschmidt, and others raised questions which would be answered definitely only after investigating a radical procedure of deriving the Boltzmann equation from Newton's equations of motion governing the behaviors of molecules with microscopic precision.

1900–1935

In 1902, Gibbs proposed the principle of statistical mechanics dealing with general mechanical systems in thermal equilibrium based on Hamilton's equations.

The effort of earlier authors to harmonize the molecular hypothesis with thermodynamical phenomena was abandoned by Gibbs. He says:

> It is well known that while theory would assign to the (diatomic) gas six degrees of freedom per molecule, in our experiments on specific heat we cannot account for more than five. Certainly, one who bases his work on a hypothesis concerning the constitution of matter, is building on an insecure foundation. Difficulties of this kind[†] have deterred the author from attempting to explain the mysteries of nature, and have forced him to be contented with the more modest aim of deducing some of the more obvious propositions relating to the statistical branch of mechanics. Here, there can be no mistake regarding the agreement of the hypothesis with the facts of nature, for nothing is assumed in that respect. The only error into which one can fall is the lack of agreement between the premises and the conclusions, and this one may hope, in the main, to avoid with care.

This philosophy of Gibbs stated in the preface of his *Elementary Principles in Statistical Mechanics* was not necessarily new in his time. His statement reminds us of Ostwald and Mach who insisted in the last century that theories which postulate hidden occurrences should be rejected from science. Regarding heat science, there had been three main approaches of treating thermodynamical phenomena in the last century. The first is based on the molecular hypothesis by Clausius, Maxwell, Boltzmann, etc. The second is similar to that of Gibbs, promoted by Helmholz, etc., and the third is purely thermodynamical as stressed by Planck. See the preface to the first edition (1897) of Planck's *Treatise on Thermodynamics*.

In view of the above statement, Gibbs obviously curbed his ambition and confined himself to a domain more secure from errors which might be caused by the molecular hypothesis. Thus his effort is concentrated on the consideration of stationary states and energy relations. He defines ensembles and postulates that the average obtained on successive trials of the same experiment will agree with

---

[†] This difficulty was solved by Ehrenfest, 12 years later, in such a way as is compatible with the molecular hypothesis; the anomaly is due to the quantum effect appearing on each single molecule.

ensemble averages.[†] (Note that the time scale of his experiment is infinitely long.) Gibbs did so in order to avoid possible *mistakes*, but he seemed to believe that there is something, although uncertain, behind the scene of his theory. In his statistical mechanics, the kinetic theory of gases in its literal sense is no more than a heuristic introduction to statistical mechanics of general dynamical systems constituting various ensembles. Gibbs begins the theory with an interpretation of the Liouville equation; he interprets the equation as one governing the evolution of the probability distribution of similar systems in the phase space,[‡] and concludes that the distribution of those similar systems belonging to an ensemble which represents a real system in thermal equilibrium will remain unchanged. Thereby he obtains a stationary solution of the Liouville equation which is similar to the Maxwell distribution function. The significance of the theory is that the individuality of a particle has been completely eliminated from the consideration; if it exists, it does so in the number of degrees of freedom of the entire system described abstractly in terms of generalized coordinates. The main interest of the theory is in the partition of energy. (In contrast, we have seen an ingenious expression of the individuality of a particle

[†] The difference between Gibbs's approach and the molecular hypothesis may be explained analogously by the following. Suppose that an astronomical observatory has recorded a series of radio waves over a period of time. One way of analyzing the waves is to find the relation between intensity E and frequency of appearance defined by $f =$ (the total extension of time during which the intensity is between E and $E + dE$)/τ dE, where f is a function of E. f may provide for us some information about the waves. This analysis is similar to Gibbs's approach. But if one believes that the radio waves carry informations of events which have occurred in succession on a star according to causality laws, including mental behaviors of intellectual beings, one has to treat the waves as stochastic signals. Here consideration of time scale and correlation of intensity from one moment of time to another is essential.

[‡] Boltzmann (1868) and also Maxwell treated the energy distribution in a gas based on Hamilton's equations of the constituent particles. They seemed to be aware that Hamilton's equations have no statistical sense. See "On Boltzmann's theorem on the average distribution of energy in a system of material points", by Maxwell (1876). There, Maxwell noticed the convenience of considering ensemble, possibly for the first time in history, with respect to thermal equilibrium.

in the collision integral of Boltzmann.) Due to the ignorance of the individuality of a particle, however, Gibbs succeeded in the abstraction and axiomatization of statistical mechanics. But Gibbs's theory is not concerned about the main interest of the kinetic theory dealing with the dynamical evolution (stochastic behavior) of a system.

Later, however, Gibbs's rather humble approach seemed to have become a positive principle. In 1938, Tolman (*The Principle of Statistical Mechanics*, pp. 67–69) says:

> Hence the older point of view, based on the ergodic hypothesis, might seem at first sight to furnish a more satisfactory justification for the methods of statistical mechanics than is furnished by the point of view which has been adopted in this book. In the first place, the older development was regarded as primarily based on a hypothesis which might be an actual consequence of the exact laws of mechanics, while our development is based on a definite postulate as to *a priori* probabilities, which can only be justified if its consequences do correspond with statistical findings. . . . It must hence be felt that the point of view of the early founders did not give due recognition to the truly statistical character of the problems to be attacked. Impressed by the exact character of the principles of classical mechanics, and also by the actual regularities in the macroscopic behavior of systems composed of many molecules, they apparently hoped to secure really precise results for such systems by the temporary introduction of a hypothesis which might itself be ultimately validated from the principles of mechanics proper, and did not sufficiently appreciate that a further essentially statistical assumption would be needed even if their hypothesis were valid.

Although we see substantially the same meaning in Gibbs's statement quoted previously, Tolman's tone is more confident and more positive. The difference may be due to the new development of quantum mechanics during the time between Gibbs (1902) and Tolman (1938); uncertainty and degeneracy are basic principles in quantum mechanics. The thoughts expressed by Tolman were probably common among many authors at the time. Of course, it should be noted that gas-dynamical phenomena occupy only a minor and exceptional part of the vast world of statistical-physical phenomena. Excluding gas-dynamical phenomena, Tolman's statement may be feasible. See for example, Appendix I of *Elements o, Statistical Mechanics* by ter Haar (1954).

In 1900 Planck proposed his theory of radiation in which he introduced the hypothesis of quantum of action. It should be noted that Planck utilized the Maxwell–Boltzmann distribution function, though in a peculiar way, for deriving the distribution of radiation energy which is now known as the Bose–Einstein distribution. The following development of quantum theory clarified the dynamical characteristics of corpuscles (electron, atoms, and molecules) and hence the mystery of specific heat: (1) Angular momenta of electron and atoms with respect to internal axes, spins, are of the order of Planck's quantum of action h. Hence they may be ignored in the approximation of ignoring h; that is, these particles may be simulated by ideal material points. [Uhlenbeck and Gousmit (1925).] (2) The intrinsic vibration of a diatomic molecule is not activated unless it is stimulated with high energies. [Ehrenfest (1914).]

Those discoveries made by Einstein, Ehrenfest, Uhlenbeck, Gousmit, Pauli, and others in the first quarter of this century were favorable for the kinetic theory, since it is not difficult to take into account those facts within the old framework of kinetic theory. At the same time, however, the quantum-mechanical degeneracy (Fermi, Dirac, Bose, Einstein) proved to exist in states of various systems appeared unfavorable to the classical kinetic theory.

Note that *degeneracy is not the result of thermalization in the classical sense, but is the basic mode of existence of a system*. Later, however, Uehling and Uhlenbeck (1933, 1934) and Massey and Mohr (1933) showed that the average magnitude of action of molecules in gases in the ordinary sense is much larger than Planck's quantum of action and hence Boltzmann's collision model is still valid. Besides, quantum-mechanical degeneracy of a state which is usual with respect to electrons bound in molecules and/or metals is thought not to be significant with respect to molecules in a gas in the ordinary sense.

Although the Gibbs–Tolman view prevailed, some authors seemed to be in favor of the molecular hypothesis.[†] See, for example,

---

[†] An observation of thermodynamical phenomena is conducted with respect to a single system whereas the statistical-mechanical prediction of the same

(Continued on p. 271)

Ehrenfest (1912). Also Lorentz, after describing the kinetic-theoretical approach of treating electrons in metals (1909), elaborated upon his statement as follows:

> This rapid review will suffice to show you that the theory of electrons is to be regarded as an extension to the domain of electricity of the molecular and atomistic theories that have proved of so much use in many branches of physics and chemistry. Like these, it is apt to be viewed unfavorably by some physicists, who prefer to push their way into new and unexplored regions by following those great highways of science which we possess in the laws of thermodynamics, or who arrive at important and beautiful results simply by describing the phenomena and their mutual relations by means of a system of suitable equations. No one can deny that these methods have a charm of their own, and that, in following them, we have the feeling of treading on firm ground whereas in the molecular theories the too adventurous physicist often runs the risk of losing his way and of being deluded by some false prospect of success. We must not forget, however, that these molecular hypotheses can claim some results that could never have been attained by pure thermodynamics, or by means of the equations of the electromagnetic field in their most general form, results that are well known by all who have studied the kinetic theory of gases, the theories of dilute solutions, of electrolysis and of genesis of electric currents by the motion of ions. Nor can the fruitfulness of these hypotheses be denied by those who have followed the splendid research on the conduction of electricity through gases of J. J. Thomson and his fellow workers.

1935–

After a settlement of quantum mechanics and general statistical mechanics, the old desire of establishing kinetic theory as based on the classical Liouville equation of a system was renewed (as

---

phenomena is done by considering an ensemble of similar systems. Why do the observation and the prediction agree with each other? Ergodic theory attempts to justify the agreement. The reasoning by the ergodic theory is that a thermodynamical observation is executed over a span of time which is extremely long compared with the time scale of microscopic phenomena in a system and hence the single system during the observation takes substantially the states of all the systems of the ensemble at a moment of time. Ergodic theory is primarily kinetic-theoretical. But it is not interested in the process of time evolution of a system, but instead in the average over an infinitely long period of time.

expected by Boltzmann in 1898,) by Yvon (1935), Kirkwood (1946), Born and Green (1946), and Bogoliubov (1946). These authors published independently similar theories from the above viewpoint. (Yvon and Born and Green seemed to be interested in liquids rather than gases.) Unlike Gibbs, who also began his theory from the Liouville equation, these authors are interested in the evolution of the state of a gas due to interactions among molecules constituting the gas. In these theories, we see the revival of old imaginations of Krönig, Clausius, Maxwell, and Boltzmann; but at the same time, we see strong influences left by Gibbs and quantum mechanics. In spite of their primarily radical intention, we see their hasty justification of the proposition that the density of similar systems in the phase-space is symmetric with respect to the interchange of the phase-space coordinates between a pair of similar particles:

1. Bogoliubov takes it for granted that the density of similar systems in the phase-space is always symmetric with respect to the interchange of coordinates between any pair of similar particles. Note that the quantum-mechanical probability density of a degenerate system, is always symmetric. Because of the assumption, Bogoliubov's derivation of the Boltzmann equation is not consistent. The absolute symmetry and the Boltzmann collision model are incompatible in their radical meanings.

2. Kirkwood stresses that the state of a system is to be averaged along its trajectory in the phase-space. He was aware of the necessity of the period of time over which the average is made to be macroscopically short so that the non-uniformity of the gas is not obscured by the average operation. Nevertheless, he states that the choice of a system to be averaged is made at random among the systems constituting one of Gibbs's ensembles. Since Gibbs's ensembles are defined mainly with respect to energy (an integral of motion of an isolated system), such a system as selected at random from an ensemble of Gibbs is not expected to exhibit properly macroscopic dynamical characteristics, such as represented by shearing stresses, heat conduction, etc., which he intends to consider in his theory. (In general, such quantities are not integrals of motion of an isolated system.) In spite

of the proper approach of time average, Kirkwood experiences a failure similar to that of Bogoliubov; he does not pursue persistently his initial approach of time average, seemingly because of his strong adhesion to Gibbs's ensembles.

Reconsideration of the implication of Gibbs's ensembles and of Bogoliubov's symmetry assumption (a manifestation of his interpretation of the hypothesis of equal *a priori* probabilities) is urgent in view of the purpose of the kinetic theory of gases in its literal sense. Considering the seriousness of its consequence, the reason for the above statement is elaborated upon in the following. Suppose that one conducts a certain procedure of experiment regarding a gas contained in a vessel. (It is misleading to assume that the vessel is made of walls which are solid, fixed, adiabatic, etc. The walls are under control in the macroscopic sense as a part of the procedure of experiment; they may be flexible, deformable, and may conduct heat, etc.) The experiment begins at time 0 of a stop-watch and ends at time T. Obviously the macroscopic state of the gas at one phase of the experiment, time t_1, must be represented by a single point in the relevant phase space, even if it is impossible for us to point out the location with microscopic precision. If one repeats macroscopically the same procedure of experiment many times, the phase-space point representing the microscopic state of the gas at time t_1 during one procedure of the experiment may be different from the phase-space point representing the microscopic state of the gas at the same time t_1 during another procedure. By repeating many times the same macroscopic procedure, however, one obtains a relation between the initial condition and the final condition. Then he believes that a good theory pertaining to his experiment is one that predicts the result from the initial condition. Considering the situation, one tends to speculate the following:

1. The average result of his repeated experimental procedures is equivalent to the result of a single experimental procedure conducted in his imagination with a gas of which the state is not represented by a certain single point in the phase space but a probability density cloud.

2. The probability density is governed by the Liouville equation.

3. The macroscopic quantities of the gas, in terms of which the macroscopic laws of the phenomena are given, are obtained by making averages over the cloud, and that the average operation is guided by the assumption that the probability density cloud is always symmetric with respect to the interchange of the phase-space coordinates between any pair of similar particles.

The feasibility of this speculation is quite uncertain and ambiguous because of the following:

1. It is obvious that each procedure of the experiment is conducted with a single system even though it is not precisely known where the state of the system may be located in the phase space at each moment of time. Regardless of the microscopic uncertainty from the viewpoint of the macroscopic observer, the system evolves with certainty.

2. Even if one takes for granted the feasibility of considering the probability density cloud, there is more than one method of averaging operation. In general each may give a different result. Suppose, for example, that one has ten spinning tops, each of which has a slight distortion in the distribution of the mass density around the expected axis of symmetry. Suppose that by making the geometrical and static (arithmetic) average of the mass distributions one obtains an imaginary top of perfect symmetry. The average of the behaviors of the ten tops and the behavior of the imaginary top are in general different, because the relevant dynamical law is not linear regarding the mass distribution.

3. The average operation due to the symmetry of the probability density in the phase space is one of many conceivable and different averaging operations. The feasibility of a choice is not a matter of axiomatic proposition but a matter of rational investigation.

Of course, we recall the great success of Gibbs in establishing his statistical mechanics based on the symmetry assumption. But there is a large difference between the purposes of Gibbs's theory and of the kinetic theory: In Gibbs's theory, the physical quantity mainly concerned is energy; energy is an integral of motion of an isolated

system (uniform integral by Fowler) and the total energy of a system is the arithmetic sum of the energies of the constituent particles. In his theory, no dynamical processes which are presented in general by equations nonlinear with respect to physical quantities of particles are considered. On the other hand, nonlinear processes such as a collision are essential in the kinetic theory. (It is not sufficient to consider simply the total energies of two particles before and after their collision. It is necessary to consider the momenta of each particle before and after the collision.) Besides, quantities such as stresses, heat conduction rate, etc., are not integrals of motion of an isolated system. These quantities appear in a secular sense in a system under restrictive effects imposed from the outside. Therefore, there is no *a priori* reason for taking a Gibbs ensemble for the basis of consideration of the kinetic theory and/or for taking the symmetry assumption for granted. The feasibility of these approaches, if it exists, must be investigated more seriously.

In short, the symmetry assumption is a realization of the hypothesis of equal *a priori* probabilities. Without the hypothesis we cannot deal with many-particle systems. But the application must be conditional. If we deal with gas-dynamical phenomena (states in evolution) in systems which are not in thermal equilibrium, scales of time and space which govern these phenomena are essential conditions to be considered in applying the hypothesis. (It is noted that Gibbs's ensembles represent systems in thermal equilibrium of which the time scale of our observation is infinitely long.) The application of the hypothesis is not a matter of postulation but a matter of investigation.

Technological interests have realized various gaseous phenomena which are not accounted for in the development of the kinetic theory of gases as stated above. For example, regarding ionized gases, the Boltzmann collision integral is known to diverge. Therefore a more radical approach based on the Liouville equation or Hamilton's equations is necessary. But the feasibility of the BBGKY approach is quite doubtful; the approach fails to derive the Boltzmann equation consistently in the simple case of the binary collision assumption.

(Of course there is no proof that the Boltzmann equation is completely correct. But the equation is known to be valid at least as an empirical formula. Besides, the relevant equation derived consistently according to the BBGKY theory does not appear to be a better empirical formula. See Section (4.3).

As to shock waves and boundary layers of hypersonic flows of neutral gases, the Boltzmann equation is generally regarded as valid. There, however, mean free path lengths of molecules are often macroscopic and gradients of change of state are steep, and hence the Chapman–Enskog solution of the Boltzmann equation does not seem plausible. In his paper, 1879, cited previously, Maxwell realized the possibility of phenomena in which his equations of transfer, as well as the Chapman–Enskog solution, would not be valid. But in his time, those phenomena were not so usual as they are today. Maxwell's consideration in the above paper was inherited by Millikan, Epstein, and others who investigated tiny objects moving in rarefied gases, and later by those investigating hypersonic flows. Kennard reviewed the development in his *Kinetic Theory of Gases*.

Grad (1949) and others attempted to derive general macroscopic equations from the Boltzmann equation with the hope that the results be valid for these phenomena with which neither Maxwell's equations of transfer nor the Chapman–Enskog theory are valid. But none of them appears to have succeeded. At this moment, we must be satisfied with *ad hoc* methods such as the method of Mott-Smith (1951) for solution of the Boltzmann equation for shock waves.

Finally it is stressed that the kinetic theory of gases to be useful in gas dynamics must be concerned with the following four points: (1) One cannot expect the existence of quantum-mechanical degeneracy of states of particles in an ordinary gas, especially of low density and of high temperature. (2) As long as we observe gas-dynamical phenomena in a gas, the gas is not in thermal equilibrium, no matter how slight the deviation is. This qualitative recognition of a state is necessary for our proper choice between the statistical-mechanical approach and the kinetic-theoretical approach. (3) Similar results of experiments repeated under macroscopically similar conditions might

276

suggest the possibility of defining ensembles. But it is necessary to note that ensembles which may represent those real systems exhibiting specific gas-dynamical phenomena are different from Gibbs's ensembles. (4) A state of a gas is not always close to thermal equilibrium. If not, the Maxwell distribution function has no priority to be chosen as the first approximation. Similar questions were raised by ter Haar (1955).

References

ALLIS, W. P. (1956), Motion of ions and electrons, in *Handbuch der Physik*, edited by S. Flügge, Springer-Verlag, Berlin, vol. 21, p. 430.

BALESCU, R. (1960), Irreversible processes in ionized gases, *Phys. Fluids*, **3**, 53.

BARDEEN, L., COOPER, N. and SCHRIEFFER, J. R. (1957), *Phys. Rev.* **108**, 1175.

BHATNAGAR, P. L., GROSS, E. P. and KROOK, M. (1954), Model for collision processes in gases, *Phys. Rev.* **94**, 511.

BOGOLIUBOV, N. N. and MITROPOLSKY, Y. A. (1961), *Asymptotic Methods in the Theory of Non-Linear Oscillations*, Hindustan Publishing Corp. Delhi, India.

BOGOLIUBOV, N. N. (1946), *J. Phys. (U.S.S.R.)*, **10**, 256; Problems of a dynamical theory in statistical physics, translated by E. G. Gora, in *Studies in Statistical Mechanics*, vol. 1, edited by J. DE BOER and G. E. UHLENBECK, North-Holland Publishing Co., 1962.

BOLTZMANN, L. (1872), Weitere Studien über das Wärmegleichgewicht unter Gasmoleculen, *Wien Ber.* **66**, 275.

BOLTZMANN, L. (1896–1898), *Lectures on Gas Theory*, translated by S. T. Brucs, University of California Press (1964).

BORN, M. and GREEN, H. S. (1946–1947), A general kinetic theory of liquids, *Proc. Roy. Soc. (London)*, A **188**, 10; A **189**, 103; A **190**, 455.

BURBURY, S. H. (1894), Boltzmann's minimum function, *Nature*, **51**, 78; also see JEANS, J. H. (1925), *The Dynamical Theory of Gases*, p. 56; BOLTZMANN, L. (1896), *Lectures on Gas Theory*, p. 40.

CHANDRASEKHAR, S. (1943), Stochastic Problems in Physics and Astronomy, *Rev. Mod. Phys.* **15**, 1.

CHAPMAN, S. and COWLING, T. G. (1952), *The Mathematical Theory of Non-Uniform Gases*, 2nd edn., Cambridge University Press.

CHU, C. K. (1965), Kinetic-theoretical description of shock wave formation, *Phys. Fluids*, **8**, 12; **8**, 1450.

CLAUSIUS, R. (1857), Über die Art der Bewegung welche wir Warme nennen, *Ann. Phys.*, **100**, 353.

COURANT, R. and HILBERT, D. (1953), *Methods of Mathematical Physics*, Interscience Publishers, Inc., New York.

EHRENFEST, P. and T. (1912), *The Conceptual Foundations of the Statistical Approach in Mechanics*, translated by M. J. Maravcsik, Cornell University Press, 1959.

EPSTEIN, E. P. (1924), On the resistance experienced by spheres in their motion through gases, *Phys. Rev.* **23**, 710.

FARQUHAR, I. E. (1964), *Ergodic Theory in Statistical Mechanics*, Interscience Publishers, London.

FOWLER, R. H. (1929), *Statistical Mechanics*, 2nd edn., Cambridge University Press, 1936.

FOWLER, R. and GUGGENHEIM, E. A. (1960), *Statistical Thermodynamics*, Cambridge University Press.

GIBBS, J. W. (1902), *Elementary Principles in Statistical Mechanics*, Yale University Press, reprinted by Dover Publications Inc.

GRAD, H. (1949), On the kinetic theory of rarefied gases, *Comm. Pure Appl. Math.* **2**, 331

GRAD, H. (1952), Statistical mechanics, thermodynamics, and fluid dynamics of systems with an arbitrary number of integrals, *Comm. Pure Appl. Math.* **5**, 455.

GRAD, H. (1958), Principles of the kinetic theory of gases, in *Handbuch der Physik*, edited by S. Flügge, Springer-Verlag, Berlin, vol. 12, pp. 205–295.

GREEN, H. S. (1952), *Molecular Theory of Fluids*, North-Holland Publishing Company, Amsterdam.

GREEN, H. S. (1960), The structure of liquids, in *Handbuch der Physik*, edited by S. Flügge, Springer-Verlag, Berlin, vol. 10, p. 1.

GREEN, M. S. (1958), Statistical mechanics and the Boltzmann equation, in *Proceedings of the International Symposium on Transport Processes in Statistical Mechanics*, Brussels, 1956, edited by I. Prigogine, Interscience Publishers Inc., New York, p. 8.

GROSS, E. P. and KROOK, M. (1956), *Phys. Rev.* **102**, 593.

GROSS, E. P. and ZIERING, (1959), *Phys. Fluids*, **2**, 701.

GROSS, R. A. (1965) Strong ionizing shock waves, *Rev. Mod. Phys.* **37**, 724.

TER HAAR, D. (1954), *Elements of Statistical Mechanics*, Holt, Rinehart and Winston, New York.

TER HAAR, D. (1955), The foundations of statistical mechanics, *Rev. Mod. Phys.* **27**, 289.

HIRSCHFELDER, J. O., CURTIS, C. F. and BIRD, R. B. (1954), *Molecular Theory of Gases and Liquids*, John Wiley & Sons, New York.

HOLTSMARK, J. (1919–1924), Über die Verbreiterung von Spektrallinien, *Ann. Phys.* **58**, 577; *Phys. Z.* **20**, 162, **25**, 73. Also see the paper by CHANDRASEKHAR (1943).

HUBBARD, J. (1961), The friction and diffusion coefficients of the Fokker–Planck equation in a plasma, *Proc. Roy. Soc.* A, **260**, 114; A, **261**, 371.

IKENBERRY, S. and TRUESDELL, C. (1956), On the pressure and the fiux of energy in a gas according to Maxwell's kinetic theory, *J. Rational Mechanics and Analysis*, **5**, 1.

JEANS, J. H. (1925), *The Dynamical Theory of Gases*, 4th edn., Cambridge University Press (reprinted by Dover, New York).

KENNARD, E. H. (1938), *Kinetic Theory of Gases*, McGraw-Hill, New York, Chapter 8.

KHINCHIN, A. I. (1949), *Mathematical Foundations of Statistical Mechanics*, translated by G. Gamow, Dover Publications, Inc., New York.

REFERENCES

KIHARA, T., AONO, O. and ITIKAWA, Y. (1963), Unified theory of relaxations in plasma, I, II, *J. Phys. Soc. Japan*, **18**, 837, 1043.

KIRKWOOD, J. G. (1946–1947) The statistical mechanical theory of transport processes, *J. Chem. Phys.* **14**, 180; **15**, 72.

KIRKWOOD, J. and ROSS, J. (1958), The statistical mechanical basis of the Boltzmann equation, in *Proceedings of the International Symposium on Transport Processes in Statistical Mechanics*, Brussels, 1956, edited by I. Prigogine, Interscience Publishers, Inc., New York, p. 1.

KOGA, T. (1954), *J. Chem. Phys.* **22**, 1633. See the appendix.

KOGA, T. (1955), *J. Chem. Phys.* **23**, 2275.

KOGA, T. (1957), *Memoirs of Faculty of Engineering, Nagoya University*, **9**, 274.

KOGA, T. (1959), *Phys. Fluids*, **2**, 580.

KOGA, T. (1961), *Phys. Fluids*, **4**, 834.

KOGA, T. (1965) *Nuovo Cim.*, **36**, 174.

KRAMERS, H. S. (1949), On the behavior of a gas near a wall, *Nuovo Cim.*, **6**, Suppl. No. 2, 297.

KROOK, M. (1959), *J. Fluid Mech.* **6**, 523.

KRÖNIG, A. (1856), Grundzuge einer Theorie der Gase, *Ann. Phys.* **99**, 315.

KRYLOV, H. M. and BOGOLIUBOV, N. N. (1943), *Introduction to Non-Linear Mechanics*, Princeton University Press.

LAMB, H. (1932), *Hydrodynamics*, 6th edn. Cambridge University Press.

LANDAU, L. D. and LIFSHITZ, E. M. (1958), *Quantum Mechanics, Non-Relativistic Theory*, Pergamon Press Ltd., p. 24.

LIOUVILLE, J. (1838), *J. Math. Pures Appl.* **3**, 348.

LORENTZ, H. A. (1909), *The Theory of Electrons*, Dover Publications Inc.

MASSEY, H. S. W. and BURHOP, E. H. S. (1952), *Electronic and Ionic Impact Phenomena*, Oxford University Press.

MAXWELL, J. C. (1866), On the dynamical theory of gases, *Philosophical Transactions*, vol. 157, also paper 28 in the *Scientific Papers of J. C. Maxwell*, Dover Publications Inc., New York.

MAXWELL, J. C. (1876), On Boltzmann's theorem on the average distribution of energy in a system of material points, paper 94 in the *Scientific Papers of Maxwell*, Dover Publications Inc., New York.

MAXWELL, J. C. (1879), On stresses in rarefied gases arising from inequalities of temperature, paper 93 in the *Scientific Papers of Maxwell*, Dover Publications Inc., New York.

MAYER, J. E. (1958), Theory of real gases, in *Handb. Phys.*, edited by S. Flügge, Springer-Verlag, Berlin, vol. 12, p. 37.

MILLIKAN, R. A. (1923), Coefficients of slip in gases and the law of solids and liquids, *Phys. Rev.* **20**, 217.

MOTT-SMITH, H. M. (1951), The solution of the Boltzmann equation for a shock wave, *Phys. Rev.* **82**, 883.

NAVIER, C. L. M. H. (1822), Mémoire sur les Lois du Mouvement des Fluides, *Mem. Acad. Sci.* [according to Lamb (1932)].

OBERMAN, C., ROS, A. and DAWSON, J. (1962), High-frequency conductivity of a fully ionized plasma, *Phys. Fluids*, **5**, 1514.

281

ONO, S. (1958), The Boltzmann equation in quantum statistical mechanics, in *Proceedings of the International Symposium on Transport Processes in Statistical Mechanics*, Brussels, 1956, edited by I. Prigogine, Interscience Publishers Inc., New York.

PLANCK, M. (1897), *Treaties on Thermodynamics*, the seventh German edition translated by A. OGG, Dover Publications Inc., New York.

POINCARÉ, H. (1881, 1882), Mémoire sur les courbes définies par une équation différentielle, *J. Math. Pures Appl.*, ser. 3, (7), 375; 8, 251.

POINCARÉ, H. (1892), *Les Méthodes Nouvelles de la Méchanique Célète*, vol. 1, chap. 6., reprinted by Dover.

POISSON, S. D. (1829), Mémoire sur les Équations Générales de l'Équilibre et du Mouvement des Corps Solides Élastiques et des Fluides, *J. l'École Polytechn.* 13, 1 [according to Lamb (1932)].

PRIGOGINE, I. and BALESCU, R. (1959), Irreversible processes in gases, I, II, *Physica*, 25, 281; 25, 302.

ROSTOKER, N. and ROSENBLUTH, M. N. (1960), Test particles in a completely ionized plasma, *Phys. Fluids*, 3, 1.

ROWLINSON, J. S. (1958), The properties of real gases, in *Handbuch der Physik*, edited by S. Flügge, Springer-Verlag, Berlin, vol. 12, p. 1.

RUARK, A. E. (1928), *Proc. Nat. Acad. (U.S.A.)* 14, 322.

DE SAINT-VENANT, B. (1845), *Comtes Rendus*, 17, 1240 [according to Lamb (1932)].

SCHAAF, S. A. and CHAMBRE, P. L. (1958), Flow of rarefied gases, *in High Speed Aerodynamics and Jet Propulsion*, 3, sec. H. edited by H. W. Emons, Princeton University Press.

SCHAAF, S. A. (1963), Mechanics of rarefied gases, in *Handb. Phys.*, edited by S. Flügge, Springer-Verlag, Berlin, Vol. VIII/2.

SIMON, A. and HARRIS, E. G. (1960), Kinetic equations for plasma and radiation, *Phys. Fluids*, 3, 245.

STOKES, G. G. (1845), On the theory of the internal friction of fluids in motion, *Camb. Trans.* 8, 287, [according to Lamb (1932)].

TAKAO, K. and FUJIMOTO, T. (1956), *Memoirs, Faculty of Engineering, Nagoya University*, 9, 379.

TAYLOR, G. I. (1912, 1935), Diffusion of continuous movements, *Proc. London Math. Soc.* ser. 2, 20, 196; Statistical Theory of Turbulence, *Proc. Roy. Soc. London*, A 151, 421.

TCHEN, C. M. (1959), Kinetic equation for a plasma with unsteady correlations, *Phys. Rev.* 114, 394.

THOMPSON, W. B. and HUBBARD, J. (1960), Long-range forces and the diffusion coefficient of a plasma, *Rev. Mod. Phys.* 32, 714.

THOMPSON, W. B. (1962), *Introduction to Plasma Physics*, Pergamon Press, p. 175.

TOLMAN, R. C. (1938), *The Principles of Statistical Mechanics*, Oxford University Press, section 21.

TSIEN, H. S. (1946), Super Aerodynamics, Mechanics of Rarefied Gases, *J. Aeronaut. Sci.* 13, 653.

UEHLING, E. A. and UHLENBECK, G. E. (1932), *Phys. Rev.* **108**, 1175.

VLASOV, A. (1950), *Many-Particle Theory and its Application to Plasma*, State Publishing House for Technical–Theoretical Literature, Moscow and Leningrad; republished by Gordon and Breach Science Publishers Inc., New York.

WALDMANN, L. (1960), Transporterscheinungen im Gasen von mittlerem Druck, in *Handb. Phys.*, edited by S. Flügge, Springer-Verlag, Berlin, Vol. XII, p. 295.

WANG CHANG, C. S. and UHLENBECK, G. E. (1948–1956), Several pioneering papers on transport phenomena in rarefied gases, in *Reports of University of Michigan:* Eng. Res. UMH-3-F, 1948; Rep. CM-579, 1949; Eng. Res. M998, 1953; Rep. 1991-1-T, 1954; Eng. Res. 2457-2-T, 1956.

WEINSTOCK, J. (1964), Theory of irreversible processes in a plasma, *Phys. Rev.* **133**, A673.

WHITTAKER, E. T. (1937), *A Treatise on the Analytical Dynamics of Particles and Rigid Bodies*, 4th edn. Cambridge University Press.

WIENER, N. (1950), The Extrapolation, Interpolation and Smoothing of Stationary Time Series, Technological Press, M.I.T., John Wiley & Sons, Inc., New York.

YVON, J. (1935), *La Théorie Statistique des Fluides et l'Équation d'État*, Hermann, Paris.

ZAHM, A. F. (1934), Super aerodynamics, *J. Franklin Inst.* **217**, 153.

ZIERING, S. (1961), Plane Poiseuille flow, in *Rarefied Gas Dynamics*, edited by L. Talbot, Academic Press.

Name Index

285

Subject Index

297